Advance Praise for

Heels Down Hall

Heels Down Hall is a must-read for fans of *All Creatures Great and Small*! You will end up engrossed in a slice of England that appeals to equestrians and non-riders alike.

—**Ron Friedson,** Saddle Designer and Avid Reader

Heels Down Hall is a fictional account based on real-life experiences and makes for fascinating reading. Set from 1967, the work records one year in the life of Alexa, a seventeen-year-old American girl, who goes to an English residential riding school as a working pupil with the dream of becoming an international show-jumper one day.

On arrival at a rambling Leicestershire mansion, Alexa little imagined the cultural shock that awaited her. In many ways, Heels Down Hall was still time-warped in the 1860s. The interactions of Alexa with the characters she meets at the Hall and various horse shows and competitions take the reader into a different world from today's as does the odd romantic encounter!

The style is refreshingly easy to read even for non-horsey people, despite technical phrases such as "leading file" and "leg yields," *Heels Down Hall* is a unique insight into a nearly forgotten time and well worth the read. I enjoyed it.

—**Charles de Beaulieu**

Heels Down Hall: Adventures of a Working Pupil by Regina Kear Reid is engaging from beginning to end. The author takes the reader along for the main character's literal and metaphorical journey as she leaves her home in the United States for a year in England.

The storyline offers a glimpse into the day-to-day activities of an English riding academy from the perspective of a young American newcomer. We follow along as Alex navigates a different culture and lifestyle, experiencing both the joys and frustrations of adjusting and fitting in while pursuing her equestrian passion. The book has a lovely pastoral feel. The setting is a riding academy in a small village, with lots of detailed descriptions of the school and the surrounding areas.

Taking place during the late 1960s, readers are reminded of a time before the pervasiveness of social media, a time of face-to-face conversations and hand-written letters to those far away. Somewhat cloistered, the rigorous schedules of the working pupils leave little time for the distractions of the outside world. With television access limited to Sunday evening viewing and occasional trips into town, students have time to focus on their instruction as well as the relationships formed within the establishment.

The individuals in the story experience highs and lows, triumphs and disappointments. The characters' many adventures are recounted in vivid detail and with a good dose of humor. All in all, the book is a very entertaining read.

—**Julia Peterson,** Independent Film Producer

Heels Down Hall is the perfect read for horse-crazy girls and their mothers! An inspiring account of the day-to-day hard work and joys of the equestrian working student. If you are looking for the perfect gift for the horse lover, look no further than *Heels Down Hall*!

—**Linda Kerstetter**

At first, *Heels Down Hall* seems to be the tale of a young girl on a grand adventure. It is so much more; it is the story of an American girl pursuing her dream to become a professional in the horse world. It takes you through the struggles of the rider to become a horsewoman, in a foreign land, in a time when the world was in chaos. It is a tale of a girl changing into a lady through sweat, determination, and true grit. I recommend it as both just a fun read and as a guide for anyone thinking of entering into the professional world of horses. You will laugh and cheer throughout.

—**Mikki Schattilly**

Heels Down Hall

Adventures *of* *a* Working Pupil

Regina Kear Reid

Illustrations by J. Johnson

Heels Down Hall: Adventures of a Working Pupil
Written by Regina Kear Reid

http://www.hoofbeatsandhorsetales.com
Cocoa, Florida

Library of Congress Control Number: 2022901441

ISBN: 979-8-9853625-0-3 (paperback), 979-8-9853625-1-0 (hardback), 979-8-9853625-2-7 (epub)

First printing: 2022

Publishing and Design Services: Melinda Martin, www.MartinPublishingServices.com
Illustrations: J. Johnson
Editorial Team: David Aretha

Heels Down Hall: Adventures of a Working Pupil is based on a true story. This fictionalized memoir aims to preserve anonymity, names of individuals, animals, and some geographical locations have been changed. Other changes include but are not limited to identifying characteristics, details of physical properties, occupations, and places. Except for public figures, any resemblance to any person living or dead is coincidental. The opinions expressed are those of the characters and not the author.

HISTORICAL DISCLAIMER: The terminology and language used in this book are proper for the time and places in 1968 and earlier. English characters speak in British English. The world was not politically correct.

Foreword

Regina, Deb McCarthy, and I are great friends and fellow horse professionals. Our lives have been interwoven for the better part of forty years. I was in New Jersey at Fairleigh Dickinson University creating and developing the Intercollegiate Horse Shows Association (IHSA) and Regina was the director of Equine Studies and Equestrian Team coach at Pace University in Pleasantville, New York. Deb was a member of one of the first Pace teams and returned to Pace years later as the stable manager and assistant coach. From Pace, she continued to support the IHSA as a coach at both Syracuse University and Cazenovia College.

Over the years, it has been a source of great pride and enjoyment for the three of us to witness the birth and growth of what is now the largest college horse organization in the United States. Today, the IHSA has over 250,000 student riders, and in its history has had four riders go on to represent the USA in the Olympics.

During her time at Pace, Regina built a prominent Equine Studies program and trained riders who became regional, zone, and national champions. Under her tutelage, the Pace University Equestrian Team achieved the title of Champion College in Region I of the IHSA. Many Pace students have gone on to become highly respected professionals as well as successful IHSA team coaches. These accomplishments not only demonstrate Regina's skill as a teacher and superb horseman but also her special ability to build relationships between rider and horse. It was the horsemanship skills she learned while a student at British Horse Society establishments in England that gave her the foundation and tools she needed to become so successful in developing riders, teachers, and horse trainers.

The special relationship between mankind and horses not only exists historically; it still flourishes today. However, the magic of the relationship between horse and human lies not in its strength and longevity; it lies in the mystery of how two different species can be drawn so closely to one another. Regina's work at Pace University and the success she and her students have enjoyed is due to that unique relationship.

Heels Down Hall is a story of a young woman who travels overseas to learn from the best teachers available. I would say the lesson was well learned. I am proud to say I have learned a great deal from Regina over the years about riding, teaching, and training horses. I have come to the conclusion that her teaching methods have become so well developed and systematic that she could teach any rider on earth.

By reading Regina's book, you will not only be entertained, you will also gain some of her wonderful knowledge as well.

—**Robert E. Cacchione**
Founder, Intercollegiate Horse Shows Association

As I read Regina Kear Reid's *Heels Down Hall*, I found myself reminiscing about my own unique journey with horses. Through each chapter, I accompanied Alexandra Goodwin and her fellow Heels Down Hall working pupils on their everyday adventures. I found myself becoming part of their story. As I became better acquainted with each of the characters, I joined in their adventures as well as the hours of hard work and study. I loved going with them on their "off-day" trips into town and was filled with nervous energy as they went to horse shows and took their British Horse Society Examinations. I felt the pang of homesickness at their first holidays away from home and the joy of being reunited with family members after a long separation. Heels Down Hall is a story all of us can relate to in one way or another. It is a coming-of-age story set in a time in history that signified great social change. It is also the story of having a dream and working very hard to make it a reality.

Alexa and I are different in many ways, but we definitely share some things in common. Horses have taught us patience and understanding, self-reliance, the value of hard work, compassion, and perseverance in the face of adversity and difficulty. The pursuit of equestrian excellence has also given us the ability to travel to wonderful places around the world, meet incredible people, and experience things that perhaps we mightn't have otherwise. Alexandra came to her experiences partly as a result of answering an advertisement for a riding school in England. My life in the horse industry came about somewhat differently.

As a college student, I had set my sights on a career in international relations. I was fascinated by foreign cultures, had a talent for learning other languages, and really enjoyed the classwork. Most of my courses were in global studies, foreign language, and political science. Filled with youthful idealism and enthusiasm, I dreamt about taking my place in the diplomatic corps. I would be able to travel, live in exotic places, and work to help make the world a better place. One fateful day, as I walked up a path at the Pleasantville campus of Pace University, I discovered something that would captivate not only my imagination but my every waking moment—the study of horses and horsemanship. It was shortly thereafter that my whole academic world was turned upside down, and I've never regretted a minute of it.

After two years in a different major, I enrolled in the Pace Equine Studies department where Regina Kear Reid was the program director and equestrian team coach. Now, looking back all these years later, taking the risk of following my dream has paid off in ways for which I will always be grateful. I have built a successful career as a horse professional, traveled to the far corners of the world, and made friends with people who have touched my life in wonderful ways. Through it all, my best friends and teachers have been the horses.

As you read this wonderful story of Alexandra and Heels Down Hall, feel encouraged to follow your dreams. If there is something you've always wanted to do with horses, find a way to do it. Invest the time. Do the work. Have the fun. Never forget to keep your eye up and your leg on. Be open to possibilities. Enjoy the adventure. It is never, ever too late.

—**Debra D. McCarthy**
Pace University
British Racing School
American Driving Society Technical Delegate
Equine Educator

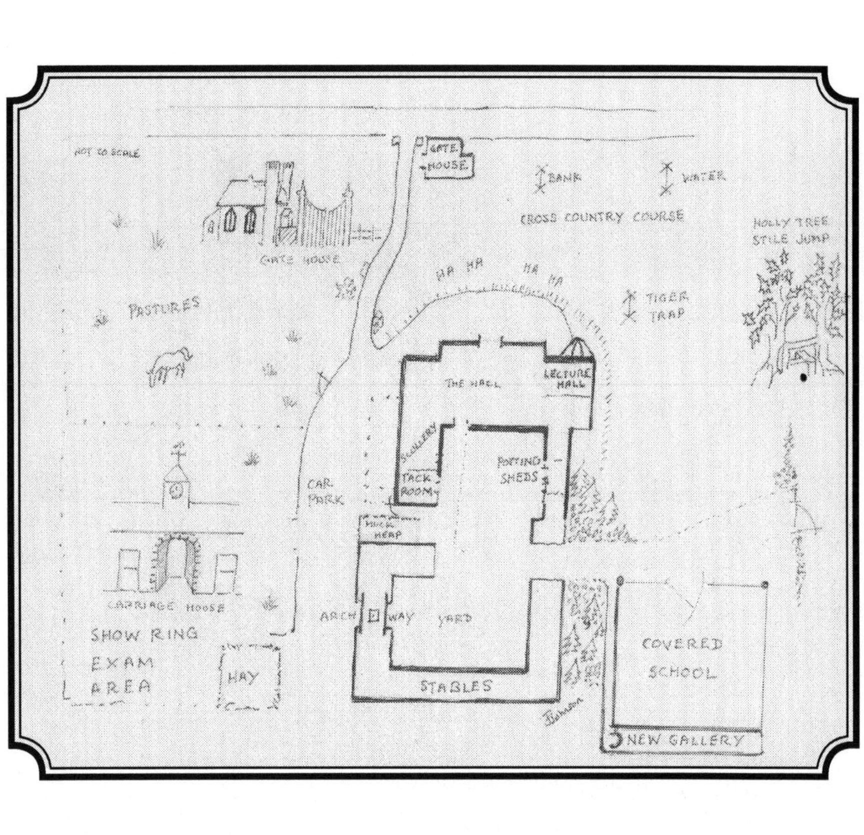
NOT TO SCALE
GATE HOUSE
BANK
WATER
CROSS COUNTRY COURSE
HOLLY TREE STILE JUMP
GATE HOUSE
HA HA HA HA
TIGER TRAP
PASTURES
THE HALL
LECTURE HALL
SCULLERY
POTTING SHEDS
TACK ROOM
CAR PARK
MUCK HEAP
CARRIAGE HOUSE
ARCH WAY
YARD
SHOW RING
EXAM AREA
HAY
STABLES
COVERED SCHOOL
NEW GALLERY

Chapter 1
Curious and Curiouser

Saturday, June 10, 1967

It was surreal. Regiments of smartly dressed soldiers riding perfectly matched horses marched in the street. Soldiers dressed in red coats and tall, furry hats stood shoulder to shoulder, forming a barrier between the densely packed crowd on the pavement and the parade. Mr. Dashet expertly maneuvered us to the front of the crowd. "It's called Trooping the Colour."

By now my friend Jennifer and I were fueled solely by adrenaline. We had been in England for only a couple of hours and now we were standing a stone's throw from Buckingham Palace. Leading the mounted band, a huge piebald drum horse with a kettle drum on each side was setting the tempo. His bridle had ornate reins attached to the drummer's stirrup irons. The sun glinting off the gold braid on the uniforms was blinding. My eyes nearly popped out of their sockets. Only a few yards away from me, the Queen of England, HM Elizabeth II, was riding past us. She was side-saddle, mounted on a bay horse, and wore a red military-style coat.

In spite of all the IRA activity during the past year, which my father warned me about, I thought the Queen looked safe enough surrounded by so many soldiers and police. Little children waved their flags and older people cheered: "God save the Queen" and "Long live the Queen."

Mr. Dashet and Sareena were my parents' friends. They had kindly met us at the central London BOAC terminal and were escorting us across London to make sure we would catch the train to Leicester. Fewer trains were scheduled on Saturdays. Mr. Dashet whisked us through the crowds and jammed us into a cab. Sareena reminded us that Leicester was two hours away. "I'll ring Mrs. Highstaff and let her know which train to meet." This was reassuring, since we had no way to make a telephone call.

Soon we were safely deposited at St. Pancras station. Mr. Dashet bought our tickets. We dragged our luggage along the platform and found some seats in a second-class compartment. Bouncing along, sitting on the train, I found it hard to believe that I was actually going to Heels Down Hall for a whole year. Jennifer and I had just graduated from high school in Greenleaf, North Carolina, two days ago. It was easy for me to persuade horse-crazy Jennifer that she would love spending the summer at a great English riding school. She had ridden at summer camps for years and her mother was a soft sell on the idea. With three teenage boys still at home, getting rid of one kid for the summer seemed like a terrific idea to Mrs. Bailey.

"Hey, Alexa, can you understand the announcements?" The garbled list of names the announcer rattled off was unintelligible.

"I know it's English," I replied, "but no." We kept our noses pressed to the window to watch for the town names on signs on the outskirts of the stations.

"We can relax for a little bit." I couldn't fall asleep.

I sat on the seat that faced backward. The towns and countryside turned into a blur. The swaying motion and clacking sounds of the train were hypnotic. I felt like Alice in Wonderland tumbling into a new dimension. In my mind England was the horse capital of the universe.

I was finally here.

I had made a deal with my parents when we moved to Greenleaf. I would delay entering college for a year so that I could attend Heels Down Hall to prepare for and take the British Horse Society Assistant Riding Instructor's Examination. My parents insisted I be a working pupil and work off my tuition, because they still had to pay a small fee for my room and board, plus an extra charge for laundry. I was always a good student. It was expected, without question, that I would receive my certificate.

My parents realized too late that they were responsible for my idea to study horsemanship in England. I had started planning this trip years ago while our family was stationed in East Africa and we were on our annual holiday in Nairobi. I thought Nairobi was fabulous. Nairobi still enjoyed the last hurrah of the fading sunset of the British Empire, but elsewhere in the vast savannahs, beyond the villages and farms, the soft whisper of discontent rustled through the branches of the acacia trees.

For me, second only to the drive-through Nairobi National Park outside of town to see the wild animals, the best thing about Nairobi was a European-style tack shop where my mother haggled with the Indian tailor who was going to make me a pair of whipcord jodhpurs. The imported ready-made ones were three times the price.

"Madame. Hard-wearing fabric." My mother hesitated. "With extra material in the seat and cuffs—plenty of room for Missy to grow!" At thirteen, I was a tall, skinny kid.

While my parents were busy with the tailor, I found a copy of *Riding* magazine, which my parents cheerfully bought for me, thinking it would keep me quiet for a while. Little did they know that inside the cover was a two-page "Directory of Riding Establishments," which I immediately memorized. Heels Down Hall did it all. The succinct advertisement read:

> *Heels Down Hall. Brickton, Leics. Residential Courses. B.H.S. Examinations. Children's Holiday Courses. Working pupils. Ponies broken and schooled. Mrs. Highstaff, I.I.H.*
>
> *Telephone: Brickton 352.*

Immediately, I envisioned myself galloping, riding with wild abandon, through the English countryside just like in the old hunting prints. Hand gallop and flat-out gallop were my two favorite gaits.

After years of listening to my relentless nagging, my parents finally agreed to allow me to write letters of inquiry to the riding schools. While I had many responses, most of them were just packets with printed brochures and mimeographed forms. Mrs. Highstaff actually answered all my very specific questions. The most important one was, "How much riding would I, as a working pupil, be doing?"

In beautiful penmanship, written on watermarked school stationery, Mrs. Highstaff assured me that "Working students receive two lessons a day and as they progress, WPs will assist with training of young horses or ponies." Of all the places I had written to, this was far and away the most generous riding time. My reverie was interrupted by the conductor.

"Ladies, Leicester is next. You may want to start gathering up your suitcases and put them by the door." I was glad that when he punched our tickets earlier, I had asked him to please come and find us so we wouldn't miss our stop. Shortly after the train stopped at Leicester station, the other passengers quickly scurried off. We found ourselves alone on the platform in a brick tunnel, surrounded by a heap of luggage. By now we were exhausted, famished, and getting nervous. It was no wonder we were feeling rather sick.

We were just about to give up hope when, in the backlit stairwell leading up to the street, appeared a handsome, athletic-looking young man impeccably dressed in riding attire. He strode over to us and confidently introduced himself.

"Hello, I'm Denis Parkhurst. You must be the Americans, Alexandra Goodwin and Jennifer Bailey. Mrs. Highstaff sent me to collect you and take you to the Hall. Welcome to England." He smiled.

Denis grabbed the two heaviest cases and easily marched back up the steps. Fortunately, his little Ford Anglia was parked close by the station. We crammed everything into the car. I sat in the front and Jennifer squashed into the backseat, wedged between the suitcases.

Along the way Denis told us a bit about himself. He had been at the riding school since February. His family lived near here and he commuted every day. He had two "A Levels." I wasn't sure what they were—English education was very different from ours—but I was too terrified to ask.

I had taken Driver's Education, but this was driving on the other side of the road. I clenched the handgrip the whole way. I thought every oncoming car was going to hit us and I averted my eyes at intersections. We zoomed around roundabouts and through the city streets and out into the bucolic countryside.

We were too tired to talk so Denis continued, "I'm taking the BHSAI exam at HDH in July." He didn't seem the least bit worried about it. About twenty minutes later, Denis chuckled. "Don't blink twice or you will miss it. This is Brickton." He enjoyed being our tour guide. "Pub, church, church hall, primary school, greengrocer, pub."

We turned up a narrow village lane: houses on one side and the other side had a drapery shop, a tiny grocery store, and an off-license/stationery/post office all in one. We passed a covered bus shelter. The lane turned to gravel. We passed some cultivated fields. Denis slowly turned the car onto a wide driveway between two large brick columns. The spiked iron gates were open. Just inside the gate, on our left, was a turreted, yellow brick miniature castle with some weeds growing out of one window. "The Gate House. We're here," Denis announced.

The massive stone and yellow brick Hall loomed ahead of us. It looked ancient. Large, mullioned windows punctuated the three-story facade.

Jennifer mused, "It looks just like in the brochure." I thought that was an odd thing to say because the brochure was in black and white. The car crept past paddocks dotted with beautiful horses and ponies. We did not, as I expected, turn onto the narrower gravel drive that ended in a circle in front of a grand semi-circular portico flanked by round fluted columns. Instead Denis drove us around the side of the Hall and stopped in front of a small sign: Stable Car Park. When we got out of the car and took a moment to stretch, we admired the impressive red brick carriage house. Centered above the big arch was a clock tower with a dovecote.

"Seventeenth century," said Denis. He picked up the bags. "Follow me." The stable yard was walled in and separated from the back garden by a narrow wooden gate. We could see a row of modern, dark-brown, wooden horse-boxes and lovely horses sticking their heads over the half doors. We followed Denis past the tack room with arch-shaped, mullioned, thick, beveled glass windows. The heavy, arched wooden door with long, iron hinges was open.

We passed the kitchen window and entered the Hall through a wide back door into a drab lobby with a flagstone floor and thirty-foot-high ceiling. You could see a railing when you looked up.

Denis was our tour guide again. "Students' dining hall off to the left. Pantry, post counter, and on the right, the butler's pantry." A few letters were neatly laid out on top of a long cabinet at the base of a staircase. I wondered for a second if there was a butler. "Coat rack." This was obvious. "Students' quarters, lounge, and loo upstairs."

At this point, Mrs. Highstaff appeared. She was a short, wiry woman dressed in a tailored herringbone tweed skirt and a hacking jacket worn over a shirt and tie. She looked old, but I could not tell how old. She had fine features and high cheekbones. Her silver-gray hair was neatly pulled back into a tight bun. Gold, round wire-rimmed glasses framed her piercing gray eyes, which were set into a weathered face unadorned by makeup. "Thank you, Denis, that will be all. You may help the others finish up in the yard."

Denis smiled at us and left.

After introductions, and a few pleasantries and rules, Mrs. Highstaff rang a small brass bell that sat on the post counter. A short teenage girl with a messy pixie haircut that topped a cheerful face appeared at the top of the stairs by the coat rack.

"Yes, Mrs. Highstaff?"

"Ruth, please show our new students to their room."

Ruth's attire consisted of a long-sleeve shirt and tie with pale yellow jodhpurs and slippers. "No boots upstairs," she told us.

Five of us had to share an enormous room in the front corner of the house. Our new room had one large, high window, wide wooden floorboards, and six ancient metal-frame beds with equally old wooden dressers standing at the foot of the beds. Beside each bed, a small threadbare rug covered a bit of the floor. Three beds were occupied, with a row of shoes and some boxes under them. Framed photos and toiletries decorated the tops of the dressers. The tan plastered walls were void of pictures. Ruth pointed out our beds. Our other roommates, Marion and Linda, were outside in the stables.

We were left to unpack. I wondered how I was going to survive. Most of the worldly belongings I needed for the next year were packed in a trunk, which was shipped over a month ago but hadn't arrived yet. I expected to find the trunk waiting for me. My stomach churned while I unpacked. The beds were old and high off the ground, which was useful because our suitcases fit easily underneath them. The beds sagged terribly and the mattresses were lumpy, but we were too tired to notice.

I don't remember much about the next few days except for some cups of tea, grooming one horse, and sleeping.

Chapter 2

Not a Holiday

By day three we were ready to start. The brochure from Heels Down Hall included a schedule:

Typical Holiday Course

8:00 a.m.	*Breakfast*
9:00 a.m.	*Grooming. Saddle Up*
10:30 a.m.	*Riding Lesson*
12 Noon	*Water and Feed Horses*
1:00 p.m.	*Lunch*
2:30 p.m.	*Riding Lesson or Lecture*
4:30 p.m.	*Tea*
5:00 p.m.	*Instruction*
6:00 p.m.	*Clean Tack*
7:00 p.m.	*Supper*

We were not on a holiday.

Before I left the USA, I imagined that the working pupils assisted the staff. I quickly discovered we *were* the staff. Heels Down Hall was a boot camp where riders were transformed into horsemen and where the horse's needs always took priority over the rider's personal interests.

I started to realize there wasn't much conversation at HDH. No talking was permitted during riding and lectures, except to answer questions; no chitchat in the stable yard unless it was work-related or if something was dangerous.

Ruth had already given us two serious "heads up" alerts. "Be careful what you say at meals, Rachael and Mrs. Fawcett are spies," and "Mr. Hobbs doesn't like a lot of chatter while he is watching television."

At quarter past six on Tuesday morning, we joined the others already in the kitchen to swill down a large mug of strong, disgusting tea without milk before we all went up to the stable yard. The milkman didn't arrive until shortly before breakfast with the day's rationed pints. Mr. Hobbs, our head instructor, had already finished his tea.

Mr. Hobbs looked old and had a slight build with very long bowed legs. He was taller than me, about five-foot-eight. Bright blue eyes peered out of a reddish, long face with sagging jowls. A thin fringe of gray hair poked out from underneath his tweed flat cap. The white tip of a handkerchief was just visible in the top pocket of his well-worn, expensive tweed jacket. He wore a regimental tie. His boots were so polished you could almost see yourself in them.

Mr. Hobbs checked his silver wristwatch.

Our day started at half past six.

To ensure there was no loitering over the morning tea, Rachael gleefully warned us, "There are *just* enough pitchforks and brooms to go around, but the last one out to the yard gets the broom with the wobbly head and the pitchfork with one tine broken off."

Rachael Hardwick, BHSAI, was the head girl. She had light-brown frizzy hair, a pointy nose, little eyes, and a pouty mouth with buckteeth. She wore glasses with cat-eye-shaped lenses. I imagined her as a weasel from the book *Wind in the Willows*.

Out in the yard, the first order of business was mucking out the stalls using a square burlap muck sack instead of a wheelbarrow. And we had to *carry* the mucky wet sack from our horse's stall, across the cobblestone yard, and dump it in the muck bin behind the carriage house.

Fortunately Jennifer and I each had only one horse to muck out.

After the stalls were clean, we watered our horses. The two thick, black rubber buckets hanging on the wall were emptied into a drain in the yard and scrubbed clean with a brush. The empty buckets were filled from the large, round, wooden water tubs located against the outside wall of the carriage house. We carried water-filled buckets back across the yard to our horse's stall.

My shoulders were spindly. As I carried two heavy buckets filled to the brim, my arms started to quiver and twist and I spilled the water onto my jeans and into the top of my work boots.

I heard a faint "Oh dear. *Tsk-tsk*!" from one of the stalls.

Inside the carriage house, Mr. Hobbs mixed the feeds according to a neatly printed chart on a large blackboard attached to the feed room wall. The horses' names were listed down the side, and the amounts of flaked maize, oats, crushed barley, bran, carrots, or swedes were listed next to the name. He mixed a large handful or two of freshly cut chaff into each rubber food tub. The chaff cutter looked like a medieval torture device. While Mr. Hobbs mixed the feeds, Marion was in the hayloft above old St. Christopher's loose box on the other side of the archway. Marion was my age and height, and our hair was the same color.

"Heads up! Hay-nets coming down." She threw the nets down through the open hatch and clambered down the wooden ladder pegged into the wall, closing the hatch behind her. We all gathered around to get our horse's hay-net. Each horse's hay-net was weighed on a hanging scale.

Rachael made sure Jennifer and I tied the nets up properly to the rings attached to the wall. "This is for safety. Practice until you can do it easily," she ordered us. Rachael was a nineteen-year-old drill sergeant. There was no time to practice. After feeding, each horse had to be quartered, or lightly groomed, before we could all sweep the yard together and go into breakfast. By now the strong tea sloshing around in my empty stomach, an hour and a half of nonstop work, and the whole time, not knowing quite what was expected of me, made me feel queasy.

Mr. Hobbs checked his wristwatch and said, "You pass inspection, and you can go to breakfast."

After the others, including Jennifer, removed their boots and put on street shoes or slippers, they trooped into the dining room and took their places on the mismatched chairs surrounding the long rectangular table.

I poked my head through the doorway and imagined that I was being scrutinized. The song "People Are Strange" by the Doors popped into my head. I dashed up the stairs without removing my work boots and threw up.

While I sat on the wooden floorboards in the enormous bathroom, I looked up. Behind the freestanding commode with a wooden seat was a large vertical pipe connected to a metal box, a water tank six feet above it. I noticed a small metal label on the underside of the tank: THOMAS CRAPPER & COMPANY 1870.

I thought that was amusing. I usually felt better after I was sick. I pulled the porcelain handle on the chain to flush. It was noisy. The water pipes were in exposed conduits on the interior of the plastered stone walls.

I decided I was hungry after all.

Opposite the long bathtub with claw feet, a chipped enamel sink was propped up on long legs, and above it, a large mirror was bolted to the wall. I tidied up a bit and went back downstairs to breakfast. I deposited my work boots on the coconut matting under the coat rack and put on my house shoes.

I sat down at the only empty seat at the table and had just started munching on a piece of toast when a very tall, stooped old lady with short, tight white curls surrounding a wrinkled face suddenly appeared in the passageway to the kitchen. Her smile revealed a missing tooth. A white pinafore covered her heavy cotton dress that hung down halfway to her ankles. She wore lace-up, stout shoes. She could have easily been mistaken for a character straight out of Dickens.

"Porridge or cornflakes?" she squawked at us with a lit cigarette hanging from the corner of her mouth.

Jennifer and I looked up, astonished.

Marion whispered to us, "You have to pick one."

"Cornflakes, please." I knew what cornflakes were. I wasn't exactly sure what porridge was; all I could think of was the old rhyme, "Peas Porridge Hot." I didn't like peas and it was summer. I did not think hot peas would be nice.

While I was eating breakfast, I saw Mrs. Fawcett disappearing upstairs carrying a broom, dustpan, bucket, and rags.

After we ate, we went to our room to change from our work clothes into riding attire. Even though I found it a bit disconcerting to share a room with four other girls, I was extremely excited. Just as Mrs. Highstaff's letter promised, Jennifer and I were having two riding lessons on our first full day.

On the way out to the stable, Ruth beckoned for Jennifer and me to detour through the kitchen. While we walked, she explained how she worked with Mrs. Fawcett, as well as taking care of two horses, including Mrs. Highstaff's Topaz. When the others were out of earshot, Ruth informed us, "Linda, a new American WP, is a skyver and you should keep an eye on her."

The single light bulb, which dangled from the ceiling on a long cord, illuminated a heavy oak table that filled the kitchen. Two orange cats, Apollo and Artemis, slept beneath it close to the drain grate on the flagstone floor.

The wooden counter was stacked with dishes for Ruth to wash. The smallest refrigerator I had ever seen was tucked under the counter. Through the large window above a shallow sink on legs, we could see the lawn and walled garden.

Rows of square canisters dotted the wooden shelves that surrounded the kitchen. I spotted the head of a mouse peeking out from behind the tin labeled SUGAR. Ignoring the mouse, I pointed to a large stew pot with some gray sludge simmering away on the back of the AGA. "What's that on the stove?" I hoped it was the duck's gruel.

"That's porridge!" Ruth laughed so hard she was holding her sides.

"Peas porridge in the pot nine days old."

Cornflakes were the right decision.

We left Ruth in the kitchen with the dishes and dashed up to the yard to get ready for our lesson.

Our morning flat work assessment lesson with Mr. Hobbs, who had previously instructed at Weedon where he molded raw recruits into battle-worthy horsemen, proved to be something of a shock. Mr. Hobbs looked terrifying with a long hunt whip draped around his neck. He barked out unfamiliar commands.

I was mounted on Marigold, a lovely large chestnut pony, and Jennifer was assigned to Ghost, a slightly smaller, sturdy gray. Fortunately, the ponies were well schooled and did everything Mr. Hobbs asked.

In our first lesson, we had to drop our self-stylized hunt seat riding, and start to ride in the modern military, knees-in, forward-seat position, and we had to understand and memorize the commands. "Don't perch on the saddle like a bird!" Mr. Hobbs shouted. We did our best.

Before we could have lunch, which turned out to be dinner, we skipped out the stalls, watered and fed the horses lunch. The skips were woven wicker baskets and they leaked. Then the stable yard had to be swept again. Not one errant straw was to be left on the cobblestones.

Fiona went to the Hall before sweeping. This week she was on Set the Table on the Weekly Rota.

Mrs. Fawcett turned out to be a terrible cook.

Dinner was some type of boiled, fatty meat, which I suspected was mutton. Mr. Hobbs thinly sliced the joint and forked a few thin slices onto a plate before he passed it around. The vegetables, to my dismay, were boiled cabbage and lumpy mashed potatoes served family-style in large crockery bowls. I swore I saw a bit of gray ash on the top of the potatoes, but Marion took that scoop. We drank tap water, without ice cubes, from glass pitchers on the table. For dessert we ate boiled gooseberries topped with lumpy yellow custard poured from a ceramic coffeepot.

Fiona dumped several teaspoons of sugar on the gooseberries.

By now I had started sizing up the others.

Petite and pale Fiona was Irish. She wore her long black hair in a braid down her back and had large brown eyes in a lightly freckled face. I noticed her flirting with Denis when they saddled their horses for their morning lesson with Mrs. Highstaff.

Like Marion, Fiona was a working pupil, and they both had been at Heels Down Hall for over a year.

Astonishingly, our fifth roommate was an American. Linda arrived a week before we did and was also a WP. She immediately told us, "My family owns Arabians in California." Linda spoke in a loud voice. She thought everything she said was funny, and her ear-splitting cackle grated my nerves. After Ruth's unsolicited warning, I immediately disliked her.

The last of our crew was a residential student. Tall, slender, and graceful, Janet hardly spoke a word.

After lunch we had a few minutes to ourselves to study, write letters, or watch TV. I lay on my bed to rest.

When we went back out to the yard, I was envious when I watched Mrs. Highstaff, astride Topaz, lead the more experienced riders, riding their training projects out to the big field beyond the indoor school for their afternoon lesson. All of them planned to take the exam in July, except Rachael and Ruth.

Linda was included in our afternoon jumping assessment in the indoor school. Jennifer and I had the same dependable ponies as in the morning. Linda rode Atlanta, a small sorrel mare that flattened her ears when she looked at you. After we warmed up, by trotting and cantering with and without stirrups, Mr. Hobbs had us shorten our stirrups and we started to jump.

After we trotted several X jumps, we started to canter over a small vertical. We followed each other around, keeping a safe distance between us.

This is more like it.

It was my turn. Marigold pleasantly cantered straight to the base of the small vertical and I leaned forward. She propped over the jump and fortunately kept cantering on landing. *Whew, that was awkward.* I was embarrassed.

Mr. Hobbs shouted out, "Don't lie on the neck like that and get ahead of your horse! You look like Queen Victoria on the commode!"

Linda started to cackle.

I really could not be mad at her. Picturing the portly old Queen wearing a long black dress and a long black veil squatting over a chamber pot made me giggle.

Before my second attempt, Mr. Hobbs reminded me, "Wait for the horse."

I made sure I did not make the same mistake.

After our lesson, the rest of the day went quickly. We threw down bales of straw and bedded down the stalls, followed by strapping your horse, a head-to-toe grooming.

Strapping the swaybacked giant St. Christopher took me an hour. Then we turned out horses, filled more hay-nets, topped up the water buckets, cut the chaff, fed and hayed the horses, and swept the yard.

At five o'clock we had a fifteen-minute tea break. I hungrily devoured the bread and jam and chugged a few cups of milky, hot tea. I quickly learned to use a lot of milk. Then everyone dashed upstairs to queue for the loo. Ruth explained the reason. "If you go upstairs at the beginning of tea break, someone might eat your bread."

After tea we went to the tack room. Every piece of tack used that day had to be scrupulously cleaned. The chart on the wall had to be initialed for each piece cleaned. Rachael disapproved of my method. "Alexa, you are using far too much water and making the glycerin soap too sudsy. *Tsk.*"

After tack cleaning, it was back to the stable to give the horses the evening hay, top up water buckets, skip out the stalls, and give the yard a final sweep. Denis left for home.

After the yard was swept, Rachael gave us our first lecture. Located across the garden from the kitchen, the lecture hall resembled a chapel with rough stone floors, high arched windows and door, and a vaulted, timbered ceiling. The front portion of the room was a foot higher than the rest and Rachael sat there. Behind her, a large niche in the front wall was crammed full of books.

We sat at old-fashioned desks with inkwells and recorded notes on the daily routine of a working stable yard, the difference between a weekday and Saturday, when there were many more lessons, and Sunday, which was the horses' day off and we could go to church with Mrs. Highstaff. Rachael then proceeded to rattle off a long list of safety rules.

At last, when we were dismissed and told to go across to the kitchen and get our supper, it was after eight o'clock. The two backless stools by the kitchen table were occupied. When we came in, Fiona removed the second tray of toast from the oven and put it on the table for our beans on toast.

Yuck. I hated baked beans, and the thought of putting them on toast was not appetizing.

Ruth grabbed a second piece of toast and cheerfully piped up, "Don't worry, tomorrow it's spaghetti on toast."

I ate some toast, without beans, said "good night" to Mrs. Highstaff as we were instructed to do, and I went to bed. It was still daylight. Even though Lights Out was not until half past nine, I was exhausted and fell asleep immediately.

Early the next morning when the alarm clocks on the dressers began to ring, I woke up and wondered where I was. My legs and my hands were stiff. My fingers were curled as though they still held a broom. Before I arrived at Heels Down Hall, I thought I was reasonably fit. I had walked to school, ridden my horse afterward, and sometimes played half-hearted tennis with Jennifer. In reality I was a suburban kid and not used to hard physical labor. Before I arrived, I reasoned with myself, *How hard could working at a riding school be?*

I had to admit I was not prepared to work from dawn till dusk. Everything was different: the people, the names for things, the food, the rules, and the way I was being taught to ride. It was a bit overwhelming. I remembered why I came. I thought of that section in the HDH brochure:

> *Students who wish to make riding their career and take the examinations have every opportunity to gain teaching experience in Equitation, Horse Management, and Training the Young Horse. They are able to assist in class lessons and as training progresses, they will instruct junior lessons under supervision.*

My goal was to obtain the British Horse Society Assistant Instructor's certificate in one year.

I was here to make riding my career. I hadn't revealed to anyone that my secret ambition was to become an international show jumper. I begged my parents to allow me to come here and vowed I would never tell them of my physical discomforts. I had a lot of pride.

I got ready quickly and went down for a cup of strong, disgusting tea. I hoped it would not make me sick again.

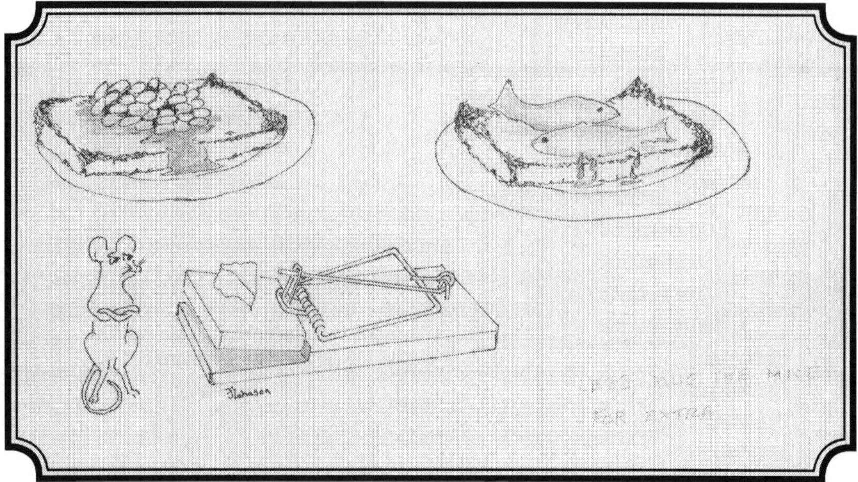

Chapter 3

Alien

During my first week in my new life of being a serf, otherwise known as a riding school working pupil, I was forced to adjust quickly.

Every minute of the day was accounted for by someone. Our lives were run by the Daily Schedule, The Red Book, in which Mrs. Highstaff recorded all the Riding and the weekly Rota. The Rota was a list of unsavory jobs to be performed, in addition to your other responsibilities, when you might have otherwise had a few minutes of free time.

By five o'clock the sun was already shining, which made waking up easy. Jennifer and I agreed to get up fifteen minutes earlier to have a few extra minutes in the bathroom. We were used to showering every day. We knew that would not happen here, but we were shocked to find a Rota of Baths taped to the wall in the WC, signed by Rachael.

"One bath a week!" Jennifer shrieked.

I hoped we didn't wake up Mr. Hobbs, still in his attic quarters. Mr. Hobbs luxuriously had his own bathroom, but he was last to get any hot water that was pumped up from the ground floor.

The hot water for the entire Hall was heated by the noisy, smoky coal and wood-burning boiler located in a small room between the kitchen and dining room. Since it was summer, the heat wasn't on.

Lazy Linda, as I had nicknamed her, was lumped into the lessons with Jennifer and me. We were mounted as before on the same trustworthy steeds. Sometimes Mr. Hobbs taught our lessons in various parts of the hundred-acre estate. I preferred this, over having lessons in the indoor school.

We had one lesson in the show jumping paddock across from the carriage house, which was all trotting poles, cantering poles, and tiny cross rails, and no jumping. Mr. Hobbs told us, "You should always watch the other riders when they are doing the individual exercises because I might ask questions about their performance."

While I was *not* watching Linda's turn, I noticed a person far away, dressed in dark clothing with his head down and stooped over, walking along the paddock fence line by the gravel road to the Hall Farm. It looked like he was carrying something.

Sometimes we practiced endless circles and transitions, riding in the dressage arena set up in the large pasture where the ponies lived.

Cross-country jumps were scattered around the landscape, freestanding in the pastures or incorporated into paddock fence lines. Mr. Hobbs would school one of the young horses while he instructed us and he would demonstrate the correct way to do the exercises. We rode with short stirrups, walk and trot, in jumping position, up and down the bank, or we trotted and cantered large circles. No jumping at all.

I spied the same mysterious person as before, this time in the bottom field near the water jump. He never looked in our direction. He appeared to be cutting the hedge.

While Mr. Hobbs taught us, Mrs. Highstaff instructed the other riders in preparation for the July 7 examination.

A cob-sized pinto gelding named Cherokee arrived at HDH for training.

I remembered the advertisement in *Riding* magazine: "Ponies broken and schooled."

The brochure elaborated:

> *Horses and Ponies for Breaking and Schooling: The same care and systematic method of training is applied to the education of horses and ponies as to students. Training is progressive and may include dressage, jumping, or combined training. Pupils may accompany their horses, horse and rider being trained concurrently.*

Later, during another of Mrs. Fawcett's astounding dinners, this time consisting of boiled riced potatoes, boiled cabbage, and another mystery meat, Rachael informed us, "Sally Brown will not accompany Cherokee for training. She is terrified of him."

"Her father probably bought the skewbald from a passing Irish tinker." Denis smiled and winked at Fiona.

After lunch when we checked The Red Book on the table in the tack room, I was extremely pleased to find out I had been assigned to Cherokee.

I had only been here a few days and I already had a training project.

I thought nothing of the fact he was a "colored horse." My first pony was a pinto. Cherokee was a good size for me, bigger than Marigold. I quickly found out he only had the right, as opposed to both leads, but he seemed quiet and willing. The real bonus was he came with a comfortable German jumping saddle with a deep seat and padded knee rolls, unlike most of the saddles at Heels Down Hall.

Later, when we were cleaning the tack, Mr. Hobbs commented, "There's a good possibility that Mr. Brown spent more money on the saddle than on the horse."

The next afternoon, in lieu of our half-day off, Mrs. Highstaff told us to change into dress clothes and gather up our passports, plane tickets, letter of acceptance to the school, and health cards because Mr. Hobbs was taking us to register with the police. I thought that was a bit unnecessary as all those documents had been thoroughly reviewed at the airport when we entered the country. My passport had Visa – Good For One Year stamped in it, but I was curious to see a real English town, and I hoped we could buy some things.

We brought our traveler's checks with us.

The three Americans took our places on the hard fold-down seats in the back of the Land Rover and Mr. Hobbs chauffeured us to the Crowsville Constabulary.

The local constables were not used to talking with teenage American girls and they seemed to be slightly amused by the unfamiliar process. In the end the desk sergeant typed, in triplicate, our information onto long forms, so Linda and I would officially be Resident Aliens.

This took quite a while.

On the forms, which we had to carefully review and sign, our Occupation was listed as Student. Even though Jennifer was a student, she did not have to register. She was only here for the summer and had a tourist visa.

Apparently, as a Resident Alien, your photograph had to be on file with the police.

"In case you go missing." The older man wearing a suit looked toward a bulletin board on the wall.

I was glad Jennifer produced a small black and white photograph of me from a stack of pictures of our high school friends that she carried in her wallet.

The older policeman wrinkled his brow. He admonished me to write home, as soon as possible, and get two more photos. One had to be attached to each form.

A dashing Bobby wearing a blue uniform complete with a dome-shaped hat checked to see that Linda and I each had an open return airline ticket. He sternly warned us, "In the event you have to go home, *for any reason*." He emphasized the last phrase. I remembered my dad complaining about how much the ticket cost because it was good for any time of year, with prior booking.

I wondered if the police were just having some fun at our expense by trying to scare us, or if they were serious.

I didn't like being an Alien, registered or not. "Alien" had outer space implications, but now that we were legal, we asked if we could go shopping. Mr. Hobbs readily agreed and said he wanted to get some things for himself.

The first shop we went to did not want to cash our traveler's checks. "They could," the elderly shop assistant waffled. "It was such a rigmarole . . . a lot of forms to fill out . . . a lot of maths are involved . . . they didn't have that much cash on hand." He nodded in the direction of the bank, a small building across the street.

While we were busy befuddling the sole clerk in the tiny bank, Mr. Hobbs told us to meet in the Woolworths down the street in half an hour.

The bank clerk checked our passports, carefully examined the traveler's checks, and telephoned London to get the daily exchange rate to convert dollars into pounds. He did some calculations, deducted a service charge, and insisted we open small savings accounts. "This will make your money exchanges easier in the future." He filled out some forms and suggested we all convert the same amount, ten dollars, into cash.

The money was funny and there was a lot of it: farthing, ha'penny, penny, tuppence, thruppence, sixpence, shilling, half crown, and crown. Then there was paper money: ten-shilling notes and different-colored pound notes for various denominations.

Ten dollars came to three pounds, six shillings.

Mr. Hobbs stood by the Woolworths entrance with a small parcel under one arm. He checked his watch. "Finish up quickly because we still have to stop at the post office."

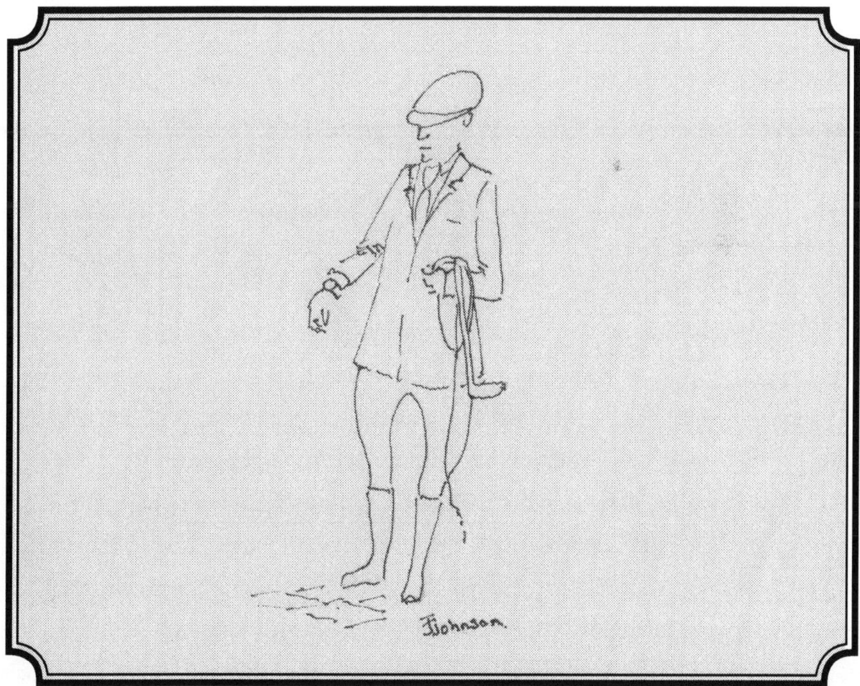

Woolworths had everything we needed. We bought washcloths and some toiletries. Only communal bars of soap and paper-thin towels were included in your board at HDH.

Mr. Hobbs led us through the crooked streets, and eventually into a magazine shop, card shop, stationery store, with a large candy counter with dusty wine bottles on a high shelf. The post office was a small counter in the back of the room. Mr. Hobbs purchased a box of ten Senior Service cigarettes, which was odd because he didn't smoke. In fact, smoking was strictly forbidden at HDH, except for Mrs. Fawcett. I remembered a full-page ad in that old *Riding* magazine, featuring a hunt gathered in front of a thatched-roof pub. The caption read, "Senior Service, the outstanding cigarette of the day."

I bought postage stamps. I promised to write home regularly. I had a lovely journal, a graduation present, and a box of stationery in my suitcase under my bed. I already had a brainstorm. I would ask my mother to save all my letters because there wasn't going to be much time to keep a journal.

When we got back to the Hall, I was happy to find the invoice for my trunk, which would soon be here, lying on the post counter along with a couple of letters from my high school pals.

Things were looking up.

The next morning, instead of our usual lesson, we wondered at the entry in The Red Book: 10:00 a.m. Long Reining. Atlanta. Mr. Hobbs. Indoor school. Alexa, Jennifer, Linda.

Back in the States, I had observed horses being twirled around willy-nilly on the end of a long lunge line by a person who periodically cracked a whip in their general direction. Most of those horses had a frantic look in their eyes, with their heads pulled inward and quarters winging out.

I didn't see how this activity was going to improve my riding.

To top it off, I disliked the horrible Atlanta, whom I had already nicknamed Attila because she threatened to bite or kick humans and horses alike. Fiona took care of Attila and they adored each other.

Linda said, "I have cramps," and she retired to the Hall.

In the indoor school Mr. Hobbs greeted us with, "Don't just stand there. Take the stirrups off the saddle." Then he attached the long reins to the bit rings. On the far side, one rein went from the bit ring and around the horse's hindquarters, just above the hocks, and back to the trainer. The other long rein attached to the bit on the near side and came back to the trainer's hand. This looked like a slice of pie with the horse on the perimeter of the circle and trainer in the center. Mr. Hobbs carried a lunge whip but never cracked it once. "The whip is an artificial aid; it is not something to be used to frighten the horse," he explained.

We were amazed as Mr. Hobbs put Atlanta through her paces. The tubby chestnut mare gracefully walked, trotted, and cantered in both directions with smooth transitions. Then Mr. Hobbs got a glint in his eye. The next thing we knew, Attila was cantering figure eights with flying lead changes. It turned out that Mr. Hobbs was an expert at handling the long reins from when he had trained artillery horses.

We each took a turn riding with Mr. Hobbs long reining us at the walk and trot with the stirrups off the saddle. I went first. He had me performing all sorts of gymnastic exercises. *Well,* I thought, *joining the circus could be a fall-back career.* But to my amazement I found out the long reining session quickly improved my position. We were starting to develop deep, balanced seats.

Saturdays at HDH were devoted to children's riding lessons, or rides, taught by the more experienced students and assisted by novice WPs. It was the busiest day in the yard. Jennifer and I were the least experienced and therefore the most expendable helpers, so Mrs. Highstaff chose us to groom for two ten-year-old girls who were competing with Mango and Marigold at the Scuthering Horse Show on the far side of Birmingham. Mango was a fizzy, pony-sized Anglo-Arab, full sister to Topaz, usually ridden by Ruth.

We were told to bring our raincoats. This was, I suspected, because it rained a lot in England.

In the pre-dawn light on Saturday morning, Julie and I were told to put our raincoats over our riding clothes and to climb into the front of the wooden Rice horse trailer. We entered through the groom's door and sat facing the ponies on fold-down seats. An emergency switch located over the high, small window between us could turn on an alarm light in the Land Rover.

The spotless, carefully plaited, and bandaged ponies were loaded into the trailer. Caroline and Jennifer sat in the back of the Land Rover with all the tack and buckets. Mrs. Highstaff and the kids' parents wished us good luck. Mr. Hobbs touched his cap, and we were on our way.

Fortunately, the ponies were well behaved, and we did not have to use the emergency switch, but by the time we got to the show, I discovered why we needed raincoats. While the ponies munched on the hay-nets, they would give the net a good pull and a shake, showering us with bits of hay and seeds.

I swore the ponies were laughing.

Chapter 4
Off to a Flying Start

When we arrived at the Scuthering Show, two arenas were running simultaneously: one for show jumping and the other for riding classes. We were provided with an accurate time schedule because the whole show was pre-entries only. After we picked up the girls' numbers from the show secretary, we gave the already impeccable ponies a final polish, tacked them up, and oiled their hooves. Fortunately for us, the ten-year-olds were seasoned competitors and knew exactly what needed to be done.

The girls' short hair was securely netted before they left the school, and they were completely dressed except for jackets, helmets, gloves, and crops. The girls warmed up the ponies under Mr. Hobbs' watchful eye until the preliminary class call was announced. We made our way down to the collecting ring to check in with the gate steward.

Our girls were riding in Working Pony:

> *Class Three: Entry Fee 7/6d. (Seven shillings sixpence) For the best WORKING PONY, Mare or Gelding, not exceeding 14-2 hands. Competitors may be asked to jump. A special award will be made to the most promising pony of 5 years or younger. Riders for this award should wear a white armband. Prizes: First prize: Headcollar in "Cortack," presented by P. Pointdexter, Esq. and £2. Second prize: £1 /10s. Third prize: £1.*

There were so many Working Ponies that the class was divided into three sections by height. Both our ponies were in Large, which was further divided into three groups of ten.

After each group collectively performed at the walk, trot, extended trot, and canter in both directions, the judge picked nine contestants for individual testing and dismissed the others.

The young riders had two and a half minutes to do an original test that included all gaits, a turn on the haunches, a turn on the forehand, a hand gallop, a halt, and canter over one jump.

The whole class took well over an hour.

No prizes were awarded after third place, but all the finalist places were announced. Mango was sixth and Marigold came in eighth. I gained some new respect for my frequent mount and these little kids.

The gate remained shut. "Before the ponies leave the arena, we will present the award for the Best Pony under Five." The announcer paused. "This year's award goes to Mango owned by Mrs. M. M. Highstaff of Heels Down Hall, Leicestershire, and ridden by Miss Caroline Timmons." There was a polite clapping of hands by the tweedy set holding ponies in the collecting ring.

As soon as the ponies were untacked, the girls took the ponies' plaits out and we laughed at the kinky manes and tails. The ponies were offered hay and water.

When everything was ready to go home, we ate our packed sandwiches and drank lukewarm tea from a flask. We ate while we watched a fancy Hackney driving class.

During the intermission some well-dressed Royals Patrons, who were smiling and waving, were driven around the grounds in a beautiful carriage pulled by a matching pair of high-stepping horses. Mr. Hobbs told us the horses were Cleveland Bays and the carriage was a landau. After the Royals left, the Featherstone Foxhounds flooded the arena. I loved watching the happy tricolored hounds bouncing around.

The Scuthering show was still going on in full swing when we left the grounds.

Julie and I were promoted to the back seat on the way home.

"It's just a little different than Flatlanders," I mused while looking out the Land Rover windows. Flatlanders was the name of the horse show circuit at home. The shows were usually held on little fairgrounds and a great many townspeople would turn out for the social occasion, complete with picnics and barbecues. The riding classes were accompanied by live music played by a professional organist. Spectators would try to influence the judges by shouting out, "There's your horse!" in the Five-Gaited and Tennessee Walking Horse classes. Only the cowboys played the gymkhana games.

When we got back to HDH, we unpacked the horsebox and cleaned it while the girls took care of the ponies.

The others were thrilled with Mango's win, but even happier that we arrived in time to help with the evening feed, sweep the yard, and clean the tack, not just from the show, but from all the lessons.

While we were eating supper, this time sardines on toast, I watched Mrs. Highstaff with her faithful black Lab, Lord Daffy, trotting at her heels, purposefully stride past the kitchen window. I was astonished. *She's smoking a cigarette!*

"Off to check the stables," Rachael informed us. "I hope you put everything away properly," even though she knew we had.

"A place for everything and everything in its place" was a frequently quoted motto at Heels Down Hall. I ignored Rachael and was busy making friends with the cats under the table, by feeding them the sardine bones and guts that I carefully had picked out.

"How often does she do that?" Linda asked apprehensively.

Fiona replied matter-of-factly, "Every evening,"

Marion added solemnly, "And whenever she takes a mind to do it."

At breakfast on Sunday, Mrs. Highstaff, dressed in a tweed skirt and a beautiful cream-colored silk blouse, came into our dining room to ask if anyone wanted to accompany her to church. Jennifer and I seized the opportunity to wear real clothes and makeup and see some real people.

Mr. Hobbs, still dressed in his riding clothes, ordered us, dressed in our miniskirts, to get in the back seat of the Land Rover. He drove us around to the front of the Hall. We saw that Mrs. Highstaff, waiting on the portico, had added a matching tweed cape, a hat with a pheasant feather, and gloves to her outfit. Mr. Hobbs popped round and opened the door for her. He touched his cap as she was about to get in.

We stopped at the village corner shop in Brickton, where Mr. Hobbs nipped in and a few minutes later came back with some newspapers and a box of Senior Service, which he laid between the seats.

Mr. Hobbs dropped us off in front of the church and said he would park the car. He never came in.

St. George's in Storkey was a small, dark, gothic church with square stone towers with pointy tops. The only light inside filtered through dark stained glass windows. The place reeked from the scent of frankincense and myrrh that floated down from a brass censer hanging from long brass chains from the high vaulted ceiling.

The Communion service was very austere and without music. I wasn't sure if Jennifer attended church regularly, but I was a confirmed Lutheran and so, when it was our turn, we followed Mrs. Highstaff up and knelt in front of the altar rail. The whole experience was a stark contrast to our church in Greenleaf, which was Swedish modern architecture, all wood and windows with a swooping roofline, and with lots of music and singing.

After the service, Mr. Hobbs was waiting for us. When he saw us walking toward the car, he put down his newspaper and jumped out to open the door for Mrs. Highstaff. While I tried to be as ladylike as possible when I climbed into the high back seat of the Land Rover, I noticed a copy of *The Sporting Chronicle* laying on the driver's seat.

When I discovered it was Mrs. Fawcett's day off, I looked forward to our Sunday lunch.

Lunch was different—cold (but not refrigerated) chicken, roasted the day before. The chicken had some tiny pin feathers around the tops of the legs. For a change, there was salad, a few leaves of long lettuce, and one tomato each. Ruth heated up a large tin of peas and they disappeared quickly.

Since there was No Riding, the horses didn't have to be groomed and there was no tack to clean. After lunch we adjourned upstairs to the student lounge, to watch a popular show on the small black and white television set. There was the usual scramble to get the best seats on the sagging couches and well-worn chairs. I took a seat at the writing table by the window. Mr. Hobbs motioned for Linda to remove herself from his favorite wingback chair.

Reluctantly, she plopped down onto the rug. The first program we watched was *Les Misérables*, a TV mini-series. We were fascinated by the hardships of the characters whose lives made ours look easy by comparison.

After evening stables and supper, which turned out to be the best one yet, cheese on toast, we returned to the lounge to watch *Top of the Pops.* Mr. Hobbs grimaced most of the time but sat through it, because afterwards, Patrick McGoohan, retired British Secret Service, now *The Prisoner* named only Number 6, would resist brainwashing, and have another exciting escape attempt from the Village. Ultimately Number 6 would be captured by a giant white ball and be returned to the Village to try again next week.

Sitting by the window, I noticed the same curious person I had spotted around the grounds a few times earlier in the week. He never spoke to any of us. Now he was suspiciously routing around in a wooden shed leaning against the garden wall. *It's almost dark. I wonder what he is doing.*

He looked like a tramp. The man was about six feet tall, medium built, and stooped, with sloping shoulders. He had a pale complexion, a vacant expression, and scraggly black hair. He wore glasses with heavy black frames and thick lenses that made his eyes look enormous. He always wore the same clothes—dark, baggy corduroy trousers and a dark pullover sweater with holes in the elbows. Curiosity got the best of me. "Who *is* that person?"

Fiona jumped off the sofa and looked out. "Oh!" She laughed. "That is Mr. Highstaff. He teaches in the aerospace department at the university."

I was mortified. "I thought he was a gardener."

Linda cackled.

"Be quiet. *The Prisoner* has just started," said Mr. Hobbs.

On Monday of the second week, Jennifer and I were each assigned full care for two horses. I still had St. Chris, as we called him. Mrs. Highstaff's retired show horse was a dark bay with a wide blaze on his face, and three white stockings on his legs. He was a big-boned, swaybacked, ancient Thoroughbred. His head still had the look of eagles, if the eagles were old and tired. He spent most of his days in the field and came in at night. He was revered in the stable.

My second horse was something the likes of which I had never seen in person before. Kris Kringle, a huge dapple gray with a gigantic head, was owned by Dr. Amsley, our vet.

"Let's call him Harry. We already have a Chris." Mr. Hobbs looked at Harry's teeth. "He's only four." Then he stood back and looked at the whole horse. "When he finishes growing, he will be too big for a heavyweight hunter."

After breakfast on Tuesday, Mr. Hobbs and I were sent to fetch two mares in foal to a three-quarter bred Thoroughbred stallion. The unborn foals of these mares were destined to become hunters or three-day event horses.

During the two-and-one-half hour journey to the farm near Chesterfield, Mr. Hobbs was not talkative. I was happy to finally be allowed to sit in the front seat of the Land Rover and just gaze out the window. At some point, we passed through a moor. I envisioned Pip finding Magwich, the criminal, in just such a place.

On the return trip, on duty in the trailer, watching the fidgety mares flatten their ears and grimace at each other, I was showered with hay again. The mares were making me nervous, but I never had to use the emergency switch. Facing backward in the swaying trailer made me nauseated and I was happy to get back.

The rest of the week I alternated between riding the giant Harry and the diminutive Cherokee. Jennifer was upgraded to Marigold. Linda was still riding Attila; she was too big for Ghost. I loved both my horses, I imagined Harry as a knight's charger, and I felt very superior getting to train Cherokee.

The exam candidates were getting worked up because next week Mrs. Ainsworth was conducting a combined training course, and the week after that, Colonel Somebody was scheduled, and then there was the exam on the seventh of July.

We newcomers were excluded from these courses, and I wondered what these guest instructors would be like.

Fortunately, Linda did not share our half-day off, and Jennifer and I were glad to be rid of her. We boarded the Double Decker red bus at the edge of Brickton and rode the bus to the other end of the line, into the market town of Leicester. The bus fare was three shillings sixpence each way. Denis's thirty-five-minute car trip took well over an hour on the bus.

We wandered aimlessly toward the center of town by following the white arrows with Town Centre printed in black letters, which pointed us in the general direction. As we sauntered along, we were window shopping.

Our first stop was a Wimpy Bar. With knives and forks, we enthusiastically downed a delicious hot hamburger on a bun smothered with fried onions and doused with brown sauce, served with chips. The server chuckled when we called them French fries. "You won't find anything French in here."

The fabled cobblestoned Roman Market was empty, and the banks were closed. We found a clock tower in a roundabout, called a square, near Belgrave Gate. A travel agency changed our traveler's checks without any fuss, and we asked them for directions to Lewes Equestrian Emporium. It was only a block from the city center.

Mrs. Highstaff had directed us to purchase riding crops.

Lewes Equestrian Emporium was a horseman's heaven. They had everything: top-of-the-line breeches, jodhpurs in every color, riding coats and shirts, short and tall boots, expensive hunting accessories, and grooming kits. The *lot*.

I asked why there were only one or two used saddles and found out most saddles were made-to-order for each horse and rider. At HDH the saddles were carefully assigned to fit the horses and generally fit the rider.

The young female shop attendant who modeled the latest equestrian fashions thought it was wonderful that Americans were studying horsemanship in Leicestershire. We purchased long crops, a useful length, not jumping bats or dressage whips. We thought the wrist loop was fun. We looked at *everything*. We promised the clerk we would be back again and started back to the bus depot.

Department store windows were full of practical fashions, but I already had my eye on expensive leather trench coats and long black fashion boots. I loved the colorful mod fashions in the boutiques, so different from the sedate preppy clothes available in Greenleaf, but I was not prepared to spend the money.

Near the bus depot we discovered the Chalet, a cheery little restaurant with a Switzerland theme. I liked how the restaurants posted menus with prices, outside by the door. For only eight shillings, and no tipping, we could get pork chops with fresh garden peas, a piece of lettuce (salad), hot applesauce, and a pot of tea. Already tired of the something on toast every night, we stayed at the cozy Chalet, savoring each bite, until it was time to catch the ten past seven bus back to Brickton. We were warned by Rachael, "Do not plan to take the last bus at eight o'clock. If you miss it, there is no way back and the riding school is over twenty miles away."

My trunk arrived the next day while we were out in the yard. After lunch, I happily unpacked everything, except for my heavy winter clothes. When I finished unpacking, I decided I desperately needed a western belt for my jeans, two books—one about American breeds of horses and the other by the Italian Santini, simply called *Riding*—and my copy of the BHS exam syllabus, which I had forgotten to pack. Obviously, I could get another one here, but I did not want to pay a shilling for a replacement, and I needed those two photos for the police. I would write home after supper.

In the afternoon Mr. Hobbs took all nine of us out to the big field for a jumping lesson. Before we left the stable yard, Mr. Hobbs snatched the new crops from Jennifer and me and promptly cut off the wrist straps. "Bloody stupid things," he said. "They are a good way to break your arm."

Getting to jump outdoors was going to be a real treat. I had just silently been congratulating myself on how well Cherokee was jumping for me in the indoor school.

Finally it was our turn to go over the small red and white striped rails on the upright fence. We energetically cantered up to it, but Cherokee somehow swerved on takeoff and my leg hit the standard. I was glad I wore tall boots.

This was an unacceptable attempt.

"Do it again and this time be ready for him. Ride straight ahead!" Mr. Hobbs shouted.

On our next try, Cherokee did not swerve on the takeoff. I was ready for him. He sailed straight over the middle.

This time, he shied when he landed. I precariously tipped over one side for three strides, but I determinedly stuck on. Then Cherokee agilely sidestepped out from under me. It seemed like a well-practiced move. That finished me off.

I heard Mr. Hobbs disgustedly mutter, "Cheeky little Arab!" as he went to catch the spotted gypsy-wonder before the pony stepped on his reins. Cherokee was grazing right where he pitched me.

I took a moment and realized I was alright, but I wished the ground had opened up and swallowed me. The seam on the seat of my breeches split when I hit the grass.

I picked up my crop. There was a titter among the class when I stood up.

Just then, Lord Daffy appeared, frolicking over the crest of the hill, closely followed by Mrs. Highstaff dressed in a headscarf, tweed coat, tan trousers, and high, green rubber boots. She carried a long, stout walking stick, and she did not look as happy as her dog.

She walked straight over to me. In her perfect, quiet, and commanding Queen's English, Mrs. Highstaff said, "Alexa, get back on and do it again. The horse is here for training. It is obvious he has done that before with Sally."

Mr. Hobbs lowered the jump and I made sure Cherokee did not pull that stunt again.

Luckily, my jacket covered most of my knickers, at least when I was sitting upright.

Jennifer was more domestic than I was. She had taken home economics in high school, and helped her mother take care of her three younger brothers. She sewed my breeches back together very neatly.

Other than the ghastly bruises on my elbow and thigh and being stiff for a few days, I survived.

Chapter 5

Ha-Ha

My bruises started to subside. The mysterious Mrs. Ainsworth was here, and during the day, we barely saw the exam candidates. Ruth was now schooling her horses with us. Mrs. Ainsworth was accommodated in one of several upstairs guest rooms, past the point that we were not allowed. She dined with the Highstaffs. I never actually saw her. I had already concluded one thing about guest instructors—more work for all those not on the course.

Riding Harry was like trying to navigate a large, overstuffed couch around the living room. My unnaturally stretched out legs ached from "riding forward and keeping straight." Even though our lessons included many segments of walking on a loose rein, Harry frequently thought he should stretch his long, heavy neck. He nearly yanked me out of the saddle and pulled my arms out of their sockets. I got really good at slipping the reins and picking them up quickly and effectively.

Cherokee and I were coming to terms with each other. He now had two leads and a fairly balanced trot. He was teaching me "to ride every fence." We had started jumping some of the tiniest cross-country jumps, a log, and a little hedge. He was gaining confidence and he seemed to like the natural fences better than the brightly painted show jumps.

When our half-day off rolled around again, Jennifer and I decided to save money and take our chances on eating dinner at the Hall. This time we were lucky; the meat was two recognizable sausages baked in the oven. Since we had been to Leicester, Storkey, and Crowsville, we walked into Brickton. Exploring the village took less time than we thought, so on the way back to the Hall, we stopped at the everything shop opposite the bus shelter at the edge of the village. We bought chocolates and cookies, which the lady told us were sweets and biscuits. In the distance, on the village green, we could see a cricket match.

Jennifer and I had both played softball, but it seemed impossible to figure out the rules. There was batting with a paddle, pitching, catching, throwing, knocking sticks over, running back and forth, and all the players wore white.

"I don't really get it," said Jennifer.

I agreed, but we watched the cricket for a while and leisurely consumed our candy. We didn't want to take any back to the Hall because we would appear stingy if we didn't share with the others, and our money was dwindling.

When we got back, the others were still out in the yard. We washed out some of our clothes with a bar of soap and cold water in the big bathtub. My mother would have been amazed that I was voluntarily doing this. I felt like a washerwoman in Bombay.

The "nominal charge of four shillings a week to cover laundry allows students to send personal items that need ironing" was only for riding breeches, shirts, and dress clothes, which would be washed in the kitchen.

Mrs. Fawcett would swish your clothes around in the old, white washing machine, a tub on legs, and crush them through a hand crank mangle.

If it was rainy, the laundry was dried on wooden racks that were lowered and raised from the kitchen ceiling by rope pulleys. It would have been entirely possible to find a sock in the soup. When they were almost dry, your breeches disappeared in the drying cupboard in the upstairs hallway for an unspecified period of time. Then Mrs. Fawcett would iron them. It was not a fast turnaround.

Jennifer and I were producing stacks of dirty clothes. We quickly realized that the other students went home on their half-day off and most of them lived within a thirty-mile radius of the Hall. Their moms did their laundry. At home, they took baths and ate normal meals. We were definitely at a disadvantage on all counts, especially the laundry issue.

I spent the rest of the evening writing letters home.

On the way into breakfast, Rachael cornered me in the cloakroom. "You may want to start wearing your Wellington boots. It's going to start raining later this week."

Start wearing my Wellington boots? I was wearing Wellington boots just as I had done since day one. My parents bought them for me from the Sears and Roebuck catalog specifically for this trip and Jennifer brought the same boots.

Mrs. Highstaff was very specific about what to bring. "You will need riding clothes. Hard hat, jodhpurs or breeches, boots or jodhpur boots, jacket, gloves, shirts, tie, Wellington boots, riding Mac, jeans or slacks, and plenty of warm clothing. Bring one or two dresses in case you want to change in the evening. I think this is all you will need."

So far, my black leather pull-on work boots that went over my jeans to the bottom of my calf had been fine. The weather had been fair, but Rachael had a point. The boots were not waterproof.

Even if she was the Head Girl, I was tired of her bossing me around. I picked up my riding crop off the shelf. With a flourish I pointed to the boots on my feet. "These *are* Wellington boots."

"Not here they're not." Rachael tossed her head and swaggered into breakfast.

I made a face. I thought about the pricey green rubber boots in Lewes. *Rats! More expense.*

Marion came into the cloakroom. "These are what you need." She pointed to her heavy black knee-high rubber boots with thick soles, the type laborers wore. "You get them at the Army Navy Store. They are a lot less expensive than the fancy ones from the tack shop. If you don't mind hand-me-downs, I'll bring you a pair on loan when I go home this afternoon."

Marion and Ruth were proving to be good friends.

Rachael was right.

Saturday morning was wet, with a thick fog and heavy mist. I was glad Marion had loaned me some boots, but I clumped around in them like Clarabelle the Clown.

It was my first time to bring the ponies in from the field for the busy lesson day ahead. When not being ridden, the ponies lived in the big field. They had a sturdy turnout shed with a zinc water trough. When the ponies were needed for lessons, they were brought into the carriage house and tied, side by side, to rings on the wooden hay manger. While the ponies were eating their hay, they would be groomed, have their feet picked out, be checked over for any possible injuries, then fed. In addition to all that, today they would first have to be dried off with straw and burlap.

I set off jauntily, with the seven small headcollars on my arm and long lead ropes draped over my shoulder, down the path, past the indoor school, and out to the big field to collect the ponies. If you were lucky, the ponies would already be at the gate. However, when you opened it, they would try to slip past you and merrily run back to the stables. This was frowned upon.

The correct procedure was to put headcollars on all the ponies and tie the lead ropes around their necks. Then you would lead the bigger ponies, Ghost and Brandy. The smaller ponies—Ivy, Dinky, Spice, Holly, and Cocoa—would follow.

The ponies were not waiting at the gate.

It was a pretty miserable morning. I thought the ponies might be in the shed, keeping dry. I walked the length of the field. The shed was empty, and there was no evidence that ponies had been here recently.

There were no ponies in a 360-degree view. The fog thickened. I thought they might have gotten out. I walked the fence line along the farm field and saw no obvious gaps, no broken rails, no ponies in the wheat field, and no ponies anywhere.

This is not good. I will have to go back and report this to Mr. Hobbs.

It seemed like a long way back to the stable yard.

The horses were being quartered.

"Mr. Hobbs, I can't find the ponies." This sounded ridiculous, even to me.

A mocking voice came out of one of the box stalls. "Ha-ha!"

I did not find that funny.

Mr. Hobbs did not answer.

Rachael's condescending voice came from a different box. "Look in the ha-ha."

"Take a tin of pony nuts with you," Ruth helpfully added.

I was impatient. "What on earth is a ha-ha? Please . . . where am I going?"

Mr. Hobbs replied matter-of-factly, "You walked right past them. The ponies are in the ha-ha, the big ditch along the edge of the stone wall. Take the tin of nuts with you. When you see them, shake the can. Let them come to you. Give each one a few nuggets when you put their headcollars on."

I jogged back to the field. The borrowed boots were getting heavier. I turned left as soon as I went through the gate and walked along the top of the deep, wide ditch. *I thought this thing was called a moat!*

Three-quarters of the way down the field, almost to the shed, a white apparition appeared in the mist. I peered into the ditch and saw our beautiful Welsh ponies up to their knees in the mucky rivulet. They seemed right at home, contentedly munching the long grass growing on the steep slope of the bank.

The promise of nuggets persuaded the ponies to leave the ditch. Soon I was mobbed by ponies trying to take the tin of nuts away from me. Finally I got them organized and led the soggy crew on the long walk back to the carriage house. It started to drizzle.

Ha-ha indeed. Now I was soaked and would make us all late for breakfast.

When we eventually went to breakfast, I questioned Mr. Hobbs about why the moat was called a ha-ha. I was a little disappointed when I found out it had never been a moat.

"When this place was built, it was fashionable to have a ha-ha surrounding the house. It's practical. It keeps the livestock out of the garden and provides a clear view of the grounds. I wish they would do it today."

Denis interrupted Mr. Hobbs and dramatically elaborated, "Imagine riding across an open field with your friends. You gallop up to the edge of a deep ditch, which you cannot see, and your horse stops. Suddenly, you find yourself in the ditch. I'm sure your riding companions would be giving a few hearty ha-has." Then he added smugly, "If you didn't kill yourself by hitting your head on the stone revetment." Denis thought he was amusing. He liked showing off his education by using fancy words.

Linda started cackling.

And, I thought, the unamused rider in the ditch would have probably replied something like, "#!&$%@@###!" instead of joining in the frivolity.

In fact, "#!&$%@@@###!" crossed my mind. I had already walked and jogged at least a mile before breakfast in borrowed workman's Wellies. I would soon be putting some more miles on the clock, jogging in my riding boots. In The Red Book, I was scheduled to assist with children's lessons for the rest of the day. My consolation was that it was dry in the indoor school.

We were looking forward to the show jumping on the telly on Sunday afternoon, but we were too busy to watch it.

Heels Down Hall jumped into overdrive.

The Colonel was coming to give his course on Monday, but even more importantly, we had to get the place ready for the exam. We spent the entire afternoon washing every window and cobwebbing the entire stable.

Because the Colonel's course had priority over the regular riding, Jennifer, Linda, Ruth, and I were scheduled to have our lesson out in the drizzle. Mr. Hobbs told us we could wear our riding Macs.

Linda was loudly singing what sounded like "It Never Rains in Southern California" when she appeared in an oversized windbreaker. Mr. Hobbs frowned but said nothing.

I wore my clear plastic riding raincoat twice before, both times in the trailer. The ponies didn't mind it at all. The broodmares gave me the hairy eyeball, but they were more interested in eating hay.

Everybody in the Flatlanders horse show circuit wore these plastic coats, over their show clothes, if it was raining. They were the latest, greatest thing.

When Jennifer mounted Ghost, using the millstones stacked near the end of the carriage house, he was nonplussed by Jennifer's plastic raincoat. He just accepted it. Cherokee did not give them a second glance.

Cherry behaved normally until I tried to mount, then he wanted no part of me. He danced around and around. I couldn't get on him. The more we moved around, the more the raincoat rustled. Rachael held his head, but he still danced around. This was embarrassing.

While this spectacle played out by the mounting block, Ruth mounted Topaz in the courtyard around the corner. She appeared, wearing a very smart off-white, rubberized cotton, military-style raincoat. It was belted, had gussets in the back so it went over the cantle, and it went down to her knees. The collar was turned up, which prevented the water dripping off her hard hat from going down her neck.

Mr. Hobbs looked at his watch. "You'll have to ride without your raincoat—we're five minutes late already."

Great, now I am going to have a soggy jacket for the rest of the day.

Jennifer and Linda were already riding down the path. Ruth jogged Topaz up alongside Cherokee. "Army Navy Store," she whispered with her pixie-ish grin. She halted Topaz until Cherokee could slide past and we dropped back into single file.

We could hear the Colonel bellowing at someone as we rode past the indoor school.

The tension at HDH was pervasive.

Chapter 6
Disinherited Knight

The exam candidates were nervous, except for Denis, who was exceedingly confident, but he was confident about everything. Fiona and Marion had failed the exam previously when they took it last year at a different riding school. Fiona knew the material upside down and inside out, and she was a pretty and effective rider, but she failed by three points, and Marion, who was very competent, missed by only *one* point.

This wasn't good news, but I thought at least now they know what to expect.

Our other exam candidate, Janet, had been a residential student here for two months. She was quiet and didn't mix in much with us. She spent most of her time in her private room reading or taking notes on assignments for Mrs. Highstaff. Sometimes she took extra, private riding lessons. She was a beautiful rider and had ridden show jumping ponies as a kid.

The BHSAI exam consisted of four sections: Equitation, Stable Management and Horsemanship, Minor Ailments, and Powers of Instruction. To Pass or Qualify, you needed seventy-five out of a possible one hundred points, but Minimum Passing Marks in each subject added up to only seventy points. It was possible to be awarded more than the seventy-five qualifying marks, but not reach the minimum in one subject and still fail. If you failed, or did not sit for, the Powers of Instruction and had the required marks, you were awarded the Horsemaster's Certificate.

Ruth, Jennifer, Linda, and I were going to be guinea pigs for the Powers of Instruction. Mrs. Highstaff told us it provided us with an excellent opportunity to preview a part of the exam.

The following evening after tack cleaning, Mrs. Highstaff asked us to assemble outside the tack room door. There were puzzled looks all around when she handed each one of us a hoof pick.

She informed us, "You will use the hoof picks to dig out all the little weeds which have sprouted up in the spaces in the brick walkway. Start at the car park, go to the stable gate, around the tack room, past the kitchen and dining hall, and to the backdoor of the Hall. When you finish, turn in your hoof picks to Rachael, and you may go to supper."

I wondered why they didn't just use weed killer, but there was no arguing. The sooner we did this, the sooner we could eat.

The day before the exam, we assembled a long list of all the equipment the examiners would need. The practical portions of Stable Management and Horsemanship would be held in the stables and at stations set up around the indoor school.

Early on the morning of the exam, six outside exam candidates arrived and assembled in the tack room together with our students. Mrs. Highstaff brought the examiners up from the Hall. The examiners were famous equestrians and very intimidating.

The exam itself went like clockwork; each stage held without a glitch. We had all the horses ready on time and Mr. Hobbs kept us busy and out of the way. The exam took all day.

A community sigh of relief rippled through the whole place when the last examiner's car drove down the driveway and we went into supper.

We would have the unofficial results tomorrow. The chief examiner was going to ring Mrs. Highstaff at two o'clock.

I was certain all our students would pass.

We went to bed with high hopes.

By tea time the next day, there were a lot of long faces.

Of all our students, only Denis had passed the BHSAI. Janet failed Powers of Instruction because she had whispered her lesson but passed the Horsemaster. Only four of the outsiders passed.

Rumors circulated through the students' quarters. The whispers sounded like "The examiners favor candidates from some schools over others" and "The whole system is a moneymaker for the BHS."

We wondered if HDH would host another exam. When I questioned him, Mr. Hobbs solemnly added, "It is my opinion that Americans, or any other nationality, are going to have to be well above the normal standard to pass. It may be hard for you to understand this, Alexa, but there is still resentment about the Yanks coming into the war too late."

The disappointing and unexpected exam results shed a whole new light on my adventure. I was an honor student and used to passing *everything*, but it was very possible to *fail* this exam. If you did fail, you could reapply and pay the fee and take the exam again, after a minimum of six months of further training. That wouldn't help me; I didn't live here. I would only have one shot to pass.

As disappointed as we were, the examiners were favorably impressed with the quality of the horses, the splendid variety of cross-country and show jumps, and the lecture hall, which was ideal for administering the written Minor Ailments test. We didn't know it, but the examiners, while sipping a glass of sherry in Mrs. Highstaff's formal drawing room before they left, had already set an exam date for June 1968.

In the week following the exam, Rachael became more condescending. Smug Denis sought to console and cheer up Fiona, whose parents said she should stay on and try again. Like the trooper she was, Marion agreed to stay on as well.

Janet left.

I befriended the Stapleford children who were Saturday regulars. The ten-year-old twins Peter and Violet and their younger sister Alice thought it was terrible that we could never go home.

The next Saturday morning, when Mrs. Stapleford dropped her kids off for lessons, she invited the Americans to join them for supper at their home. The kids cheerfully stayed all day. They loved it here and were happy to groom ponies and help us clean tack.

We were a little surprised when Mr. Stapleford arrived in his Bentley to drive us to Blakemore, their home in historical Ashby de la Zouch. I thought la Zouch must have been the name of some invading Norman.

The back garden at Blakemore was a delight, filled with flowering plants and large trees with colorful Japanese lanterns strung between the branches.

We were entertained by the children's stick horse steeplechase, and we admired their pet guinea pigs. We laughed because we had recently been guinea pigs ourselves.

Violet knew I loved reading and she presented me with a handmade horse magazine. She had written the whole thing herself, all the articles, some poems, and even letters to the Editor.

Dear Sir,

I would like to start a riding school. How would I do it?

(Mrs.) R H Birde. The Stables. 41 Spring Lane. Leics. England

Editor's answer:

I am afraid it would take a long time to write, so I will telephone you instead.

After our entertainment, we enjoyed a picnic, with cold ham slices, corned beef, lettuce and tomatoes, real potato salad, and for dessert, strawberry flan.

Taking advantage of the long summer evening, we sauntered over to the ruins of the castle. Mrs. Stapleford neatly condensed the castle's eight hundred-year history. "Since the days of King John in the twelfth century, this place has been known for daring feats of horsemanship. Great Jousts were held here. In Sir Walter Scott's *Ivanhoe*, the Disinherited Knight, a champion for King Richard, defeats all comers on the lists on this field."

Peter started cheering, "Long live King Richard! King Richard-Lionheart!"

Mrs. Stapleford calmly continued, "By the 1400s the Hastings family built the castle."

Violet excitedly interrupted, "Mummy, don't forget to tell them Mary Queen of Scots was a prisoner here."

Mrs. Stapleford finished her story. "After the Civil War, Cromwell ordered the Roundheads to blow out one wall in each room of the castle to punish the Royalist Hasting family."

As soon as I heard this, I instantly disliked Cromwell.

We arrived at the castle ruins. The admission gate was closed, but not to be deterred, the children led us around the side to a crumbling tower. We clambered through the open window and explored everything.

Peter suddenly raised his arm as if holding an imaginary sword and shouted out, "To the Ramparts!" And we boldly climbed to the top of the one tower that was still standing and surveyed our kingdom.

Peter warned us, "Enemy approaching. Time to escape. Follow me." We stealthily crept through an underground passageway.

When we emerged from the dark, narrow tunnel, we found ourselves standing on the ancient jousting field outside the castle wall. I imagined the Disinherited Knight and his big black charger, both clad in full armor, thundering out onto the field, the knight's deadly lance lowered and ready for battle.

I was sad when we left the castle and returned to the Hall.

Cherokee was going home next week.

A letter from home waited for me on the post counter. Instead of going to bed like Jennifer and Linda, I took my letter, went into the lounge, and sat at my favorite place, the writing table by the window.

The letter contained clippings from our local paper in Greenleaf. "Brawl in Leicester Pub."

Characteristically, my parents questioned whether or not I should go into Leicester.

The article was just another example of tabloid news. The incident occurred fourteen miles away from Leicester in a Chinese restaurant. After a closely won match, two buses full of drunken football supporters from opposing teams had booked the same restaurant for the same time.

I wondered with all the real problems in the world, like the Vietnam War and race riots, how this relatively insignificant piece of international trivia even made the pages of the *Greenleaf Daily Journal.* But then again, football brawls were a distraction from the real world.

Other clippings featured my brother, Richard, winning game after game for the Tobacco Bank Little League Baseball team. Making fantastic plays every game, and being voted Most Valuable Player, Richard was a local star.

Some bittersweet news from home was that the college I was accepted to had just been granted full university status. Now I would be graduating from a university, but my acceptance had been to the college. Acceptances were being carried over, but one had to reapply. The worst part was that my promised academic scholarship was in jeopardy because I did not use it immediately after graduating from high school.

I naively thought that living and working abroad for a year would impress the provincial college administrators, but my dad said the dean, whose daughter showed Saddlebreds on the Flatlander circuit, seemed to think it was just girls playing around with horses and I would have to take further testing.

I briefly wondered if I could be deported for not providing the photos to the police in a timely fashion. The exam results were foremost on my mind *and* Denis's anecdote of the rider flying into the ha-ha made me remember what Mrs. Highstaff had told me.

I replied to my parents:

> *Please don't forget to send the two photographs for the police.*
>
> *We don't have much spare time, and I have loads of studying to do, so please don't get upset if letters don't come so often. I shall try to write at least every two weeks.*
>
> *Dad, this is important! Mrs. Highstaff must have a letter, giving her authority to tell a doctor at a hospital that I can have anesthetics. This must be signed by both parents.*
>
> *Lots of love,*
>
> *Alexa*

I laid my letter for home on the post counter downstairs and went to bed.

During the next week, I was appointed librarian in addition to my other duties. A wall-sized bookcase was installed in the lecture room. I got to organize Mrs. Highstaff's accumulated treasure trove of equestrian literature. I enjoyed this, and I had to watch the amount of time I spent in the library.

On our next half-day off, Jennifer and I went back to Leicester. We skipped Lewes Equestrian Emporium altogether, and instead, we went directly to the Army Navy Store to buy our proper workman's Wellies and mounted police surplus riding Macs.

Chapter 7
Halcyon Days of Summer

The summer school holiday officially started. Heels Down Hall was invaded by people and equines. The first to arrive were Jeremy, accompanied by his horse Falstaff, and Julian, a fourteen-year-old HDH regular.

Miraculously, Linda switched from working student status to being a resident student "so she could study more." She moved out of our room into private quarters. This situation was fine with the rest of us because we didn't like living with her, and she did not pull her weight in the stable. Her parents now paid more money for her to do less work.

Cherokee left much more trained than when he came. Mr. Brown paid Mrs. Highstaff, which made her happy. He gave us a large box of chocolates to share, which made the other WPs happy. Mr. Brown was happy because he had a buyer for Cherokee. Sally was getting a pedigree puppy, which made Sally happy.

I was sad. I was the one who did most of the pony's training, and I was starting to really like Cherokee.

I wasn't to be sad for long because Bombay arrived, along with another pony named Pewter. The welfare of these two ponies was added to that of my other charges, Chris and Harry. I was also on the Rota for Tack Room this week and there was a lot more tack to clean and organize.

Now I was riding the two grays, Harry the plodding giant or Bombay the nimble dancer, in our lessons with Mrs. Highstaff or Mr. Hobbs. Jennifer rode the saintly Pewter. Jeremy rode his amazing horse Falstaff; Falstaff could do the Spanish walk and kneel on one knee. Denis commented that with

Falstaff, Jeremy could always join the circus as a ringmaster. Jeremy was tall, thin, and gawky, but well-groomed and had excellent manners. I liked him because he was helpful.

Rachael left us alone; she was busy teaching the holiday course.

Two typical thirteen-year-old, horse-crazy girls and their ponies arrived. Susan with Miami and Mary with Ladybug. Even though the girls were unrelated, when they weren't on their ponies, they were hard to tell apart. Julian was a regular Saturday rider. He rode Meteor, another of HDH's homebred Anglo-Arabs. In his spare time, Julian played harmless practical jokes on people and asked a million questions.

After the kids were in bed one evening, Rachael started to complain that Mr. Hobbs or Mrs. Highstaff would unexpectedly drop by and observe her lessons or lectures.

I didn't envy Jennifer on the Rota for Breakfast tomorrow morning with fourteen places to set and more tea and toast to make.

I had been here a month and I finally qualified for my first full Sunday off. As it turned out, my first full Sunday off coincided with that of Rachael's.

I didn't fancy spending a fine summer day at the Hall but there was no point in going to Leicester or even Brickton. Everything in England, it seemed, was closed on Sundays except for corner shops that were only open in the morning until noon.

Early Sunday morning, Rachael and I were in the kitchen with the others who were working. We gulped down our morning cup of tea, and out of the blue, Rachael asked me, "Alexa, do you want to go home with me for the day?" I was mystified by Rachael's offer. I didn't get on that well with her, but after weighing my limited options, I was happy to accept a chance to see another part of the country and I would enjoy eating some home-cooked food.

Mr. Hardwick picked us up after breakfast and drove us to their suburban home in Derby. I was quickly instructed to pronounce the name "Darby."

While I happily sat in the back seat and watched the countryside roll by, I gleaned tidbits of Rachael's background from her discussion with her father. She didn't know if she could stick it out another year. Mr. Hobbs was always grousing at her—blah, blah, blah. To top it off, when she said goodnight to Mrs. Highstaff, my ears perked up like a German Shepherd's. Mrs. Highstaff suggested to Rachael that she should cut back on her biscuit consumption because her hacking jacket was getting tight.

She had been having tea with the holiday kids who got biscuits, in addition to eating the bread and jam later in the afternoon with us.

Personally, I didn't see how anyone could gain weight at Heels Down Hall. I had lost five pounds in a month and, even as a picky eater, I was eating more than I ever had before.

After I had dinner with the Hardwicks, I could see how Rachael was gaining weight. She plowed right in. We devoured a traditional roast beef dinner with Yorkshire pudding, roast vegetables, fresh garden peas, and a massive fruit and cake trifle for dessert, followed by a cheeseboard. I was very relieved when there was not a cabbage in sight.

Mr. Hardwick suggested we walk off our dinner by touring nearby Kedleston Hall.

The Hall was a prime example of Palladian architecture set in magnificent grounds, with a row of serpentine lakes punctuating long swaths of green lawn and unusual ornamental trees that provided shade canopies. The manicured lawns and paths were edged with flowers.

We wandered through the immense house filled with antique furnishings and old master paintings, but I wasn't too impressed until we went to the original Chapel built by the thirteenth-century baron. The triple-panel stained glass window depicted a king in armor flanked by two soldiers. It was the Crusaders' version of Christ and his generals, Joshua and David. Spooky life-sized, life-like, stone knights peacefully slept on marble slabs on the tombs. I started thinking, *At least these Christian soldiers made it back from the Holy Land to be buried in England. I wonder if they ever encountered the Disinherited Knight.* It was strangely awe-inspiring.

After the visit to Kedleston Hall, we returned to Rachael's comfortable home to have tea. This time tea meant a light supper. Mrs. Hardwick poured the tea from the pot and passed the steaming hot cups around. I thought that was a potentially hazardous practice.

"It is my dream," she said, sighing wistfully, "to have high tea in the Palm Court at the Ritz in London. I would be dressed in my finest clothes and politely nibble tiny fancy sandwiches and delicious creamy pastries served on delicate china and sparkling silver." Listening to her fantasize about being prim and proper didn't stop us from greedily finishing off our thick roast beef sandwiches and helpings of salad.

It was a pleasant evening, and we had an hour before Mr. Hardwick planned to drive us back, so Rachael and I, along with her fawn-colored spaniel, Hermione, walked over to visit her friend's pony kept in a nearby paddock.

Rachael wasted no time starting her campaign. "I was a Head Girl before I came to HDH . . . blah . . . blah . . . blah." She brushed her frizzy hair away from her face. "I passed my AI on the *first* try. I have already been with HDH for a year, but you must be twenty-one to take the BHS Instructor Exam . . . blah . . . blah . . . blah. . . . I keep up to date by reading the modern horse magazines, not just that dated War Department information."

She paused. "By the way, Alexa, what do you think of Mr. Hobbs?"

I thought Mr. Hobbs was tough, but he could hop on and sort out any horse, which Rachael could not do, and he was a walking horse encyclopedia. I hesitated to answer.

Rachael did not give me time to reply. "He is so old-fashioned. He won't listen to any new ideas," she said haughtily.

We arrived at the paddock. It was empty.

The Hardwicks had been very gracious hosts to me.

I wasn't going to argue. In the US, the police always had to read the Miranda warning before questioning their suspects. I knew anything I said could be used against me.

On the way back, I threw sticks for Hermione and made a great fuss of the dog, so I could avoid further discussion. I wasn't interested in Rachael's woes or career aspirations.

The drive back to the Hall was relatively quiet.

❧

The horse show season was at its height.

I was chosen to accompany Mr. Hobbs. Caroline and Mango were competing in a big show in Lincolnshire. On the way to the show, we passed a Robin Hood-Sherwood Forest motorway stop. "Mr. Hobbs, if this is a forest, why aren't there more trees?"

He replied, "That is a fair question . . . the word Forest in medieval times just meant a hunting ground, regardless of the amount of vegetation." I was disappointed. Robin Hood was one of my favorite Saturday morning TV heroes, and *that* Robin Hood was always hiding in and jumping out of big trees to surprise the unsuspecting sheriff's men.

To put it mildly, we had a spectacular day. Caroline earned third place in Best Rider, competing against much older children. But that was just for starters.

Mango scored a double victory, winning both Best Novice Pony and Best Pony over 13-2 hands. Novice Pony was sponsored by *Riding* magazine. The winner received a challenge trophy and a smaller trophy to keep, and more importantly, the winning pony and rider had a photograph and full-page write-up in the well-respected magazine. Because of the unusual double win, Caroline was interviewed by reporters and photographers snapped photos for another popular magazine called *Pony*.

Mrs. Highstaff was delighted. Mango was a homebred and Caroline had been riding at Heels Down Hall since she was four.

When we got back to the Hall, Vivian and Tina had arrived to join the holiday course. Now there were sixteen places for breakfast.

The following Monday another big horse show was scheduled for Market Bosworth. It was the summer holiday in Scotland, and the holiday was also being observed here. In addition to taking Mango to this show, Jazzy was making his debut under saddle.

Four-year-old Jazzy was Rachael's sole stable charge and her training project. Last year at the prestigious Leicester County Show, Jazzy was Champion in his In-Hand division. He was another HDH homebred, a dark bay, 14-3 hand Anglo-Arab. He looked like a small, very refined Thoroughbred.

Prior to the show, Rachael had been confident, but now that we were actually here, she was getting nervous and she ordered me around endlessly. She was worried because Jazzy was the youngest and greenest horse in his class.

To top it off, Mrs. Highstaff didn't tell us she was coming, but Mr. Hobbs told us he had sighted her in the tea tent.

After Mango's big win at Lincoln, we were disappointed when she only got one rosette for third in Novice Pony. Mango placed fourth in Best Pony, but no award was given for fourth place.

On the other hand, Jazzy was a disaster. He placed sixth, but only because he did not bolt like the eighth-placed horse did when the seventh-placed horse started bucking.

During the intermission, the Featherstone Foxhounds grandly paraded around the arena. I had seen them before at Scuthering. I admired the dashing hunt staff in their pink coats mounted on stately, well-groomed horses, and I loved the exuberant pack of tricolored inquisitive hounds.

The brochure from Heels Down Hall mentioned foxhunting:

> *Hacking over roads, fields, and tracks is available in the surrounding countryside, and in winter advanced pupils have the opportunity to hunt with the Featherstone Foxhounds.*

Winter has never been my favorite season, but I was looking forward to hunting. This is exactly what I first imagined I would be doing when I got the *Riding* magazine in Nairobi.

Just a flicker of doubt crossed my mind over the words "advanced pupils." As a rider I was fearless, almost foolhardy, but would Mrs. Highstaff consider me advanced enough to go hunting?

I resumed my fantasy.

Chapter 8
The Great Escape

Every Monday we switched jobs on the Rota. It was Linda's turn for Ponies this week. One of the required duties listed under Ponies on the Rota was to turn them out in the evening. After another long, busy day we said our good nights to Mrs. Highstaff and went to bed. Every night I slept like I was in a coma, mostly from exhaustion.

Around eleven o'clock Mrs. Highstaff was in her study finishing some correspondence when she looked up and saw Ghost ambling across the lawn in front of the window. Peering out into the gloom, she spotted Ivy and Holly, two little greys, heading toward the drive. Spice, a light chestnut, was munching the hydrangeas. Brandy, a dark liver chestnut, Cocoa, a dark bay, and Dinky, a black, were not visible.

Mrs. Highstaff summoned Rachael and told her to quickly wake up Mr. Hobbs and get everyone else up. Rachael scurried from room to room, pounding on the doors and shouting, "Pajamas, coats, and Wellies. No time to get dressed!"

As he passed by on the way down to the stable, Mr. Hobbs knocked on the doors again. "Hurry up."

It was a crazy dream. There seemed to be a lot of commotion and a faint distant phantom calling my name. I pulled the covers up and rolled over.

The ponies headed for the road to Brickton.

In the stable yard, torches were issued to everyone.

Fiona pelted down the drive to check that the gates to the main road were closed. Others dashed to get tins of nuts, headcollars, and lead ropes.

The ponies were not keen on being caught by dark shapes lurching around with darting lights.

It took a long time to collect the ponies and to thoroughly check them over for possible injury, before returning them to the big field. It was well over two hours when everyone wearily and nosily returned to bed.

I never woke up.

The next morning, I cheerfully went down to the kitchen for my early cup of tea.

Only Rachael and Fiona were there. They barely looked at me, and there was no "hello" or "good morning." This was odd. The others were late.

Okay, everyone's grumpy today. I didn't care. I was never very talkative at six in the morning.

When the others finally straggled into the yard, I got the same silent treatment, but morning stables were not usually a time for chitchat anyway.

I didn't know it, but I was in Coventry.

After morning stables, Linda went directly up to her room.

At breakfast I was surrounded by long, tired faces.

I was not amused by the averted eyes and lack of conversation. "Everyone seems to be in a bad mood. What is the problem this morning?"

Apparently, lazy Linda did not shut the gate to the field securely when she turned out the ponies last evening.

Well, that has nothing to do with me.

"*And* all the ponies got out during the night," Mr. Hobbs said while he munched his toast.

"What? Why didn't you wake me up?" I was indignant.

Even my best friends Marion and Jennifer chimed in, "We tried!"

"I called you!" Rachael said sharply.

I was really upset. "You know I would help!"

"You just laid there."

"I thought I was dreaming! Why didn't you shake me?"

"We didn't have time."

It was hard for me to convince them that I had not intentionally ignored the calls and I actually had slept through all the commotion.

Why the ponies wanted to go to Brickton when they had loads of grass to eat and everything they wanted at the Hall was beyond me.

Linda's act of negligence, of not securing the gate properly, resulting in the escape of the ponies, was the last straw for Mrs. Highstaff.

Shortly after the ponies' great escape, Mrs. Highstaff made an expensive intercontinental trunk telephone call from Brickton to California.

Linda departed from us to attend a riding school in Scotland. I thought this was a disservice to Scotland, but I was happy to see her go.

The summer was clicking along.

I thought HDH was busy with these extra kids living here, but on Wednesday I found out what busy was really like.

Forty-two Featherstone Foxhounds Pony Club kids and their ponies descended on Heels Down Hall for their summer riding rally. The courtyard was a sea of assorted sizes of ponies and children.

With the authority of a General, Mrs. Highstaff quickly sorted them out into levels.

I was to review "position" with a group of little kids who were preparing for the D-level tests, and then hand them over to Denis for a lesson in the little paddock. Before I fully realized I had just taught my first solo teaching assignment, I was sent off to another paddock to assist Marion with a dozen children of varying ages who were working toward their C level.

After the Pony Club Rally, Mr. Hobbs disappeared.

Ruth speculated, "I think he has a young wife and a child somewhere in the West Country."

He was gone for four days.

During his absence, Mrs. Highstaff was murder on us.

She was fanatical. Everything had to be done the BHS way. We weren't even allowed to drop the handles on the water buckets. "The noise annoys the horses." Worst of all, she required Jennifer and me to attend Rachael's stable management lectures for the holiday students. I am sure we learned something, but it was a little humiliating.

The kids brightened up the place. They adored us. We were the goddesses of the horse. The dining table was a bit cramped, but no one minded. Two more girls, without ponies, joined the holiday course.

It was a fine afternoon. After tea, Tanya and Marcy were the first ones out to the stables. They liked to gaze into the stalls and converse with the horses. Unless the staff was in the yard, the holiday students were not allowed to go into any loose boxes.

We were in the cloakroom getting our hats and kit for the afternoon rides.

The backdoor flew open. The girls came through the door as fast as they could without running because running was strictly forbidden. They were breathless and frantic.

Tanya shrieked. "*Help*! *Help*! Come quickly!"

"Something's terribly wrong!" Marcy had tears running down her cheeks.

"Calm down," Rachael firmly told them. "What's the problem?"

"Rob Roy and Minstrel are lying down and making terrible noises! We think they are *colicking*." Marcy's voice was quavering. Yesterday Rachael gave us the lecture notes on Colic for Minor Ailments. We knew that colic could be fatal.

We wasted no time getting out to the stables. We had been taught to observe the horses without disturbing them, so we could accurately assess the situation. We strode along silently, keeping calm and carrying on.

The late afternoon sun was shining directly through the open tops of the stable doors, but there were no happy-to-see-you faces hanging over any of the stable doors.

Piteous loud and terrifying noises were being emitted from two loose boxes.

Terrible scenarios raced through our minds. *The horses are down! Are they cast from rolling? What did they eat? Are all the horses going to get sick?*

We knew we should get the horses onto their feet as quickly and safely as possible. Mr. Hobbs would want to know pulse, respiration, and temperature. He would be here in a minute.

We tiptoed up the stall doors and silently peeped into the boxes. We watched the horses for a minute.

Rob Roy and Minstrel were soundly sleeping with their chests heaving. The young horses were lying down, comfortably stretched out flat on thick, clean beds of straw, snoring their heads off.

A low ripple of chuckles started to grow louder, and then Rob Roy yawned and rolled his eyes, and a wave of relieved laughter erupted.

Rob Roy ridiculously had his mouth open with his teeth exposed and his tongue hanging out. His ears flopped out to the side and his partially open eyes looked glazed.

It was easy to see why anyone would think he was dying.

On a warm summer afternoon and with the sun shining on me, I wouldn't have minded having a kip on a soft straw bed, without the snoring part, myself.

That evening Julian had us in stitches imitating the noises and faces of the sleeping horses.

The next morning when I looked at the Rota, I was disappointed to see my name next to Ducks.

Until now I had been pretty indifferent to the four scruffy white ducks. They didn't seem to have names, so I called them Donald, Huey, Dewey, and Louie.

During the day, the ducks waddled about, greedily gobbling bugs and whatever they could find. The ducks were kept out of the stable yard by a gate. Stepping on slimy duck droppings was dangerous for those wearing leather-soled riding boots.

If the ducks wandered into the stable yard, they created more work for us by swimming in the wooden water tubs. Then the heavy tubs would have to be emptied, scoured, and refilled.

The ducks had to have fresh water every day, but as soon as you put it down, they walked around in it. They ate duck meal mixed with a disgusting, smelly concoction of potato peels, leftover cabbage, and god knows what else.

The ducks lived in a small metal hut, which reminded me of a prisoner cage in *Bridge on the River Kwai*, and it had to be mucked out once a week.

Much to my amazement, while I was squatting down inside the hut, removing the stinky straw, I found three eggs in the back of the shed.

Rachael ordered me, "Take those three eggs into the kitchen."

At breakfast Mrs. Fawcett's curly white-haired head poked through the open dining hall door. "Who wants a boiled duck egg?"

The duck eggs were twice the size of the chicken eggs. Mr. Hobbs and Denis both claimed one immediately. Jeremy declined.

Denis winked at Fiona. "Real men eat duck eggs."

Fiona blushed. Jeremy looked stunned.

"*Eeeewwwwwwuu!*" A spontaneous chorus of dismay erupted from all the adolescent girls around the table.

Earlier that morning on her mile-and-a-half walk to work, Mrs. Fawcett noticed that the blackberries in the hedgerows along the lane had ripened. *Better get to those before the birds do*, she thought.

She wondered if she would have the energy to stop and pick them on the way home. If she did stop, she would get home even later than usual. On the other hand, berries were expensive in the greengrocer shop. Free food, especially fresh food, was always welcome.

She grimaced; a bunion was bothering her. She rubbed her foot and then an idea occurred to her.

As soon as Ruth came into the kitchen, the very practical Mrs. Fawcett got right to the point. "Mornin', Ruth. You and your friends could pick those blackberries I saw this morning on my way to the Hall. If you gather enough, I'll bake crumbles for the lot of you. While the oven is on, I suppose I could make a little tart for myself to take home."

Mrs. Fawcett would not repeat her offer.

Ruth's face lit up. It was a challenge that had to be met. "How many would you need?"

At lunch Ruth sold us on the idea. We would get scratched picking blackberries, but the end result would be worth it. We were sick of eating the nourishing and free—but boring—gooseberries that grew along the back garden wall. Every day it was gooseberry this, gooseberry that, and gooseberry something else.

After supper we gathered in the kitchen. While Ruth distributed the pots and pans that Mrs. Fawcett left for us, she instructed us, "Don't eat *too* many berries—we have to fill the pots. The point is to get enough for blackberry crumble." Given that advice we rushed off to the hedgerows.

The next morning when Mrs. Fawcett opened the wooden plank door to the kitchen, she lit a cigarette and grinned. Tin pots filled with juicy blackberries were lined up on the wooden table.

While we were enjoying our blackberry crumble at lunch, we received an important announcement. The Highstaffs were going to Ireland for a month in September. We were jubilant.

Then it dawned on me. My pal, Jennifer, would be heading back to the US to start college soon. Thinking of her departure made me anxious about my admission to the University.

That evening, I wrote home:

Dear Everyone,

Please send me the University application so I can get started on it.

Jennifer is going to bring the presents I bought for everyone home with her. I bought Richard a suede tie, but if he doesn't like it, please keep it for me. What would Dad like?

I am planning to accompany Jennifer to London. We are planning on going down the night before.

I bought a roll of color film, so we are taking pictures. Jennifer will get them developed in Greenleaf since this is awfully expensive over here.

Rachael and Wizard went to a Prix Caprilli, which is a dressage and show jumping event where the rider is judged as well as the horse. I thought they did reasonably well, but Mr. Hobbs grumbled, "If Rachael would have ridden him better, they could have won."

Congratulations to Richard and the Tobacco Bank Little League team on making it to the State play-off!

Mom, good luck on getting your job as a trainer with President Johnson's Job Corps.

By the way, Mom, I wore my brick breeches yesterday. They are fabulous! It seems they have not started making riding breeches in denim here yet. Ruth said she'd like to get a pair because we are supposed to wear jodhpurs or breeches and a shirt and tie from breakfast onwards and canaries get dirty too fast.

I had a postcard from Sherry, my high school friend who is now in Denmark. Maybe she will visit me at HDH before going home."

I've been riding Kris Kringle, a 16-2 dapple grey. Mr. Hobbs told me to buy a pair of blunt Prince of Wales spurs and spur straps which will cost me $5.32. I will only be allowed to use the spurs on certain horses at specified times.

I only have about $50 left.

Love,

Alexa

Chapter 9

All Change

The holiday kids went back to school. The ponies went home. Pewter went back to Mary, who decided to buy a Thoroughbred. Personally, I thought Mary would be better off sticking with Pewter. Mary was not a gutsy rider, and a three-year-old Thoroughbred would probably kill her.

The Highstaffs left for Ireland.

Before she left, Mrs. Highstaff agreed to purchase all the straw directly from the Hall Farm. Since the farmer would not have to store and stack the straw, and sell it later in the year, and the baled straw, straight from the field, would be delivered next door, he was happy to make a deal. Mrs. Highstaff saved a bundle.

The golden wheat in the farmer's field next to our pasture was waist high. The heads of grain were mature and ready to harvest. Combines chugged back and forth, clipping the corn tops off the long stalks.

As we rode out in the field, more than one horse spooked from the ungainly machine's clanking and banging. Then the baling began. Even scarier, noisier machines picked up the cut straw and spat out rectangular bales directly onto the ground.

Rain was likely in the forecast.

Straw bales dry out faster if they are aerated. This is accomplished by leaning them against each other to form windrows. If stacked wet, straw can combust or get moldy, then Mrs. Highstaff's precious straw would be rendered worthless for horses and sold off cheaply as mulch.

On Saturday, after the children's rides were over, *we* were going to windrow the straw bales and stay at it until the whole field was finished.

Windrowing requires gloves and a long-sleeve shirt since straw is prickly. The baling string was rough hemp twine. I had never lifted or carried more than a few bales of straw at a time. I chose the wrong shirt, my favorite: a navy blue, shimmery top with a round neckline and long sleeves, which I had bought in a boutique in New York City. It looked great with my faded blue jeans.

Mr. Hobbs told us exactly how he wanted the job done. "To make the windrows, two people work together as a team. One person goes down one row of baled straw, and the other person walks down the row next to them. Pick up a bale by the two strings; try not to hit your knees or drag the bales on the ground. The bales can break. Meet the other person and tilt the bales together in an inverted V. The next pair of bales leans against the first ones, and so on."

By the end of the windrow, the straw looked like a long, yellow snake. After a few hours of windrowing, my shirt was ruined; covered with pulls and snags. My riding gloves had holes in them. My back ached.

When we finished late Saturday night, we climbed over the fence between the field and our pasture.

Looking back at the field, I had to admit there was something rustically beautiful, almost Van Gogh like, about the long, pale gold windrows of straw.

Everyone was starving, but we hadn't cleaned the lesson tack. Amazingly, Mr. Hobbs, who was as tired as everyone else, said, "You can clean the tack Sunday morning."

The Sunday schedule changed. All staff was now on duty, no days off, no half-day off, no church, and no TV. All of the usual Sunday stable chores had to be done before lunch, plus cleaning the Saturday tack. After lunch, we were going to help the farm lads stack the straw into ricks.

The lads arrived with the first of many flatbed wagons loaded with straw. We stopped whatever we were doing and went out to help them unload and stack it. The farm laborers never spoke to us. They only spoke to Mr. Hobbs. Mr. Hobbs directed us.

In the end, we had four massive ricks of straw, all with tarps neatly tied down over the tops. There was enough straw to supply HDH for the next year or possibly more. When it finally dawned on me that I would not be here at this time next year, I was happy.

Unexpectedly, Marion had to leave. Her usually robust father had taken ill. She was the oldest child and had to return home to help out on their farm.

Her mother had a chronically poorly back and couldn't do heavy work. I thought Mrs. Button probably injured her back while stacking straw, but this was no joking matter.

No one knew what the outcome of this illness would be.

Marion went home on Monday morning.

One day during the week, I realized Mr. Hobbs was here alone, teaching a lesson in the indoor school. It was Rachael's afternoon off. Mr. Hobbs could not be everywhere at once like Mrs. Highstaff seemed able to be.

I was scheduled to exercise Harry. I recently discovered that if you were riding with spurs on, Harry was a terrific jumper. Fully aware that unsupervised jumping was strictly prohibited, I confidently decided to trot down to the bottom of the field and sneak in a few cross-country jumps. I rationalized my decision. "Harry will be cubbing in a few weeks and he needs to jump some bigger jumps."

Harry was so big that normal cross-country jumps, like the real park bench, looked tiny. On the way to the lower field, in the fence line, there was a dandy wide stile hidden by shrubs, plus at the bottom of the field there was a large, shallow ditch. By putting a rail jump over the middle of the ditch, it could become a Liverpool.

Apparently, I wasn't the only one who thought of riding out of sight in the lower field. As I jumped over the stile into the lower field, I saw Fiona and Denis remounting their horses. Fiona was putting something in her top jacket pocket.

This was curious. I had seen Fiona and Denis catching a quick kiss in the tack room once before, but I really didn't care what they did as long as it did not involve me. I wasn't crazy about either one of them. At least they couldn't rat me out for jumping.

Before she went on holiday, Mrs. Highstaff made it very clear that two unchaperoned seventeen-year-old girls were *not* going to London the night before Jennifer left for home.

So, on Wednesday, September 6, Jennifer said her farewells before dawn.

We trundled into Brickton loaded with Jennifer's luggage and caught the earliest bus into Leicester. The bus was crammed with factory workers who spilled out noisily in front of big, smoke-belching, brick buildings on the outskirts of town.

We absolutely needed to connect with the bus that left Leicester City at 7:15 a.m. for the Victoria Bus Station. This would put us near our destination, the BOAC downtown terminal.

There was only one snag in our carefully mapped-out plan. The bus we needed only operated on Monday, Friday, and Saturday. The only alternative was to speed-walk to the train station, carrying the cases. We managed to catch the 7:35 commuter train into north-central London.

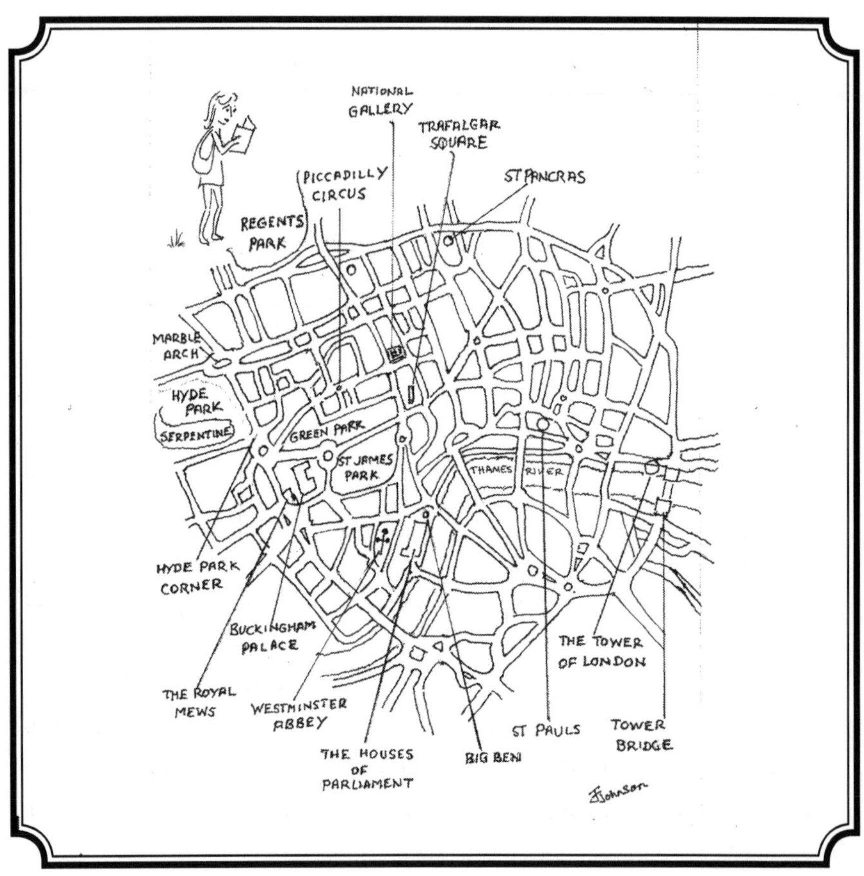

When we arrived at St. Pancras, Jennifer stowed her luggage in a locker. We jumped on a red Double Decker bus. The open-air upper deck had a good view of the sights on the way to Westminster Abbey and the Parliament buildings. Big Ben sounded off as we wandered around inside the rambling Abbey. We thought it would be easy to get lost, so we went back out and strolled through St. James Park over to Buckingham Palace. We were a little disappointed; there was no Queen anywhere in sight.

Checking the time, we decided to catch a bus back to St. Pancras and collect Jennifer's luggage and proceed directly to the airline terminal.

We were seriously cutting it close. We splurged on a cab to save time.

The downtown BOAC terminal seemed like a very civilized idea. It would have cost us a fortune to take a taxi to Heathrow Airport, which was miles away.

In the downtown terminal, Jennifer presented her passport. The counter lady told her, "Your checked-in luggage will go directly to the plane." Then she gave Jennifer a seat assignment for the flight and a multi-page paper ticket with tear-off pages like coupons. "The bus will deposit you at the airport in front of the correct boarding area for your flight. Please hurry—the bus is leaving in three minutes!"

After I left Jennifer at the airline terminal, I went directly to J. A. Allen, the horseman's bookshop, near the Royal Mews, which was only a few blocks away. I purchased *Animal Management*, prepared by the Veterinary Department of the War Office, because it was a required textbook for my exam.

I still had three hours to explore London before returning to Leicester. I checked how much I had spent today. The roundtrip train ticket had cost me fifty-four shillings and sixpence, or two pounds, fourteen shillings, sixpence. Bus fares, admission to the Abbey, and the taxi set me back more than I wished. The book cost fifteen shillings; almost another pound gone.

I studied the free London city map, which I picked up at the train station. It was about five miles from the bookshop to St. Pancras. I decided to walk. I could walk the distance in an hour and a half easily.

I quick-marched the length of Buckingham Palace Road, up the Birdcage Walk, which skirted St. James Park, and onto Horse Guards Road. I was thinking that in a former life I might have been a Horse Guard, or maybe one of those Crusaders from Kedleston Hall.

I continued hiking through Charing Cross to Trafalgar Square. The Square was actually a roundabout. I admired old Nelson perched up there on his triumphal column. Only the year before, on O'Connell Street in Dublin, the IRA had blown up his Pillar and the poor man toppled off.

I made a face at the millions of pigeons descending on the people. Large birds flapping around and landing on your head, shoulders, and arms, was not my idea of a good time. The other people in the Square were delighted and thought it was a perfect Kodak moment.

Adjoining the Square, the National Gallery was open. Some of the rooms were free to the public. I only had time to go in the front rooms, which housed the gigantic Monet Water Lily paintings. In the few minutes I had there, the Impressionist's paintings made a vivid imprint in my imagination.

Leaving the museum, I strode rapidly along Aldwych, past the Royal Shakespeare Theater. I hoped I could see a production there before I left England. In school, we studied *Julius Caesar*, *Romeo and Juliet*, and *Macbeth*. I fancied myself a poet and Shakespeare was a hero of mine; he wrote entire plays in poetry.

By the time I got to Kingsway, I needed a little break.

I bought some birthday cards and paused outside the card shop door to look at my map. I still had about an hour left and I was pretty close to the train station.

"Hello there! Are you lost?" A cheery male voice startled me. I was engrossed in my map. I had not seen anyone approach me.

"Not really." I knew where I was and where I was headed. I just needed to reorient myself. I didn't have time to waste.

I glanced up from the map and saw an attractive young man standing next to me. He was taller than me, but he didn't look much older. He was nicely dressed and fair-haired, with light gray eyes, and quite tanned, too tan to be English.

"Are you American?" He knew I was. "Would you like to get a cup of coffee?" He sounded Australian. I was good at picking out foreign accents after hearing so many in East Africa.

I had been traveling nonstop all day and I hadn't eaten anything since half past five. I was starving. I spotted a Wimpy Bar on the corner. "I was just going to grab a quick hamburger."

"May I join you?"

I couldn't see a reason why he should not. He had every right to go into the restaurant with or without me; and unlike in America, if a place was crowded, it was very possible a stranger would sit at your table. Of course, normally, you wouldn't speak to them.

Between bites of hamburger, I found out that Trevor was traveling around the world. "Next, I'm heading to France. I started in the Orient, went to Alaska, and then crossed Canada. After France, I'm going down to Italy, then across Africa, and finally home. I plan to catch a steamer from Africa back to Australia for the last part of my trip."

I told him I was working at the riding school, but I had lived in Africa a few years earlier. I told him about the Revolution in Ethiopia and advised him, "I think you should stay well clear of the place."

"Alexa, you know a lot about Africa. Would you like to come with me?"

I considered it briefly. I loved Africa and I knew there were a lot of horses and ranches in Australia.

I said, "Sorry, Trevor, as tempting as your offer is, I can't go with you. My passport is back at the Hall. I have to get going."

I wrote my addresses for HDH and Greenleaf on the back of a napkin.

Trevor graciously paid my check.

We wished each other good luck, and without Trevor, I marched steadily to Holborn and up the entire length of Gray's Inn Road. I was close to the train station when I spotted a wacky-looking building topped with a revolving restaurant. With a 360-degree view of London, the Post Office Tower was all the rage with jet setters.

When I arrived at St. Pancras, I popped into a bookstall and bought a paperback copy of Vance Packard's bestseller, *Hidden Persuaders*. The Cold War had intellectuals around the globe obsessing about mind control. The Mad Men of Madison Avenue were accused of brainwashing Americans.

I had ten minutes to spare when I finally plunked down into my seat on the train. I still had a bus ride after the train, and a walk after the bus, to get back to the Hall.

Tomorrow morning it would be back to life as a serf.

I wondered what adventures I might have had if I had gone away with Trevor. I wondered if he was a spy. Or a white slaver? Was he just a young man going on a world tour? In East Africa we had met many people like Trevor, people struck by incurable wanderlust. I wondered if he would get imprisoned or killed in Africa and if he would make it back to Australia. I wondered if I would ever see him again.

The next day I completely forgot about Trevor.

Rachael's long-running feud with Mr. Hobbs over horse care had come to a head. They had been scraping over little things ever since Rachael arrived at the Hall. During morning stables, they had an argument about Jazzy.

After breakfast, Rachael stomped into Mrs. Highstaff's office, even though she didn't have permission, and telephoned home. Then she stormed upstairs and packed up. An hour later her parents arrived to take her home.

We weren't sure if she would come back.

The few of us who were left secretly hoped she wouldn't return.

As if Rachael's sudden departure wasn't enough, on Friday morning Mrs. Fawcett arrived at the Hall all in a flap and gave her notice to Mr. Hobbs.

Her older sister was sick, and she was required to come, as soon as possible, to be a nurse. We all were sad for Mrs. Fawcett and her unfortunate sister but secretly relieved for our stomachs' sake.

On Friday at lunchtime, a postcard arrived from Ireland. Mrs. Highstaff would be back at HDH next Tuesday.

Mr. Hobbs pleaded with Mrs. Fawcett to stay until the end of next week so Mrs. Highstaff would have some time to find a replacement. The side benefit of her staying would be we could still get cooked meals in the meantime.

Suddenly reality set in. Linda had left earlier in the summer, the Highstaffs were not back yet, and now Marion, Jennifer, and Rachael were gone.

We still had the same number of horses to take care of and we were down by four people, and as terrible as she was, Mrs. Fawcett, our cook and housekeeper, might leave before a replacement could be found.

Chapter 10

Dodgy as a Fish

The critical staff shortage resulted in not only the same number of horses needing care with three fewer WPs to do the work, but there were also more horses that needed to be exercised.

With Mr. Hobbs in charge and fewer riders, we had one lesson a day and we exercised the other horses. It made Mr. Hobbs' scheduling easier if he had us ride the same horses every day. While we were riding in the field, Mr. Hobbs, on Topaz or another young horse, would ride over to us and correct whatever we were doing, or give us exercises to practice.

The "more horses to be exercised" is how I came to be riding Meteor. I had only ridden him once before in a sedate lesson with Mrs. Highstaff in the indoor school. I wasn't too heavy for Meteor. I was too tall.

Meteor was Anglo-Arab, 14-1 hands, and he lived up to his name. He rocketed around and was as dodgy as a fish. He had a lot of chrome. He was a dark bay, with black points, a blaze, and four long stockings with ermine marks.

On Friday afternoon my instructions from Mr. Hobbs were to take Meteor out in the field, to "take the edge off of him and get him sorted out for Saturday," when Julian would be riding him.

I mounted Meteor by using the millstone mounting block at the end of the carriage house. Even though Meteor was small enough to easily mount from the ground, he was a short-backed, round-bodied pony. It would have been easy to pull the saddle off center by mounting from the ground.

We started the short walk down the lane, which passed the indoor school, to get out to the field.

There just happened to be a large, shallow puddle in front of the indoor school on the way to the field.

All of the Anglo-Arabs at HDH seemed to have an aversion to walking through water. They would happily jump over water, which was not convenient if you were leading them, but they did not like getting their feet wet. I thought this was ridiculous, especially because of the amount of rain in England. The other WPs had an elaborate excuse: "Desert horses didn't experience puddles of water in their native land." I thought this was rubbish because these horses were born here in "Puddle-land."

I decided that Meteor should walk through this puddle as part of his training program. My idea was sound. Ride straight to the middle, just like a jump.

Meteor definitely had other ideas about the puddle. At the edge of the puddle, Meteor made a quick bow. He dropped his left shoulder, bent his left knee, and dropped his neck.

Before I knew what happened, I was standing on my feet with the toes of my boots in the water. Startled, I quickly glanced around to see if there were any witnesses. Nobody was coming down the path.

I checked the girth. All of our horses were taught to stand squarely and be still, so I was able to remount. We went *around* the puddle this time and proceeded to have a lovely hack as if nothing had ever happened.

On Saturday morning I was to ride Meteor before Julian's lesson. I was determined that Meteor would not outwit me again. My unplanned emergency dismount yesterday really pissed me off. I didn't like getting dumped by a crafty pony. I would try a new plan—more impulsion. I would trot Meteor through the puddle.

Once out of sight of the stable, we approached the puddle with great enthusiasm. Meteor's ears were up. He was attentive.

Trot, trot, trot. I almost expected him to try and jump it.

Dead stop.

I landed on the muddy edge of the puddle on my hands and knees. The puddle had dried up a bit; at least I wasn't in the water. I could clean the mud off my boots with some grass. I hoped the mud on the knees of my breeches would dry while I was riding so I could brush off the evidence and it would not be so obvious that I'd bought some real estate, or as Mr. Hobbs would say, made a purchase.

I would not have time to change my breeches until lunch. I was running low on clean clothes. My first instinct was to give the pony a good wallop with my riding crop, which now also had mud on it, but I had learned long ago never to hit an animal in anger.

I composed myself and remounted without being spotted. After his moment of fun, Meteor was a pleasant and perfectly obedient ride.

Before lights out on Sunday evening, Ruth came to my rescue. She pulled me aside and whispered, "I can see over the garden wall into the lane when I'm cleaning the gallery window on the first floor. Meteor always ducks out at that puddle. Back him through it and he won't try it on you anymore." Ruth was too good of a friend to squeal.

Backing Meteor through the puddle was the only thing I would have never thought of on my own.

Monday was my last opportunity to figure out this nut case of a horse. Luckily it hadn't rained all week. I made certain I was the last one out of the yard for the afternoon ride.

We nonchalantly started toward the indoor school. The puddle had dried up a little more. Instead of proceeding forward when we got near the puddle, I turned Meteor around as if we might return to the stable, and I halted. Then I asked him to rein-back, step by step. When Meteor's hind feet went into the puddle, his ears went back, and he tensed up like he might rear. He didn't, and he crossed the whole puddle by backing up, one step at a time. When he saw he was *facing* the puddle from the going home side, Meteor seemed slightly amused. Not satisfied with one victory, I rode him straight across the puddle as if we were going back to the stable. He walked right through. Then I decided to push the limit. With a half turn on the haunches, I turned him around and rode through the puddle a third time and hustled out to the field.

When I reached the field, Mr. Hobbs, aboard Minstrel, trotted over to me and looked at his watch. "Where have you been?" He spotted Meteor's dirty wet stockings and grinned. “Don’t be late again. Make sure you clean and dry your horse’s legs properly.”

Mrs. Highstaff would be back tomorrow. Everything would be inspected thoroughly before we could have our supper tonight.

Chapter 11

Squiffy Mini

I was happy when Mrs. Highstaff returned.

She brought presents for everyone. Mine was a headscarf. It had a black center with foxhunters galloping around inside of a wide red border. It was a thoughtful, practical present, very much in fashion. Even the Queen wore headscarves outdoors in inclement weather.

Mrs. Highstaff quickly sorted out Mrs. Fawcett's dilemma and arranged for her move. By Thursday we had a new housekeeper and cook, a pretty young woman named April, with curly, peroxide blonde hair. At twenty-five she was already divorced and had a small daughter, Cricket, a four-year-old with a cherub face surrounded by short, curly blonde hair.

With the first meal, the cooking standard, even with the same limited ingredients, improved to very close to acceptable. April's mashed potatoes were delicious, light, and fluffy, with some milk and a duck egg whipped in and then browned in the oven, and she actually roasted the joints of meat. She dumped the pot of gray porridge into the ducks' food.

April brought with her a secret weapon—a handheld electric whisk.

Advertisements for electrical gadgets to make a housewife's day easier filled the pages of *Woman's World* and *Good Housekeeping*, which April read every month at the hairdressers while her head was stuck under the hair-dryer dome.

The plan was that she and Cricket would move into the Gate House in a few weeks. The little brick castle with towers and turrets had not been occupied for years. For now, they occupied the little semi-private room off the lounge, with a staircase that led down to the kitchen. This made sense because April was the cook.

Cricket was quite the live wire. It was hard for her to cope with the "No Running" policy at the Hall. April gave Cricket a sleeping pill to put her to sleep. The Rolling Stones seemed to think everyone in England rushed to their doctor for pills to cure their problems.

I wondered if there was a pill to cure excessive work.

Mrs. Highstaff knew we had all been working very hard. She cheered us up by letting us know Marion was coming back this evening and staying; and three additional pupils would be arriving soon.

Two new girls were starting in October, with Jeremy soon to follow.

We adored Jeremy. He was thoughtful and helpful. Denis, now that he was a BHSAI, was generally less helpful than before.

Colonel Alois Podhajsky's book *The Complete Training of Horse and Rider* had just recently been published in English and it was Mrs. Highstaff's reading material while she vacationed in Ireland:

> *The training of the rider commences with the teaching of the correct seat, which is the basic requirement, for any kind of riding [. . .]. In outward appearance, riding should present itself as an art. Horse and rider in all movements should give the impression of two living creatures merged into one [. . .]. The best way to obtain a correct seat is [. . .] without stirrups.*

Starting on the Wednesday after she returned, and for many days thereafter, "No Stirrups" was the rule for lessons. After Mrs. Highstaff spent an hour trying to mold us into centaurs, we would stagger around the yard on our jelly legs.

Finally we were scheduled to go on a hack. After weeks of no stirrups, I was looking forward to a pleasant ride in the countryside *with* stirrups.

Plans changed abruptly when Rodney, our farrier who was always in great demand, telephoned that he was in the area this morning, and so we had to stay at the Hall.

Mr. Hobbs knew we needed some fun, so we had a bit of a competition over part of our cross-country course.

I was assigned to Atlanta, and Denis got to ride Harry, which I thought was unfair, even though Harry was very green and Denis was a more experienced rider. The course was a half-mile or more. We started by jumping a single rail into the manège, then out of the manège over a hedge, through a double, and then down the steep ramp (slide), turn left, come back up over the stile, gallop the length of the field, over the two logs by the farmer's field, and return to the group.

Periodically throughout my round, Attila would give a loud squeal, buck a few times, and try to bolt. I never allowed her to take off and we managed to go clear, which I thought was an accomplishment in itself.

Harry was faster than he looked, but Denis was pushing him too hard. Harry took off too far away from the jump and crashed through the stile like a bulldozer. Fortunately Harry was not remotely fazed or injured by the knockdown. He was checked over carefully, and, as a precaution, cold-hosed.

Fiona's round was *Hors de Concours* on Sword of Justice, a 17-2 hand, bright-as-the-sun chestnut ex-steeplechaser who sailed over every jump like he was in the Olympics. Immediately on landing after every jump, Fiona would use all her might to pull him onto a large, pre-planned circle.

At lunch, I was particularly happy when Mr. Hobbs announced the results of the cross-country. "Marion on Wizard: first with a clear round and a time of one minute and thirty seconds. Alexa on Atlanta: second with a clear round and a time of one minute, forty-five seconds."

Rats. The bucking episodes added to our time. Otherwise, we might have won.

"Fiona HDC."

Denis last.

The next day at lunchtime Mrs. Highstaff came through our dining room carrying The Red Book. "Alexa, you are going to start teaching some beginner children's rides on Saturday and you should have your lesson plans ready."

This is a nice promotion from just being a lesson helper. Later I realized that everyone was promoted because we were understaffed.

My half-day off was switched to Friday. I was at a bit of a loose end ever since Jennifer went home. I didn't feel like doing anything by myself in Crowsville or Leicester, and I had spent a lot of money in London.

I decided to be useful.

I offered to help April get the Gate House in shape.

After a few hours of sweeping up, cobwebbing, and scrubbing, the brick and stone Gate House looked much brighter. At least all the windows were still intact. Once a wood stove could be installed in the fireplace for heat and cooking, April and Cricket could move in. Furniture would be supplied from the attic in the Hall.

As we finished cleaning, I thought about walking back to the Hall to do some studying. April surprised me with the news. "My boyfriend, Tommy, is coming over shortly to pick us up."

The plan unfolded. "Tommy said he is going to splash out and treat us all to dinner. He was just paid a big bonus for finishing a European run with his lorry."

"This morning when I walked Cricket to school, I deposited a small case with some clean clothes and a bag of makeup inside the Gate House."

She decked me out in a clean shirt—a pink peasant top, which I would have never chosen for myself, to go with my jeans. For herself, she chose a black jumpsuit with big gold zippers with a white collar and white cuffs. Like a makeup artist, she applied a pale shimmering pink to our lips, painted our eyes with a dark smoky color, and ringed our eyes with dark lines. I thought we looked like raccoons.

She even teased my hair. I thought this was outrageous, but I went along with it. Back in Greenleaf, I tried to look like a folk singer with my long hair ironed straight.

Then April doused us with strong eau de toilette, which was probably a good idea since we could only wash up with a little cold water.

I scarcely recognized myself. We looked like a couple of Carnaby Street birds.

Tommy rolled up in a tiny car. April, Cricket, and I piled in, and we were away.

We were off to Storkey to drop Cricket off with Auntie, Tommy's mother, and collect Derek, his nineteen-year-old brother who still lived at home. Derek worked as a laborer at the famous Storkey brickworks. He appeared wearing a bright paisley shirt, black slacks, and a leather jacket.

This was turning out to be more of an adventure in wonderland than I'd signed up for, but I was excited to be taken out unexpectedly and I was hungry.

Dinner turned out to be a pub crawl. We went to this pub and had drinks, and then to that pub and had more drinks.

I was approaching eighteen, the legal age for drinking in pubs, but I was never asked for identification.

Drunk driving penalties in England had just been stiffly increased. Police were setting up roadblocks outside of the popular pubs. Tommy listened to his Citizens Band radio and carefully avoided the potential problem areas. He boasted, "I know every backroad in the county," and he explained, "I can't afford to get a driving under the influence summons or I will be done in."

The only dinner we got was a bag of crisps each at one pub and a plate of chips to share at another one.

Before coming to England, I did not drink much alcohol. My parents allowed me to have one small glass of wine at holiday meals a few times a year. I ordered a gin and tonic at each pub, just because I thought it sounded cool. I liked the fact the tonic water came in little glass bottles. The warm tonic water bottle came off a shelf, and no ice was available. Since his brother was buying, Derek thought it was a dandy idea to drink as much as possible. Tommy, to his credit, drank slowly. He was more interested in playing with the zippers on April's jumpsuit.

Derek guzzled two or three pints of beer at each pub. I didn't see how anyone could drink that sheer volume of liquid. *Well, he is going out to pee a lot.*

"You don't buy beer—you just rent it," Derek slurred as he swayed off to find the bog located behind the pub.

"You just rent it." He repeated the phrase over and over again between peals of his own laughter, as if he were the first person who ever thought of that line. At the brick factory where Derek worked, he and his mates would brag about the number of pints they could drink without throwing up. After the third pub, my stomach was feeling a little queasy.

I was afraid if Tommy got too drunk, I might have to drive. April and Derek did not know how to drive. I knew how to drive an automatic car, but I didn't have a clue how to drive a stick shift car on the wrong side of the road. I didn't even possess an American driver's license.

Tommy abruptly decided he was taking us all home. He was getting very randy. I was ready to go. We hurriedly abandoned the spartan comfort of the Widows Arms pub.

I was stuck on a tiny hard back seat of the Morris Minor with an oversized drunken octopus. I was used to the college boys putting one arm around your shoulders and with one hand (from outside your shirt) trying to unfasten your bra. Derek was not that smooth. He would not keep his hands, or any other part of himself, to himself. I kept battling him off with my elbows and knees. I was glad I was wearing jeans and not a miniskirt. The peasant top wasn't helping.

"Whiter Shade of Pale" was blaring out of the radio. *How appropriate . . . I might be sick at any moment.*

Derek reeked like a brewery. The window in the back seat did not roll down, so I cracked the vent to get some air. When we finally reached Storkey, Tommy stopped the car in front of his mother's row house. He yelled at his brother, "Get out of the car!" Without waiting, Tommy reached back into the back seat, opened the door, and gave Derek a push. Derek lurched out onto the pavement and promptly tripped over the foot-high hedge that bordered the postage stamp-sized front garden, and he fell flat.

Tommy drove off.

"Aren't you going to help him into the house?" I asked. I was relieved that Derek was out of the car. I hoped I never saw him again.

"Serves him right for spending all my money." Tommy laughed. He sped off toward Brickton. "If he doesn't wake up and go in, his mates will find him there on their way to work in the morning." I realized that we had not picked up Cricket at Tommy's mother's place. I didn't mention it. If Cricket was given one of her little yellow pills, she would be fast asleep by now.

April and I were dropped off *before* the gate at the end of the drive. Tommy told April he would park the car in the layby, and he would be back in a few minutes. April told me she would be down to the Hall later and went into the empty building.

Another reason why April wants to move into the Gate House, I thought. I hoped she was taking the new pill to prevent pregnancy.

While I stealthily walked down the drive back to the Hall, I tried not to startle the horses in the paddocks. I was praying I could sneak past Mrs. Highstaff and get into bed without talking to anyone.

Mrs. Highstaff would have never approved of any of the evening's activities, and she was supposed to be formally introduced to any young men who came to take us off the premises. I thought I would get told off in the morning, but if I was going to be told off, Mrs. Highstaff had forgotten about it entirely.

By good fortune, my father's check for the next quarter's tuition arrived even before Mrs. Highstaff had sent out the bill. This pleased her immensely. I was less pleased. My father did not include any quarterly allowance for me. I had been hinting I needed more money in my last letters home.

My boots were in a terrible state. Tall black dress boots were not designed for walking around in most of the day. The other WPs, except Denis, wore paddock or Jodhpur boots. I had been wearing tall boots since I was thirteen when my instructor in Africa gave me her old pair of brown field boots for my birthday. I was not reverting to Jodhpur boots now, and anyway, I only owned breeches, not jodhpurs.

During my first four months at HDH, I had my boots re-heeled and stitched once. Now the soles were practically worn through again, and they leaked like mad. The leather on one foot was separating from the sole. *Rats, now I have to get the boots resoled again.* Luckily, I could do this in Leicester, where I could drop off my boots at the shoe repair shop before lunch and pick the resoled boots up on the same day.

The October days were getting shorter and colder.

I received some cards and letters from friends in America, which cheered me up a bit. I opened a package first. My Danish Aunt Helga sent me a lovely green dress. It fit me and I liked it. I was very picky about the clothes I wore. I admired my Aunt Helga, a cosmopolitan world traveler who had married an American and lived in Hawaii.

Then I was really sad to hear that our old cat Piewackit had died. My brother had adopted another kitten. I was also sad that the new kitten wouldn't know me when I returned home next summer.

I sat down to write my parents a letter. I wanted to impress them with my knowledge.

> *I have started studying Minor Ailments. There are sixteen different types of lameness in the hoof alone and that's only the beginning.*
>
> *There is a new requirement from the Royal Mail. An official postal code must be added on to the end of the address on any correspondence to me. It is letters and numbers. I hope it all fits on the envelope.*
>
> *I am working hard, taking care of three horses' full livery. Grooming alone takes almost three hours a day, now that old St. Christopher has come in for the winter.*
>
> *Dad, please remember my boots were a year old when I came here, and now I wear them from morning until night. They are literally falling apart. I think they should be retired to a museum.*
>
> *Please send my allowance.*
>
> *Love,*
>
> *Alexa*

I would never tell my parents that I had my heart set on a twenty-guinea suede coat.

THE Squiffy MINI
THE QUEENS ARMS
HOT FOOD
THE KINGS HEAD
THE BLACK DOG
DISGUSTING FOOD
x
FILTHY ALE

Chapter 12
Autumn Leaves

An unintended consequence of people leaving, and other people not arriving yet, was that Fiona was promoted to Head Girl. For numerous reasons, she was the logical choice. The only other possible contender was Marion, and Fiona had been here longer. Although Fiona failed the exam twice, she knew the material thoroughly. On the cross-country, Sword of Justice recently proved that Fiona was a very capable rider.

Fiona's lunchtime flirting with Mr. Hobbs increased. Their constant jokes were mostly aimed at putting *me* off my food. They loved haggis, blood pudding, boiled sheep's head, and other vile Celtic dishes. While this conversation was going on, Ruth would pull a face and try to make Marion laugh. Denis would look at his plate.

It was incredulous to me that anyone civilized would eat a sheep's stomach or this other rubbish. In Africa, the Masai drank milk mixed with blood from the same living cow. Some Orientals ate live insects. *Savages will eat practically anything,* I thought smugly.

After these food reviews, Fiona would bat her big brown eyes at Denis and ask him to pass her something or get her something.

Fiona's romance with Denis was getting hot and heavy.

As big as the place was, it was hard to be alone at Heels Down Hall. On numerous occasions, I would spy Fiona and Denis slinking off together for a moment.

While we were watching TV on Sunday afternoons, I would see the two of them, sitting next to each other on the settee, leaning against the big flat radiator, secretly holding hands and hogging up every bit of heat.

Along with her promotion, Fiona got the coveted Head Girl's room, which was a room to herself.

In the stable yard, Fiona was rapidly developing a little Hitler attitude toward her former comrades and even her boyfriend.

To top it all off, the Dubliners, a popular Irish folk group, just released a song, "The Black Velvet Band."

Our leprechaun played this for all it was worth. Instead of the way she usually wore her black hair in a long braid or neat bun, she came down to breakfast with her hair tied with a black velvet ribbon and hanging loosely over her shoulder. It really was more than one could take.

There were not enough staff, at present, for anyone to have a whole Sunday off, so when we were scheduled for a half Sunday off together, Marion invited me to go home with her.

The weather was clear and crisp, a great day to visit the Buttons' dairy farm.

The cows lived in a modern steel beam, concrete, and corrugated metal building.

The Buttons' house was an old, converted stone barn, with log rafters and a thatch roof. The kids' bedrooms were up in the loft, reached by climbing a ladder. The large fireplace in the sitting room provided heat for the whole building.

We sat around a picnic table under an apple tree in the garden while we waited for dinner to finish cooking. Marion's dad treated us to a few glasses of Shandy. I would have never imagined that beer mixed with lemonade would taste good.

Her mother cooked us a delicious dinner, everything from the farm straight to the table.

After stuffing ourselves, we strolled to a field where Mr. Button was keeping some ponies at grass. We laughed trying to pronounce the Welsh Mountain names, which were longer than the ponies were high.

From the ponies' field, we walked over to the adjoining farm where Marion's friend Tina was trying to sell a bay horse named Kilkenny. At Tina's request, Marion and I both pretended we were prospective buyers and put him through his paces. It turned out Tina had been a pupil at HDH and passed her AI while she studied there.

Then we went back to the farm for tea—more homemade food and baked goods.

After tea, Marion's father went out to milk the cows.

Marion started complaining about friendly Fiona, who always had been a bit of a diva, suddenly transformed into a tyrant, now that she was Head Girl.

Her mother coolly responded, "Don't get your knickers in a knot, Marion. You will have your turn at being a Head Girl. Right now, you are learning what *not* to do as well as what to do."

Marion, her mother, her younger brother Marvin, and I played dominoes on the rug in front of the blazing fireplace until Mr. Button finished milking the cows and drove us back to the Hall.

The next day, Mrs. Highstaff started giving us two-hour lectures on the Theory of Equitation after supper. Topics included subjects such as: Turn on the Forehand Halted and Turn on the Forehand in Motion, Turns on the Haunches, and detailed explanations of all the aids, natural and artificial. This indicated something was going to happen and it did.

The Stapleford children came to stay at the Hall while their parents went on a trip. Peter, Violet, and Alice arrived after school on Friday. On Saturday, in addition to their regular riding lesson, they were kept busy exercising ponies. When they weren't riding, we put them to work cleaning tack or brushing ponies.

On Sunday morning after breakfast, Marion and I herded the kids past the paddocks with horses and down the drive to the Family Service at the church in Brickton. Just getting them to the church on time was an accomplishment. St. Cuthbert's was much less formal than St. George's. Vicar Hanleigh was delighted to see more young people in the church. He introduced us to his daughter, Penny, who was about our age. We felt welcome.

The first of our new working pupils arrived on Sunday afternoon.

Marcy Davidson, like Ruth, was going for the Pony Club B, as well as the BHSAI. Marcy was cheerful and eager to learn everything. I liked her right away. She joined us in our quarters in the large bedroom.

On Monday morning before we went in for breakfast, Colonel Jamieson, retired Army, former Army Show Jumping team, arrived in his dark green MG to teach us a four-day course in preparation for the BHSAI examination.

The Colonel was the chief examiner and commissioner for the Pony Club, and he owned a small point-to-point and show jumping yard in nearby Rugby. He rode to hounds regularly and he still did some show jumping occasionally.

Colonel Jamieson was tall and physically fit. He had an officer's haircut with slightly graying brown hair above a tanned face with hazel eyes, and under his Grecian nose, he had a neatly trimmed, slightly graying brown mustache. He was a perfect gentleman in manners. He dressed impeccably.

We all were in love with Colonel Jamieson, and we were terrified of him. If we were slow in answering his questions, he impatiently tapped his riding crop on his boot. He turned into an absolute tyrant when teaching riding.

The Colonel had been here earlier this summer, but I had not been included in his course. Up until this point, courses at HDH, held by outside instructors, just meant more work for me in the yard.

This time we were all included, even Margaret, who only arrived yesterday, and Grace Edwards with her young horse Jasper. Grace had been riding with Mrs. Highstaff for the past ten years. Jasper had just placed second at a Horse Trial last Saturday.

We rode with the Colonel from ten o'clock to half past eleven and then came in for a cup of coffee. We only drank coffee with hot milk when we had clinics, so this was a treat. At three quarters past eleven we remounted and rode until one o'clock, which the Colonel called thirteen hundred hours.

After the morning ride, we watered and hayed the horses. Fortunately, since most of the stabled horses were in the clinic, the stalls were cleaner.

After our dinner, we bedded down the boxes, tacked up again, and rode until about four o'clock. Then we came in, fed the horses, and had our afternoon cup of tea.

After tea we had to clean the entire day's tack, groom the horses, and set fair for the evening.

After evening stables Margaret and I were called in for a lecture. The other WPs had taken the Colonel's courses before, and they had the lecture notes. Sometimes we had an additional lecture after supper. Topics included were Jumping, How to Lecture, Shoeing, a Progressive Set of Jumping Lessons, and Qualities of a Good Instructor.

On Wednesday night Colonel Jamieson asked *me* to give a talk for all the students on the gaits of American horses. For twenty minutes I dealt with the mystifying five gaits of the American Saddlebreds and the running walk of the big stepping Tennessee Walking Horses. Sadly the Walkers were sometimes subjected to cruel showing practices, but they actually were a lovely breed, much in demand in the Old South for bird dog trials and as pleasure horses.

I demonstrated the paces for the slow gait, rack on, and the running walk, the best I could using my arms as front legs and my legs as the horse's hind legs. I made Margaret try it. It wasn't easy.

Thursday was the last day of the Course.

The morning ride was an hour and a half session in the indoor school.

After the morning tea break, we went out to the cross-country course and jumped a lot of the cross-country jumps, including many I had never negotiated before.

The course was much longer than our previous mock competition. It included the tiger trap, which was a deep ditch under an inverted V of logs. You could see down into the ditch between the logs. You weren't supposed to look at the ditch.

The tiger trap was part of a double with two strides out over the post and rails and then on to some stone walls. The course also included the stile.

We did about three fences at a time and worked our way around the course. Often the last jump of the group was the first jump of the new group of fences.

The Colonel added a small rail over the top of the slide, which turned the slide into a drop. The horse would jump over the rail and fly out into the lower field. "Don't look down. Look where you will be landing and gallop away." Colonel Jamieson cut an elegant figure, giving instructions while mounted on Rob Roy.

I was riding the chestnut horror, Attila, who behaved reasonably well, considering I gave her an occasional hearty *whack* with my crop. It was a miracle that we only had one refusal on the whole course. The other horses were refusing fences left and right. If Mr. Hobbs had been here, he would have cracked his hunt whip at the first hint of hesitation from horse or rider. Our horses rarely refused.

I loved cross-country. It combined galloping, my favorite gait, with jumping, which was like flying.

Mrs. Highstaff was waiting for us as we rounded the corner into the yard. Colonel Jamieson was just telling me, "Alexa, if you get bored here at HDH, you can come and spend a weekend with my family in Rugby." With her acute hearing, Mrs. Highstaff overheard the invitation.

I wondered if Colonel Jamieson was impressed by my jumping on the cross-country course, or whether my antics of imitating gaited horses had given him any other ideas, or if he just thought Americans were amusing.

Mrs. Highstaff drolly suggested, "Colonel, the next time you come, you could *drive Alexa* to Rugby so she could save the money she would otherwise need for the train."

Mrs. Highstaff realized this excursion was never going to happen. Mrs. Jamieson would not appreciate an American teenage girl and her husband driving for over an hour in his two-seater sports car. When she married him, Lillian had firmly established a firm "look, don't touch" policy with the Colonel.

Marcy, as Margaret preferred to be called, had just dismounted from Wizard, and she was standing near me, shivering. She had forgotten to wear her gloves. The weather was raw, and her hands were cold. She stuck her hands in her pockets.

Mrs. Highstaff spoke softly as she passed Marcy, "Take your hands out of your pockets, dear. We don't want the Colonel to think you belong to the common laborers."

I doubted if Marcy would ever forget her gloves again.

The weather forecast predicted snow in Scotland.

It was cold enough to snow here. I was used to warmer climates. I was already wearing a turtleneck, a flannel shirt, and a pullover. I thought I was going to freeze to death and melt with the spring thaw.

Friday the thirteenth of October was Marcy's and my half-day off. After sitting on the top of the Double Decker bus into Crowsville, and not wearing my new headscarf, I came back with an earache and sore throat, which was getting progressively worse.

On Saturday a new horse arrived from Ireland, a stunning blood bay. Mrs. Highstaff allowed us to name him. I said, "Let's call him O'Connell." The horse had a wild, lofty look like an Irish revolutionary. I was soundly outvoted. By popular demand, he was named Heathcliff, a character from the TV series *Wuthering Heights*. I didn't see the connection between a tragic Yorkshire orphan and a horse from Ireland. Heathcliff was a terrific mover. After he was schooled, he was going to be fantastic. Right now, he was five years old and was as green as the grass in Ireland.

Another new working pupil arrived on Saturday evening, Gillian Benson from Northamptonshire. She was shorter than me, with dark brown hair and brown eyes.

Gillian took the empty bed by the window in the big room with the rest of us. She was quiet. She had spent some time at Art School and liked fashion design. I told her my mother made clothes from her own patterns. Gillian thought that was cool. I didn't talk too much because I had a sore throat.

On Sunday morning I went to St. George's in Storkey for Communion with Mrs. Highstaff. No singing was fine with me. I could barely talk.

Chapter 13
Useless

By Sunday night Mrs. Highstaff sent me to bed early. I spent the whole of Monday in bed with a fever. By Tuesday I felt a bit better and got up, but Mrs. Highstaff made me stay inside all day. Twice a day Mrs. Highstaff made me sit with a towel draped over my head and lean over a bowl of boiling water with Vicks, a eucalyptus and menthol gel, dissolved in it and inhale the steam. It actually helped.

I thought I was getting off lightly by taking some aspirin and steaming my head. Two of our ancient ponies had green treacle syrup with arsenic added into their feed to relieve their coughs. I had read of cases of horses being overdosed with arsenic by overzealous grooms. In Captain Hayes' book *Veterinary Notes for Horse Owners,* he strongly warns owners against the overuse of arsenic.

Mrs. Highstaff was licensed to have belladonna, arsenic, and god knows what else in her medicine chest. Students were not allowed to touch it. I thought HDH probably had enough poisons on hand to wipe out the whole village of Brickton.

I felt sorry for the others in the yard taking care of my horses while I was inside. However, I thought I could take advantage of the situation and at least get some correspondence knocked off my list and do some studying.

Outside, the day was rapidly deteriorating.

As everyone was just sitting down to dinner, Marion came in and announced that Wizard was colicking. Mr. Hobbs and Fiona left immediately to give him a drench and the others had to take turns eating and going out to walk him.

It was just turning dusk at tea time when Fiona ran into the Hall, crying hysterically.

A man from the village had just driven his car into the yard, rolled down his window, and shouted out that Lord Daffy had wandered into Brickton and had been hit by a lorry. The dog was still alive when he left.

Mrs. Highstaff told Mr. Hobbs to ring Dr. Amsley, and she jumped in the Land Rover and drove off, tearing after the man, to find Lord Daffy.

Mr. Hobbs was left in charge of Wizard.

Wizard recovered but Mr. Hobbs kept watch on him every hour.

Shortly thereafter, Mrs. Highstaff returned and informed us, "Lord Daffy does not seem to have any broken bones, but he is spending the night in the Crowsville Animal Surgery."

Later that same evening, Marcy's father arrived at the riding school unannounced. He quickly found Marcy and told her, "Pack everything. You are going home immediately."

While she packed, Marcy told me why she had to leave HDH so abruptly. "Foot and Mouth has broken out in Shropshire. Our neighbor's herd of sheep might have to be destroyed. If that happens to my family, we will be ruined. In any case, if I stay at school and the outbreak gets worse, I may not be allowed to go home."

Marcy told me I was the only American she had ever met, and she invited me to come and visit her at Christmas.

Mr. Davidson squared up with Mrs. Highstaff, and, after a tearful good-bye, they left.

Writing home was a diversion from the chaos around me. I was listening to the transistor radio that Gillian had brought with her. She had graciously loaned it to me because I was sick and staying inside. We were not allowed to play the radio in the stable yard except on Sunday afternoon. "Up, Up and Away" by the 5th Dimension was playing. I loved this song. A balloon ride away from HDH would have been a welcome change right now. I started daydreaming.

Before I left Greenleaf, my dad and I were hatching a scheme whereby he would buy a new car in England and ship it back via sea freight, free of charge, from Marseilles, France to the USA. To qualify, the new car had to be purchased by a State Department employee and have so many miles on it before shipping it home.

Mom was coming over in the summer, and I thought we should take a grand tour. Mom could drive our new car and I would ride shotgun and watch for road signs and all. My plan was to see all of Great Britain, then ferry over to France and drive around and see everything there.

I thought my mother should bring Mrs. Highstaff a present from America, something that could not be purchased in England. I was having a hard time trying to think of something. The English had all the same stuff we had in the USA except smaller versions like littler cars, littler TVs, littler refrigerators.

I knew Mrs. Highstaff would like cigarettes and they were cheaper in tobacco-growing Greenleaf than anywhere in the world, except maybe Richmond, Virginia, where the cigarette factories were. My mother would object to the cigarettes and there might be customs on them.

I wistfully thought that Mrs. Highstaff might like some *effective* central heating, and then in a more realistic moment, I thought maybe she would be happy with a book on American horse breeds.

My dad finally sent me my allowance, which I would now have to deposit in the Crowsville bank and wait two weeks for it to clear before I could collect any cash.

Along with my allowance, my dad thoughtfully included International Reply Coupons (worth £7), which I could trade in at the Brickton post office for Aerogrammes or Air Letters, a useful page of blue writing paper that when folded up made its own envelope. Each prepaid and stamped form cost nine pence. This would save me a lot on buying more stationery and postage stamps, and due to the small size of the Aerogrammes, even with tiny handwriting, I would not have to write as much.

I was feeling better, and I was to start back to work in the stable tomorrow morning after breakfast.

The next morning I was in the dining hall getting a cup of tea when the others came stomping in for breakfast. Fiona was saying something to

Mr. Hobbs in the butler's pantry. I overheard him tell her, in quite a heated but not loud voice, "Bloody useless Head Girl, look at what has happened. You would be better suited to working at Woolworths."

Fiona started crying and went clattering up the stairs.

Mr. Hobbs came in and sat down at the table and ate his usual hearty breakfast. He did not allow silly girls to ruin his meals.

A lot had happened since Fiona had become Head Girl, but I never did find out what had happened that was Fiona's fault.

The changing weather meant the easy horse care of summer was over. Clipping took priority. *"First, clip [the horse] sometime in October." There were many types of clips: full clip, hunter clip, blanket clip, and a high trace clip. "It is a lengthy process."*

We were covered in more hair than one could imagine. It was all drawing lines on horses with chalk, holding horses, and taking turns with the noisy large clippers, which got hot pretty quickly.

The blades on the clippers had to be changed frequently. We had stacks of clipper blades in different sizes.

If we were making a mess and cutting steps into the horse's coat, Mr. Hobbs would help us after he called us "useless."

Naturally, Fiona was good at clipping. Clipping horses for the hunt could earn a person quite a bit of pocket money. She already had several of her half-days booked.

I had never done it before. There was no need for clipping where the climate was milder, and we had only pleasure horses.

After all the clipping, which removed the hair that naturally kept the horses warm, we now had to start using all the different types of man-made horse clothing to keep the horses warm.

The following articles of horse clothing were now in use daily: day rugs made of heavy wool used with a roller, night rugs made of hemp or jute, leather rollers, roller pads, and a breast strap, if the roller slips back. Completing the clothing list were: arched rollers reinforced with metal bars for horses that were likely to roll and get cast in the stall; heavy wool horse blankets under the rugs, which had to be folded back in such a way as to tuck under the roller; and four-inch-wide wool stable bandages to keep horses' legs warm.

We had the latest in turnout rugs. The New Zealand rug was made of waterproofed canvas and partly lined with jute or wool, and they had leather leg and tail straps. They stayed on pretty well but weighed a ton if they got soaked. If a wet rug fell on you, they were so unwieldy, you couldn't get up without assistance.

Rugging up and off rugging—changing all this horse clothing added to the time it took to groom and get the horses in and out, in ever increasingly short days.

Another Irish horse arrived, along with a little spindly looking bay pony.

Tara, a 15-hand, sweet Connemara mare, was as green as the Emerald Isle and was a very gentle soul. Tara and Biscuit were supposed to be on the same ferry as Heathcliff but the farmer who sold them mixed up the dates.

The pony Biscuit was free; buy one, get one. Mrs. Highstaff only had to pay his shipping from Ireland to the Hall. He didn't know a thing except how to be led. Mr. Hobbs told us, "Many ponies like Biscuit are purchased as children's pets and are never trained. People seem to think that because ponies are small, they will automatically be suitable for inexperienced children."

Gillian and I were to train Biscuit by following the outline in *Training the Young Pony*. We played with Biscuit and trained him every day for a few minutes. We taught him to lunge and how to wear a saddle and other tack.

Apparently Mrs. Highstaff collected horses instead of souvenirs while she was on holiday in Ireland. Other people collect crystal or linen.

When Gillian and I went into Leicester on our half-day off on Tuesday, I showed her my favorite restaurants and the tack shop. I dropped my boots off at the repair shop, and while we were waiting for them, we went to a terrific movie, *A Man for All Seasons*. I was going to recommend the movie to my parents. I knew my father admired the courage of Robert Moore.

Gillian liked doing the same things I did, and we were hitting it off. We had both traveled extensively and had a lot of strange adventures to share. I hoped Gillian would last longer than a few weeks like Marcy and Linda.

While we were eating omelets at the Chalet, Gillian told me a bit about herself. "Since I was twelve, I worked on Saturdays. I rode my bicycle thirteen miles, one way, to a riding school. In the morning I would take the lesson my father paid for; and then I would stay around and work all day, to earn an extra ride. Then I would bicycle home."

When I asked her why she chose to study at HDH, she looked stunned for a moment, and then answered, "Why? To ride horses, of course!" We both started laughing so hard the other patrons in the restaurant were looking at us.

The apron in front of the row of four new loose boxes had finally been paved, making the whole courtyard area blacktop with drains, except in front of the carriage house, which was original cobblestones. It was nice not to have to wallow through the mud to get your horses in or out of the boxes. My feet were keeping drier, thanks to the new paving, and the fact that I had my boots resoled.

Now that the stable yard was finished, the next and final building project at HDH was an enclosed visitor's gallery for the covered school.

The weather had been foul, which slowed down the construction. I thought it would take ages to finish the gallery. I was looking forward to the completion of this project so the wind would stop whistling through the school like a wind tunnel.

Gillian took over the care of St. Christopher. I was now looking after Wizard, Sword of Justice, and Rob Roy. Rob Roy was Marion's training project, and she normally took care of him.

An exercise rider at Major Everett's stable had taken ill. Marion was leaving us for two weeks to replace the sick girl, starting on November 1. Fiona was miffed that Marion was offered the paid job, but she couldn't say anything. As newly appointed Head Girl, Fiona could not just go away.

When I went in to say good night one evening, Mrs. Highstaff gave me an unexpected compliment. "Alexa, your riding has gone up another level. While Marion is away, you will be riding Rob Roy."

Mrs. Highstaff had recently started letting me ride some of the young horses, Jazzy twice and Cashel once. Rob Roy was a full brother to Jazzy, but he looked more like a giraffe than a miniature Thoroughbred.

It was no wonder that my riding improved at Heels Down Hall.

The lessons were tailored to the level of training of the horses. We learned by riding wonderful schoolmasters before we were allowed to school the young horses. Every school figure and dressage movement had to be done precisely with quiet and correct application of the aids.

Horses, riders, and tack were inspected before every lesson began. There was no talking among students in lessons.

Mrs. Highstaff taught with a quiet, firm, clear voice, very BHS lessons, *leading file, the whole ride, change the rein*, even, *make much of your horses.* The last one meant to put your reins in one hand and with the other hand, pat the horse's neck. There were prescribed ways the mounted ride should stand when a demonstration or explanation was given. Mrs. Highstaff's eagle eye would detect the slightest nuance of error, even how your fingertips were placed.

She asked questions at the end of every session to make sure we understood everything.

Chapter 14

Poor Old St. Christopher

Mr. Hobbs's lessons, by contrast, were louder, more active, and more military. "Prepare to trot! And *ter-rrrrot*!" and occasionally included a rude remark. "If the bloody horse isn't doing it properly, you're asking it wrong."

His philosophy was the horse first; what the rider looked like, a distant second. "If what you're doing isn't working, try something else!" A mistake was never the horse's fault.

Mr. Hobbs also had us do fun things like go through the jumping grid with no reins and no stirrups. When you could do that pretty well, the next time through the grid, it would be "take off your hacking jacket." The next time through the grid you had to "put your jacket back on."

We even practiced adjusting our stirrups while mounted *and* moving, as in cantering. "Take your feet out of your stirrups." We would ride a few strides with our stirrups dangling and then he would say, "Now find your stirrups," which meant put your feet back in. There were physical exercises on horseback that a gymnast might have trouble performing.

Every spare minute in the stable yard was spent clipping. With all this practice I was sure Clipping was one subject on the BHS Exam we would certainly pass.

From the *BHS Manual of Horsemanship:*

> *The use of clippers is not recommended on the back of tendons or fetlocks. . . .*
>
> *Some weeks after a horse has been clipped it will be found that long hairs, known as cat hairs, appear in various parts of the coat, giving an untidy appearance to the pony . . .*

> *'Singeing' used to be the method employed for their [cat hair] removal, this being done by the flame of a special lamp called a singeing lamp.*

Earlier in the week, Mr. Hobbs had given us a demonstration of singeing. Of course, Fiona had to have a go, and she was brilliant.

When at the last minute, Mrs. Highstaff was invited to bring some advanced students to audit a nearby riding clinic on Sunday afternoon, Gillian and I were asked to do the afternoon stables because we had gone to church in the morning.

Somehow, I am sure completely unintentionally, Gillian and I were the only two people in the yard that afternoon. Mr. Hobbs had the day off. Even April was up at the Gate House.

Gillian and I worked well together as a team. We had everything finished with some time to spare. Normally we would watch TV at this time on Sunday.

St. Christopher's stall was still set up for clipping. All the bedding, hay, and everything else, except the filled water buckets, had been removed from the stall. Chris's stall was ideal as it was large and all brick, even the floor. The stall had good lighting and high ceilings in case a horse reared. There was a hook hanging from the rafters for the electric cord from the clippers to go through, which prevented the horse from stepping on the cord. However, at the height it was hanging, you had to be careful. You could hang yourself on the cord.

We decided that the stabled horses were getting all the attention and that poor old St. Chris was getting neglected. How happy Mrs. Highstaff would be when she saw her beloved horse looking spectacular.

We brought Chris in, and he was happy to oblige. We gave old Chris a nice grooming, but he still looked like a hedgehog with cat hairs sticking out and hairy feathers.

Our singeing lamp was antique. It may have been an original fixture of the Carriage House. After some fiddling we managed to get the singeing lamp lit. There was no knob to adjust the flame.

The plan was Gillian would hold Chris.

I was crouched down singeing the longest feathers and cat hair off the hind legs. The hair was wet, and it started to steam and smoke a bit. A long flame shot out of the singeing lamp, and—

"Oh my God!" The end of the horse's tail caught on fire.

Gillian shouted, "Quick! Stick it in the bucket!"

I grabbed the bucket and stuck the horse's tail in it.

"Whew, that worked!"

Now we had a horse with the end of a tail that looked like a burned shaving brush.

Once again, poor old St. Christopher had become a martyr at the hands of the working students.

After a worried conference in the kitchen over a cup of tea, we quickly reviewed "grooming for hunters." We concluded we should bang Chris's tail.

We did a nice job on that.

We put his New Zealand rug back on him and returned him to his pasture. His tail still vaguely smelled of burning hair.

When she returned from the clinic with the other students, Mrs. Highstaff drove past his paddock.

She noticed right away. "How did Christopher's tail get so short?"

We got off lightly. We got a scolding for banging a grass-kept horse's tail too short.

From the *BHS Manual of Horsemanship* (on singeing): "The task is better left to the expert."

Halloween came on a Tuesday.

Disappointingly, in England, Halloween was nothing. In Greenleaf, it was dressing up in crazy or scary costumes, going door-to-door trick-or-treating for candy, or going to costume parties.

All Saints' Day on November 1 was a Holy Day on the religious calendar in England, but not much ado was made about revering saints in 1967.

We decided to take turns telling spooky stories while we were settling into bed in our drafty dorm room. Ruth had a story about witches, and Marion told of the banshees of Ireland.

I think Fiona might be related to the banshees.

Outside of the window by Gillian's bed was a large cedar of Lebanon tree, the type of trees traditionally found in cemeteries. She looked at the tree and thought of a story about owls.

She began in a quiet voice, "On a dark and windy October night, the dead leaves blew wildly around the stable yard, like dry brown shrouds of summer gone. It was the thirty-first day of the month, All Souls' Eve, when the dead walk out to claim their own.

"Mrs. MacSkittles bolted all the doors and secured the windows of her house."

Gillian was an excellent storyteller, and we were completely silent.

The call "Lights out!" came from Fiona. It was very dark.

Gillian continued, "But the Spirits are like the mist floating on the stream; they see no bolts or fastenings.

"A silent owl flew from her hide in the belfry to alight on Mrs. MacSkittles' leaded windowsill.

"In her haste to close the house up, Mrs. MacSkittles forgot to pull the curtains together.

"The owl silently peered into the dark room. '*Too-whit, too-whoo! Too-whit, too-whoo!*' called the owl. 'I have come for you!'

"The owl's shining eyes and curled talons reflected in the bedroom mirror.

"A gasp was heard coming from the bed.

"Mrs. MacSkittles did not wake up the next morning."

After Gillian's story, we lay there in silence.

Just then a huge, long-eared owl appeared on *our* windowsill, looking right at us. Our eyes became as large as the owl's. He had been perched in the cedar tree when he saw our lights flash off.

"*Who! Who-who!*" screeched the owl. He was annoyed by the glass.

The owl looked at us for a long time, then hopped, turned around, and glided silently into the night, wondering why he had bothered to land on the windowsill and be gawked at by silly girls. It went elsewhere to look for something to eat.

I couldn't think of any stories to tell after the owl flew away, but I did recall the passage from *Macbeth* (Act Two, Scene 4):

> *Old Man: "'Tis unnatural. Even like the deed that's done. On Tuesday last, A falcon towering in her pride of place. Was by a mousing owl hawked and killed."*
>
> *Ross: "And Duncan's horses . . . a thing most strange and certain . . .*
>
> *Beauteous and swift, the minions of their race*
>
> *Turned wild in nature.*
>
> *Broke their stalls, flung out*
>
> *Contending 'gainst obedience as they would*
>
> *Make war with mankind."*
>
> *Old Man: "'Tis said they ate each other."*

Halloween was Tuesday, but now it was after midnight. I knew the others were already asleep. I lay there with my eyes wide open, watching the window and wondering if the owl would come back, if our horses were going to go mad, and knowing we would be short one WP in the morning.

Marion was leaving for two weeks. Would everyone else survive?

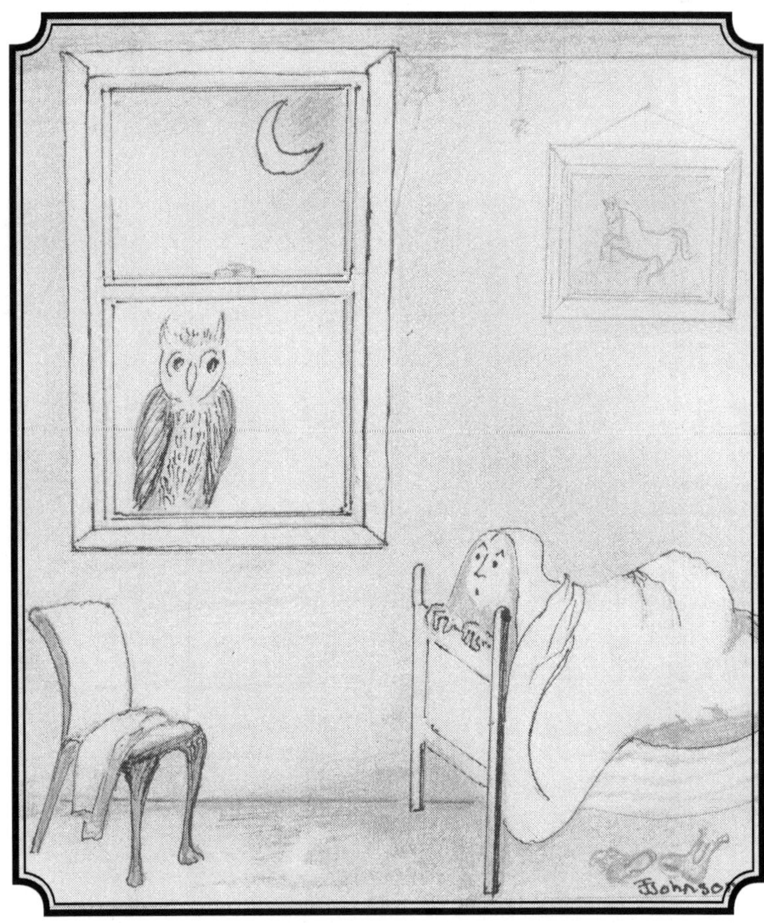

Chapter 15
Lord Daffy

On Wednesday morning Marion left to work for two weeks at Major Everett's. The good news was that I started to ride Rob Roy. I was also riding Sword of Justice quite a bit and had been assigned to ride him in our upcoming evening Dressage competition on Friday.

Mrs. Highstaff decided we should have schooling shows at least once a month on Friday evenings throughout the winter.

On the first Friday evening in November, we had our first student Dressage competition. There were two classes, one for the Young Horses and one for the School Horses.

Jeremy Howard, who would be joining us soon as a WP, was invited to compete with Falstaff.

For the Young Horse test, I scribed for Mrs. Highstaff, our judge. We both sat on stacked straw bales in the still unfinished visitors' gallery. Thankfully, Mrs. Highstaff brought a blanket to put on top of the prickly straw. My job was to quickly and neatly write the scores and the remarks for the various movements, such as circles or transitions. I liked this way of judging; it took the guesswork out of the awards.

After the first class, there was a short break for riders to change horses and loosen up their mount for the School Horse class, a Prix Caprilli. I got Justice ready and had high hopes. Being new to dressage, I had practiced the test several times on Justice but without the two small jumps. We knew it perfectly.

During our test, we proceeded according to plan until Justice came around the corner to the trot diagonal line and spotted the small cross-rail jump. His eyes bugged out and he stopped cold. I was completely surprised; at 17-2 hands, Justice could have walked over it. On the canter line, Justice refused the little upright. He stopped so resolutely you would have thought he had never seen a jump before. I thought this was odd behavior for an ex-steeplechaser, considering how tiny the jumps were, but Justice *memorized* the test without the jumps. In fact, he memorized the test long before I did, and anticipated the whole time. It shocked him to see jumps interrupting the pattern he knew so well.

Jeremy and Falstaff won hands down.

Sword of Justice and I had predictable but very disappointing results: sixth place out of six. I chalked my loss up to experience. Another competition was scheduled for December 1. I vowed I would never make that mistake again.

Next time, we would have some real competition. Mrs. Highstaff invited five riders, who rode in the clinic our students audited, to compete against us.

I was appointed the secretary-treasurer of the competitions and didn't mind the secretary part of the job because all I had to do was put the horse and rider into the correct class, fill out the class sheets, and label the dressage tests. It was not too difficult with the limited number of entries. Tracking down our students and collecting the half-crown entry fee (two shillings and sixpence) was not something I particularly enjoyed. We planned to eventually buy rosettes and invite members of the Featherstone Riding Club to a spring competition.

Sunday was Guy Fawkes Day. It rained all day. I didn't know anything about Guy Fawkes, so Gillian told me a little bit about him. "Guy is an interesting chap. He was an English Catholic and a professional soldier fighting for Spain. In 1605, a group of Catholics in England decided to blow up the Parliament. However, their bold Gunpowder Plot was discovered through a security leak. Guy Fawkes, one of the leaders, and others were caught and hanged, and King James I declared the day a holiday."

I thought it was a bit odd to celebrate a hanging, but Guy Fawkes Night quickly became a tradition with people throughout England, lighting huge bonfires, setting off firecrackers, and burning an effigy of Guy every fifth of November.

Vicar Hanleigh invited us to the Brickton Village bonfire.

It sounded like fun. Denis offered to drive us down after evening chores. Even though it was still tipping it down, Ruth, Gillian, and I happily joined him. Fiona reneged at the last minute with some made-up excuse.

We were pleased that about twenty village kids had already turned up in spite of the rain. Like a good shepherd, the Vicar herded us into the Church Hall to play some games and sing songs. Around eight o'clock, the rain let up a little. We dashed out into the drizzle and ran up to the churchyard. It took about forty-five minutes to get the bonfire blazing. In the meantime, we watched the fireworks and hungrily ate the hot dogs with soggy buns that Denis had bought. We were drenched through to our skin. Our wet coats steamed while we stood close to the fire.

We had to be back at HDH by half past nine. We were elated when Denis volunteered to drive us back; otherwise, it would be a long and wet walk. We had the car radio blaring, and we were singing our heads off. *What a great time!*

When we pulled into the car park by the stable, Fiona was waiting.

"L'Amour est Bleu" started to play on the car radio.

After quickly thanking Denis for the evening, we dashed into the Hall to dry off and get out of our wet clothes. I muttered "*Bonne chance*, Denis" under my breath as we rounded the corner of the tack room. We dripped our way into the kitchen and huddled around the warm AGA.

April and Cricket did not go to the bonfire; they stayed at the Hall with Mr. Hobbs and Fiona to watch the telly. From the window of her little room adjoining the lounge, April could see the stable car park. The headlights and music attracted her attention. Even though it was quiet in the countryside, because of the rain and the radio, April couldn't hear what was being said. She saw Fiona reach inside her shirt and pull out a chain, unclasp it, remove something, and then hand the something to Denis. April could see them waving their arms around. Then the two just stood there a minute in the pouring rain. Finally Denis hugged Fiona, got back in his car, and drove off.

Later that night April heard Fiona sobbing (only one wall separated their rooms). April wondered if the two were engaged. She figured the only way Fiona could wear a ring would be on a chain inside her shirt. Except for stud earrings, we weren't allowed to wear any jewelry around the horses at Heels Down Hall.

Denis was late on Monday morning. He made an excuse about car trouble even though the car was running perfectly well last night. Denis apologized to Mrs. Highstaff and worked through breakfast to get his horses mucked and groomed.

Fiona was in a foul mood.

I wasn't particularly interested in the star-crossed romance between Denis and Fiona.

I had my own significant problem.

My laundry was piling up.

We had to be well turned-out for riding. April, like Mrs. Fawcett, was only supposed to wash and iron breeches and a few riding shirts. When Jennifer was still here, she encouraged washing out as much stuff as possible by hand because she was more domestic than me. After Jennifer left, my new theory was I would wear my clothes as long as possible. Unfortunately Jennifer had been gone for two months. My laundry was at critical mass.

Now in addition to dirty clothes, thanks to Guy Fawkes, I had new layers of wet, dirty clothes. I kept my dirty clothes stashed under my bed in my dad's old Army duffle bag. The laundry bag reeked, but then again, so did the whole place.

Since his narrow escape with the lorry, Lord Daffy was being watched much more closely and he was not allowed out of the Hall without Mrs. Highstaff.

Ruth was upstairs sweeping and dusting. Mrs. Highstaff was in her study downstairs. Everyone else was out in the yard.

As he frequently did when the door was open, Lord Daffy wandered into our room. Without finding anyone to play with him, Daffy started snooping around, a favorite pastime for Labrador Retrievers. He wiggled under my bed and nosed around until he opened my duffle bag.

Daffy was having a lovely time rooting around inside the crammed bag.

At eleven o'clock, Mrs. Highstaff blew her dog whistle; it was time to walk around the fields.

The obedient Lord Daffy obliged instantly. He proudly trotted down the steps to his mistress, with his tail wagging, a strap of a white bra around his neck like a collar, and the bra draped over his head. Ruth tried to stop him. "Daffy, come back!" But she was in such fits of laughter, she couldn't catch him. She never told us anything about it.

I never knew that the whole dog/duffle bag incident took place until the next day. We had just finished our now (thanks to April) recognizable dinner, when Mrs. Highstaff popped in. "Gillian and Alexa, please come to my study after you are finished with your gooseberry crumble." Then she looked at Marion, who had just come back from the Major's this morning, and still shared our bedroom. "Marion, I think you should come too."

Ruth kept silent and kept an amazingly straight face. Marion, Gillian, and I looked puzzled.

Mrs. Highstaff was sitting at her desk when Ruth knocked, and we were told to enter. "Does anyone recognize this?" She held the garment up for us to see.

"Not mine."

"Not mine."

"Not mine."

Apparently the bra belonged to the famous WP named Not Mine, who was undoubtedly related to the other notorious working pupil, Not Me.

"One shouldn't leave dirty small clothes lying about." Mrs. Highstaff droned on and on, ". . . unsightly, unsanitary . . ." But this is one crime we had not committed.

Fiona, who didn't get scolded, thought the bra episode was hilarious.

Later that evening when I was hanging out in the kitchen with April, she made a deal with me. "Alexa, if you take everything to the Laundromat in Crowsville and get it clean and dry, a fresh start so to speak, I will wash most of your clothes for the same four-shilling laundry fee."

Fortunately for me, April realized I was the only WP who could not take my laundry home to be washed. Since she washed her clothes at the

Hall, she could easily throw a few more items into each load. This was great; the new plan would save me quite a bit of time, aggravation, and money. The trip to Crowsville, ten miles away, was hardly convenient and would use up your entire half-day off. The closest Laundromat had coin-operated machines that were not cheap, and it took several cycles to get your jeans dry.

I was excited about the prospect of wearing clean clothes in the near future.

To further the cause, April kindly loaned me a big paper shopping bag with string handles to carry my laundry into town.

On our next half-day off, Gillian decided to accompany me to Crowsville to do our laundry and to take in a movie. Even though Gillian lived in a neighboring county, her parents were only going to fetch her on her full Sundays off and holidays.

By the time we reached the bus stop in Brickton, my arms were getting tired from lugging the heavy bag. The string handles were carving red lines on my hands. I didn't realize it, but the damp clothes from Guy Fawkes Night were making the paper bag weak.

While I climbed the steep steps to get into the bus, the paper shopping bag hit the edge of every step. I deposited the coins for the fare into the glass container. Because the center aisle on the bus was narrow, I had to carry the large bag behind me.

The bus route to Crowsville was more heavily traveled than the midday runs into Leicester. The bus was crowded. The only available seats were in the back of the bus. They were hard and without windows, except for a small one behind you.

Fortunately, Gillian hopped on the bus right after I did because as I was going down the aisle, the bottom of the lovely shopping bag split open. Unbeknownst to me, my filthy socks and underwear were spilling out behind me on the floor like Hansel and Gretel's trail of breadcrumbs.

Using her coat as a catch-all, Gillian picked up the dirty clothes as fast as they were falling out.

The old ladies on the bus were having quite a little titter over this unfortunate turn of events.

"Well, I never . . ."

"And did you see . . ."

"Must be from the riding school . . ."

"Look how they're dressed . . ."

"They might be hippies . . ."

"Never seen them before around here . . ."

Gillian was wearing a leather miniskirt, multi-colored tights, and paddock boots with a quilted coat. I was wearing my leather Wellington boots, wheat-colored American jeans with a cowboy belt, and a western-style shirt under my jeans jacket.

If Mrs. Highstaff thought one bra on a dog's head was an outrage, what would she say about this?

When the bus made its stops, and someone got off, the other passengers moved up and took the vacated seats nearer to the front.

I am sure the laundry stunk like rotten cabbage and that we looked strange to these stalwart citizens of the countryside. They may have thought we were hippies, but we worked twelve to fourteen hours a day, something any self-respecting hippie wouldn't be caught dead doing. And we certainly didn't take drugs, which were highly illegal and not available, and we wouldn't have had money to buy them if there were any. Personally, I wasn't interested in doing anything that might get me deported or ruin my chances of becoming an international show jumper.

At the first shop we came to in Crowsville, I bought a large cloth carry-all.

While the laundry was spinning around in the washers, we went to see the movie *Bonnie and Clyde*. I wished we hadn't gone because there was too much blood. Bonnie and Clyde were not American Robin Hoods, robbing banks and giving money to poor people as folk legend portrayed them. Bonnie and Clyde were little more than cold-blooded killers.

When we got back to the laundromat everything was still in the washers. Fortunately, no one in Crowsville wanted to steal underwear, socks, and work clothes, so while we waited for the laundry to dry, we went to the Fish and Chips shop across the street.

"I'm just closing now, my ducks," said the kind man behind the counter, "but if you take what I have cooked, I'll give it to you for half price." This was exceptionally good news to poverty-stricken WPs, and I remembered the shop and noted the time, for future reference. The price cut on supper helped to offset the cost of the laundromat and the movie ticket.

Chapter 16
Justice for All

My favorite horse, Harry, was going home to hunt soon. I would be sorry to see him go.

Vicar Hanleigh pleasantly surprised us by inviting us to the Vicarage for supper on Tuesday evening. Anything was better than beans on toast, so Gillian, Ruth, and I cheerfully went together. Gillian and I convinced Ruth, whose parents weren't very religious, that going to church was a good excursion. Mrs. Highstaff approved of us going, which was another bonus. The object of the supper invitation was for us to get to know some of the village kids better. It obviously worked.

Soon thereafter Mrs. Highstaff located an old ping-pong table in the attic of the Hall and Mr. Highstaff set it up for us in the lecture room. Penny, the Vicar's daughter, and a half a dozen others, personally selected, were invited to come and play ping-pong with us. We had quite a heated tournament and mixed up the teams, so we got to know more people. I hoped the kids would come back again because we had nice sandwiches, biscuits, and lemon barley water for refreshments. Being involved with the Brickton church was turning out to be food for the body as well as the soul.

On Friday evening, we held a competition for all the HDH lesson children. Each level included show jumping and three different gymkhana games. With lots of laughing, clapping, and a little fiddling, we ensured the tiniest kids won some of the chocolate bar prizes. I think we had at least as much fun as the kids did.

On Saturday morning, Mr. Hobbs appeared with a red poppy in the lapel of his hacking jacket. When Mrs. Highstaff walked through the yard with Lord Daffy, I noticed she also had a poppy in her lapel.

At breakfast Mr. Hobbs told us, "Synchronize your watches. At eleven o'clock on the dot, you will all stand at attention, and observe two minutes of absolute silence. This is to honor all those who died in the line of duty to their country." I thought he had a tear in his eye. After a slight pause, he solemnly added, "World War I ended on November 11 at 11 a.m." We proceeded as usual with the Saturday rides, but at eleven o'clock, it was so quiet you could have heard a raindrop land on a pony's ear.

In the afternoon a horse van arrived and Harry, my heavyweight charger, went home.

Jeremy joined us on Sunday. While I chatted with him, he told me, "I left school at sixteen, and worked as a hotel waiter to pay for Falstaff's livery and to buy my car. To save money I lived at the hotel. I finally saved enough money for my tuition fees at HDH. I am already twenty and I plan to take the BHSAI here in June. Then I want to stay on at HDH to get the British Horse Society Instructor's certification. Mrs. Highstaff told me that when I pass my AI exam, I can bring Falstaff to the Hall." Right now, Jeremy couldn't afford to board him at HDH, and part of our training was to ride as many different types of horses as possible. "I've temporarily leased Falstaff to Grace Edwards. Her yard is close enough that I can still ride Falstaff on my half-days off."

Jeremy's new digs was a small room in the attic next to Mr. Hobbs.

Another package from home arrived for me. It may have been intended as a birthday present, but I eagerly opened it. It contained a book of my favorite comic characters, *Peanuts*. My brother Richard often called me Lucy after a particularly crabby older sister character in the popular comic strip.

By my request, my parents had obtained some official North Carolina tourist brochures. The pages were filled with photographs of beautiful sandy beaches, the lovely Piedmont district, and the wooded Blue Ridge Mountains. The scenes of North Carolina the booklet failed to show were shabby wooden sharecroppers' houses, women and children working the fields with mules, crews of migrant workers picking fruit, and slummy neighborhoods on the wrong side of the tracks.

Denis was genuinely interested in anything from America, so he read the brochure avidly. He was amazed at the size of one state and the vastness of our country. North Carolina alone was about half the size of England, and there were forty-nine others.

Because Denis read the brochures, Fiona did too. Fiona might have secretly been trying to make up with Denis, but he had already moved on.

Marion confided to me that Denis had asked her out on her next Sunday off. With his car, he could easily pick Marion up from her parents, treat her to a pub supper, and have her back at the school by half past nine. Marion wasn't a big fan of Fiona's, but they had been at the school for nearly two years together. For that reason and some more personal ones, Marion firmly told Denis to shove off.

April borrowed the North Carolina propaganda to show to Tommy. She had elevated Tommy from boyfriend status to fiancé, so when they moved into the Gate House, Mrs. Highstaff would allow Tommy to stay over. About a week after Tommy read the pamphlet, April asked me to please find out how much lorry drivers earned in the USA.

My parents had enclosed my university entrance application that I had been badgering them about for months. I couldn't answer half of the questions so I filled in what I could and returned it to my parents to have them fill in the blank spaces. There was not enough time to write back and forth, answering questions. Mail service to the USA was at least a two-and-a-half- to three-week turnaround. The December deadline for submitting the application was rapidly approaching.

Our training continued seriously, and we were riding outside as much as the weather permitted. The indoor school, without sun, was colder. Since the school was virtually a wind tunnel, riding in it was only an improvement when it rained. If it rained too hard, the noise of the rain on the metal roof prevented you from hearing the instructor.

Today Mrs. Highstaff was giving us a lesson on hunter exercises out in the top field. Mr. Hobbs was riding Heathcliff in the exercises. So far Mr. Hobbs and Denis were the only two people riding Heathcliff. I had unflappable Cashel, and Gillian luckily got Marigold.

Hunter exercises are performed to develop individual control of a horse, with a group of horses, in an open space. The exercises make the horse more manageable.

We practiced having one horse ride ahead, stop and wait; passing at all gaits; circling to the rear of the ride; and, turning away from and passing the ride the opposite way. The exercises were fun, and the horses were enjoying it. It was a hint that we might get to go hunting this season. Being able to control your horse in a group, at all paces, is a requirement for foxhunting.

Mrs. Highstaff had just called us to "Ride in!" which meant to form a semi-circle around the instructor to hear the explanation of the next exercise. We had all assembled and were standing at ease on a long rein when a piercing "*Da dah! Da Dah!*" broke the silence. Our horses' ears stood up at attention. Horse and human heads simultaneously swiveled toward the sound.

The Featherstone Foxhounds were barreling through the field where we had windrowed the straw. The hounds, noses down, were streaming along. The Huntsman galloped behind the hounds. Because it was open land, the small field of riders was pretty tightly packed together behind the Field Master. Toward the back of the pack, I spotted my pal Harry with Dr. Amsley, our vet. I knew old Doc would be alright. Harry could jump anything around here. I was proud of Harry; he was keeping up with "Leicestershire's best."

Just then the huntsman blew another blast on his horn. "*Da dah!*"

Sword of Justice started quivering and suddenly, from a standstill, shot off like a bolt, leaving Jeremy to gather up his reins as they flew along.

Sword of Justice blazed in the sun as they careened around on a wild ride. Justice was stretched out and flying; trying to stop him was out of the question. Justice had the bit firmly locked between his teeth. He was going faster than any horse I had ever seen.

Staying balanced and steering Justice was all that Jeremy could manage. Trying a pulley rein at that speed might have put his or the horse's balance at risk. We were praying Jeremy would not panic, give up, or let Justice fly at a fence, any one of which could have been deadly at the speed they were going. We just watched in amazement as Jeremy and Justice raced around the big field in ever so slightly smaller circles. I thought of *Little Black Sambo* and how the tigers ran round and round and round and round until they all turned into butter.

The hunt galloped down into the valley and then up the hill behind the village. Soon they were out of our sight. After what seemed like an eternity, Justice slowed down and lurched into a very rough extended trot. He had huge strides. It would have been possible to still fall off at this point. After a run like that, your legs and arms would be like gelatin and you would be exhausted physically and mentally.

Finally Justice walked. Jeremy was red in the face and panting. The horse was dripping, lathered, and puffing. We applauded. I would never underestimate Jeremy in the future.

Mrs. Highstaff quietly said, "Well ridden, Jeremy! You kept your wits about you and kept riding." Then she ordered him to walk Justice around the very field where he had been going full tilt until the horse was cooled down. There was little danger Justice would run away again today—he looked pretty tired.

Denis had been doing a stellar job in the hunter exercises with the young horse Minstrel, and he had been looking forward to getting many compliments at lunch. Instead, he had been upstaged by a broken-down, nutty old racehorse ridden by a hotel waiter.

Jeremy blushed when Mr. Hobbs congratulated him and put his hand on his shoulder as they walked into the dining room. "Lester Piggott couldn't have done a better job himself." I had discovered that Mr. Hobbs had been an apprentice jockey in his youth, and he was a huge fan of Lester Piggott.

Before she walked out on us, Rachael was always rubbing it in that because she was the Head Girl, she would get to go hunting first. It depended on how things went if I would even get an opportunity. Fiona was Head Girl, Denis was BHSAI, Marion and Ruth had both been here nearly for two years, and Jeremy just proved to be a fearless rider. Gillian and I would be low on the list.

Denis might have been upstaged in the hunter exercises, but he was not to be deterred in the romance department. Denis asked Gillian if she would like to go out with him. Gillian could be a fresh start; she was new at the school. Gillian replied coolly, "My boyfriend back in Braefield won't think too much of the idea of me dating you!"

I wondered why Denis didn't look for a girlfriend somewhere else. True, he was at the riding school six and a half days a week. There was not much time to meet other people.

A few days later, I was a little miffed when Denis asked *me* out. Of course, I already knew of his romantic advances toward Marion and Gillian, and so I said, almost truthfully, "If you hadn't asked me *last*, Denis, I might have considered it. Buzz off!" Although he thought very highly of himself, Denis was good-looking and smart. He was a good rider, and he had a car and money to spend. But not now. Forget it.

In Leicester on our next half-day off, while eating our Wimpy burgers, Gillian and I had a good laugh over the woes of Denis and Fiona. Gillian said, "And Jeremy and Justice and their one-horse race reminds me of Mr. Toad's wild ride."

I told Gillian about the *Legend of Sleepy Hollow*. "I think Jeremy looks like Ichabod Crane." Jeremy looked like an Ichabod, but much more physically fit. We laughed some more.

It was too cold to be pleasant for walking around, so we went to the movie *The Taming of the Shrew*, starring Elizabeth Taylor and Richard Burton. Aside from keeping us warm and entertained, the movies gave us topics other than horses to talk about. I had seen an amateur production of the play. I argued that any play was better than any movie because it was a *live* production. In a play, one had to do right the first time, like in a riding competition. I did reluctantly admit, the acting was better in the movie. Elizabeth Taylor personified an excellent shrew.

Gillian and I debated on whether or not women should be submissive to men. We agreed they should not be, but we thought a woman could be assertive and agreeable at the same time, and certainly should not turn into shrews.

Chapter 17
Pilgrim

The weather in England in November was more like New England than North Carolina; in other words, it was horrible. Usually, November was my favorite month because it was my birth month. I was Sagittarius, the Centaur, the hunter, the archer, half-horse and half-man. To top it off, in November there was a four-day school holiday, kicking off with a big feast on Thursday, Thanksgiving Day. Some years my birthday was actually on Thanksgiving Day. I had 4-to-7 odds I would not be at school on my birthday.

Thanksgiving meant a trip to Grandma's for an extended-family turkey dinner and all the trimmings. Unfortunately, just like Halloween in England, Thanksgiving was nothing—no feast, and no days off. No wonder the Pilgrims (I stressed the *grims* syllable) escaped from this place.

The best thing that we had to be thankful for at HDH was that the visitors' gallery on the covered school was actually shaping up and would soon be less of a wind tunnel.

It was dark much longer now. The sun didn't rise until eight and it set at half past five.

My birthday was going to be on Monday this year, not during the uncelebrated four-day weekend. I would be eighteen. I was getting a tinge of homesickness. I had started to get some cards from home. They cheered me up. My grandparents and my uncle had both enclosed $10 checks in their cards. I started feeling a little better.

My brother even sent me a letter. He had made the varsity basketball team as a high school freshman.

Richard was the best baseball player in his age bracket in the county. While Richard was playing on the high school baseball team, the coach ordered him to get a haircut, which even my parents agreed he didn't need. After that episode, Richard refused to play baseball for that coach.

I thought the real reason for the confrontation was because the coach's son was also on the baseball team, and he was likely to get picked for a college scholarship or maybe even the Big Leagues. Baseball was a huge deal in the South. Major League and college scouts watched some of the games. The coach didn't want to harm his son's chances by competition from Richard.

Coach Andrews went to our church and knew the whole story. He needed athletes. He could teach them the game and produce a winning season. Richard quit baseball and was now a forward on the varsity basketball team.

At supper on my birthday, the WPs threw a little party for me. Jeremy and Marion gave me a fluorescent orange stuffed shaggy dog. Fiona bought me a furry brown whatnot. Whatnots were nondescript mousy figures dressed in silly clothes, and they were quite the rage. Jennifer sent me a care package filled with food, which we immediately consumed, and another *Peanuts* comic book.

Ruth and Gillian bought me something much more practical. It immediately became my favorite article of clothing, an army surplus Auxiliary Territorial Services official jerkin. It was light-brown smooth leather on the outside, lined with a green army blanket, and belted in the back, and had large buttons down the front. It was warm, and best of all, it could fit under my tweed hacking jacket since I was skinnier than when I came.

The Beatles gave me an unexpected birthday present. Their *Magical Mystery Tour* album was released on my birthday. I thought that was significant. The whole previous seventeen years in my life had been a mystery tour. I had already been around the world and crossed the equator many times and seen a lot of strange sights.

Gillian and I planned that I should come home with her for the Christmas holiday, although she hadn't cleared this with her parents yet. We didn't even know which days off we were going to get. Everyone could not have Christmas Eve and Christmas Day off.

I envisioned buying myself a stylish leather coat with my birthday money. Gillian warned me not to buy it in Leicester. "In Northampton where the leather factories are, the coats will be quite a bit cheaper." The leather coats came in every color in the rainbow, every length, and many styles. *Which color and style would suit me best?*

I knew that international mail could take a long time to be delivered, so I was rather pleased that I was getting my Christmas cards out early.

I explained my mission to Mrs. Highstaff and received permission to walk to the village post office during dinner. Being friends with April had some advantages. "I'll save you a plate of food," she promised. I hoped to buy a chocolate bar at the post office.

I had a real shock when the post lady standing behind the iron grille explained that since I had *sealed* the envelopes, each card was going to cost me one shilling and sixpence to send. "Oh dear." She sighed. "That is too bad. If you just tucked the flaps in, the stamps only cost seven pence per card."

I had already sealed ten cards. Ten shillings! More than a half-pound squandered right there. This extra postage was an extravagant waste of money when I was trying to buy a leather coat.

In the true spirit of Scrooge, I stood at the wooden counter and very carefully reopened the envelopes and tucked the flaps inside. The results were mixed. Some envelope flaps had straighter edges than others. I borrowed a pen from the post lady and hastily scribbled a note on the back of the card to my family. "Mom, if you get any complaints from our relatives about tattered envelopes, please explain that I had to do it to save money."

I told my mother to expect a small package from me after Christmas. I had finished my Christmas shopping, but this postage fiasco set me back quite a bit, and I still had to mail cards to my friends.

In our Friday Evening Dressage competition, Ruth on Mango won the Young Horse division. Mango was an exquisite mover and Ruth was a tactful rider. Fiona and Jazzy took second. Rob Roy and I came in third of seven entries and my whole experience was better than the last time.

Ruth also won the School Horse class riding Topaz. Other than Mrs. Highstaff, Mr. Hobbs and Ruth were the only people allowed to ride Topaz. Ruth's win was especially exciting because the five riders from Meadowbrook competed in this class.

I liked the way dressage was judged. The rider received a score and remarks for every movement ridden. Our top three places were only four marks apart. On the scale of marks, I received: seven - 7s (fairly good), three - 6s (satisfactory), and two - 5s (sufficient).

The judging in the Flatlanders Horse Shows back home looked completely subjective to me. I often wondered if there was any real criteria for picking the winners.

After the competition, we had a coffee break in the dining hall with our guests from Meadowbrook before we did the final check of the stables.

Mrs. Highstaff made an announcement. "We are pleased to announce the students of Heels Down Hall are donating all the entry fees from the competition to a Christmas fund for orphans." There was a weak round of applause at this news. The instructor from Meadowbrook thought it was a wonderfully generous idea. As the competition secretary-treasurer, this was the first I had heard of the charitable donation. The rosettes we were going to order had just been put on hold.

Before we went out to the yard, Mrs. Highstaff cheered us with some good news. "By the way, we will be holding a Jumping Competition on Tuesday evening, the twelfth of December."

I was excited. In the show jumping competition, I would have as good of a chance to win as anybody else. After all, my secret ambition was to become an international show jumper.

After the coffee break, Denis started on his way out to his car to go home, but he changed his course, and instead he followed Ruth into the carriage house where all Mrs. Highstaff's favorites lived. Topaz, Mango, Meteor, and St. Christopher occupied four large loose boxes with wooden wall dividers and vertical iron railings around the tops.

"Congratulations, Ruth, you rode beautifully."

Ruth had just finished checking Mango's rugs. She smiled and blushed. She hated a fuss. More like a pixie than a teenager, Ruth was tickled to get some extra attention. "I give all the credit to my wonderful horses." In reality, both Mango and Topaz were hot-blooded and extremely difficult to ride.

Denis had Ruth backed into the space between the stalls where the pitchforks and yard brushes were kept. He put one hand across to the other stall to block any easy exit. Then Denis leaned in and gave Ruth a congratulatory kiss on the mouth. He hadn't even gotten to the "take you out for dinner" part of his pitch.

Mrs. Highstaff was in Topaz's stall, bent over, examining the clenches on a shoe she thought might be a little loose. With Topaz standing between herself and her two WPs, she would not have been visible to Ruth and Denis. After overhearing the romantic conversation, Mrs. Highstaff decided Topaz's shoe would be fine until Rodney could get here.

She stood up.

In a quiet, solemn voice she spoke deliberately. "Denis, I will be arranging for a meeting with you and your parents tomorrow as soon as they can get here. Go home now. Come back tomorrow with your parents."

At eleven the next morning, I was turning out horses in paddocks. A Humber Super Snipe limousine rolled up the drive, right past me, with a chauffeur driving, and Mr. and Mrs. Parkhurst and Denis sitting in the back. The maroon and black limo pulled up to the portico and the Parkhursts went inside the Hall. We never knew what went on at the meeting, but at 11:22 the same cortege in the Humber drove down the drive and out through the gates. Denis never returned to Heels Down Hall.

We weren't surprised. Denis's departure had been in the offing for a long time.

His year as a working pupil would have been up in February. As disruptive as he was, Denis's dismissal meant we had one less worker in the stables for the upcoming winter.

In the evening when I went in to say good night, Mrs. Highstaff told me, "Alexa, I am pleased to tell you that you have reached another stage in your riding."

I was delighted. This was my best birthday present yet.

On December 5, the first snow flurries arrived. We came in from riding in the field with a white frozen crust glazing our hacking jackets. Because of a polar depression, the air was clear as crystal, and on the sixth, we had another hard frost.

The next morning I went down to make the tea at ten past six. I wore a thermal undershirt and a turtleneck under my riding shirt and tie. I was cold, but once I got moving and warmed up, it was bearable.

When I tried to open the door to let the two orange tabby cats out, I had to push quite hard. When the door finally scraped open, much to my surprise, I found two inches of snow.

For the next two days, it kept snowing on and off, and on December 10, there was a blizzard. A strong wind blew the storm in from Greenland. Wales had seventeen to twenty inches of snow and Brickton got about a foot.

Before we could even start the regular morning chores, we had to shovel the snow, clear the courtyard, and ensure the stall doors would open.

I was on Rota duty for the Pasture Water Troughs. I had to go around to all the fields and break the ice in the troughs with a pickaxe. The troughs were freezing over in less than an hour.

Since the blizzard occurred on Sunday, the road crews were not going to be plowing or sanding the backcountry roads until Monday. Even driving the four-wheel-drive Land Rover would be foolhardy. You couldn't see the verge of the road.

We came in for breakfast, frozen, forty-five minutes late. Mr. Hobbs immediately discovered there was not enough milk.

"This is completely unacceptable." He stomped off to see Mrs. Highstaff.

A few minutes later, Mr. Hobbs appeared with a scarf wound around his head to hold his flat cap on and wearing thick, wooly string gloves and his tall riding boots.

We were ordered to get Ghost ready and tack him up.

Mr. Hobbs acquired a large burlap sack, which he slung over his shoulder like a paperboy. He mounted Ghost and they disappeared down the driveway into the blizzard. Soon Ghost, the white pony, and Mr. Hobbs, who was quickly being covered with snow, became a snow horse ridden by a snowman.

About an hour and a half later, Mr. Hobbs and Ghost reappeared, with as many bottles of milk that the corner shop could spare, the *Sunday Times* for Mr. Highstaff, a *Sporting Chronicle* for himself, a chocolate bar for each of us, and a package of Senior Service cigarettes.

"Thank you, Robert," Mrs. Highstaff said quietly. "Do come into the study to warm yourself by the fire and have a sherry."

It looked like we might have a white Christmas.

Chapter 18
Drench

The weather got warmer and melted much of the snow. As a result, the ground was slippery and muddy, a condition called "grease." A thick, damp fog set in; the nasty gray air was enriched by the soot from coal fires. Visibility was as far as the end of your arm. Riding in the field was an eerie experience. I hoped the horses could see better than I could. Misty apparitions appeared to float in the distance. It would have been easy to run into someone or something. Jumping was out of the question.

Miraculously, by mid-afternoon the fog lifted, and we went forward with our Tuesday Night Jumping Competition.

My prediction was right: I had as good of a chance as anyone.

Riding Wizard, I won the School Horse class after four jump-offs against Ruth on Mango. Wizard was a real champion, always giving his best effort. The final height was over four feet.

My beloved baby giraffe Rob Roy was something of a disappointment in the Young Horse class. Under this table of faults, you were not eliminated for falling, if you both could continue. We racked up a cricket score, seventeen faults: two refusals, and at the second refusal I had a fall but landed on my feet. I rationalized that Rob Roy was only three and it was the first time he had ever attempted a "proper" course. Mrs. Highstaff was still pleased by his performance. "He shows good form over the jumps when he is properly engaged."

Ruth on Meteor handily won the Speed Class. Fiona came in second on Jazzy. Rob Roy and I were eliminated in the first round. Under this table one refusal was enough to take us out of the running. It was Fault and Out.

The large ponies dominated the High Jump. Ruth and Meteor won again. Deidre, a Scottish girl who arrived just after the roads were cleared, came in second on Wizard. Deidre was here on a week-long course. Gillian took third on Marigold. The final height was four feet six inches.

Ruth and Meteor reminded me of Marion Coates, a daring young English rider, and her famous show jumping pony Stroller. For years I kept a newspaper clipping of Marion and the diminutive Stroller sailing over a Grand Prix jump. That photo fueled my childhood dream of becoming a show jumper.

The next morning, I was mucking out Wizard, and Mr. Hobbs was feeding Meteor. He called me over. "Leave that and come here quickly."

Meteor thrashed about in his stall and was trying to roll. Our champion show jumping pony had colic. I got his headcollar. We got him up and Mr. Hobbs put a blanket and an arched roller on him immediately.

Fiona ran to the Hall to get Mrs. Highstaff and have April put the kettle on to make the drench.

I knew from studying *The Owner Groom* that there were "different mixtures for different colics. Flatulent colic may also require an enema." I hoped that would not be necessary.

The recipe for Meteor's spasmodic colic was "a half pint of linseed oil, two tablespoons of turpentine [to prevent gas from formulating], and at least two shots of brandy." The brandy helped the horse to warm up and to relax. The recipe was then mixed with enough warm water to fill the large bottle.

I helped Mrs. Highstaff give Meteor his drench. To drench a horse, you must hold the horse's head up high. Since I was a head taller than Mrs. Highstaff that was my job. The warm mixture was administered via the horse's mouth through a long-neck, leather-coated bottle. The neck of the bottle was inserted into the corner of the horse's mouth with the bottom of the bottle tilted upwards. Usually, the groom gets drenched during the process, so I learned to make double the amount of the mixture and to remember to wear a raincoat.

After the drench, I took Meteor down to the indoor school. We walked, walked, walked, and walked around the school. I started singing Christmas carols, partly to keep my spirits up and partly to give Meteor something else to think about. I am a terrible singer, but I know most of the words to most of the carols. I can sing with great enthusiasm, and it helped me to forget I was cold.

After I had walked Meteor for about two hours, he finally pooped and behaved normally. I was told to bring him back to his box.

At that point, I would have recommended at least two shots of brandy for the person walking around for hours in the cold with a colicky horse, but no one asked me, and none was offered.

Mr. Hobbs volunteered to watch Meteor for a while, so I ran down to the kitchen and gobbled my breakfast in five minutes flat. Then I went back and stayed with Meteor in his stall until the others came back out to the yard.

Fortunately Meteor recovered and he had no ill effects from the colic, the drench, or my singing.

Mrs. Highstaff appointed me organizer, judge, and announcer for the HDH Annual Holiday Competition for junior riders. The kids loved Mr. Hobbs, who made a dashing ringmaster, decked out in a Pink hunting coat and a smart top hat.

Even though they were only ten, Caroline and Julie, the show pony riders, did a great job keeping the ponies coming down to the school in a timely manner. The other WPs assisted the children in getting ready or they worked as ring crew and gatekeepers.

We had two different age groups of riders with five events for each group. Mr. Hobbs awarded chocolate bars for prizes. At the end of the show, he reached into the bottom of the bag. "Guess what, Alexa? Two extra bars! We'll just have to eat these ourselves."

"Happy Christmas!"

"Happy Christmas, everyone!"

"Happy Christmas, horses and ponies!"

"Happy Christmas!"

"Happy Christmas!"

The chorus of children's voices got fainter as the parents dragged the children into the car park after the show.

On the third Sunday of December, Gillian and I went to the Family Service in Brickton. The Christmas Candlelight Service of Carols was next Sunday, Christmas Eve, and we immediately planned to go.

On our way out of the church after the service, Vicar Hanleigh said, "Girls, why don't you come to the Vicarage tomorrow evening to help make decorations for the church Christmas tree?"

After church we walked back to the Hall. When we reached our driveway, the Land Rover and horsebox were parked outside the Gate House. Cricket poked her head from the window in the turret and yelled, "Father Christmas gave Mommy and me our very own house!"

At that moment Mr. Hobbs appeared with Jeremy right behind him. "Will you give us a hand getting this last load in?"

It was not a question. Dressed in our Sunday clothes, we helped carry the furniture into the Gate House. Jeremy huffed, "All this stuff came from the Hall's attic. This is the second load." There were two beds that matched ours, dressers, tables, and an odd assortment of chairs and some boxes of mismatched dishes. A cheery fire crackled in the fireplace. April smiled ear to ear. "I've never had my own place before."

On Monday evening, Fiona came to the Vicarage with us. Now that Denis was gone, she made an effort to be part of our clique. Christmas season was making us all a little homesick. The Vicarage promised to be warm and to supply us with some decent food. It was nice to walk into a warm room filled with friendly faces.

St. Cuthbert's turned out to be a real blessing for us. There was no real entertainment for teenagers in the rural outposts of Leicestershire. Brickton was about as close to having a swinging London nightclub as Heels Down Hall was to having a NASA lunar launch pad.

We had a thoroughly good time making the ornaments while we drank cups of tea and munched sandwiches, homemade mince pies, and Christmas biscuits.

"We are making Chrismons!" I said confidently. Vicar Hanleigh was surprised I knew the names of the religious symbols that we cut from the silver and gold paper.

I politely reminded the Vicar, "You know, Vicar Hanleigh, Lutherans are the German version of Anglicans, and Martin Luther has the credit for the tradition of decorated Christmas trees." After a pause, I added, "And they didn't divorce any queens or chop off their heads in the process." Fiona, being Catholic, laughed. I always questioned Henry VIII's motives.

Christmas cards began to arrive in the post, a very tropical one from Aunt Helga in Hawaii and traditional ones from my parents' friends. We strung the cards across our lounge to make a garland. Everyone added their cards to it and the colorful greetings cheered up the place.

Mrs. Highstaff assigned each of us a Saturday ride to teach starting on December 23. My ride, the Low Intermediates, the Cs to Ds in Pony Club, started at half past eleven. Gillian got the tiny tots. We would teach our class and assist each other. We had great ponies and kids. I looked forward to this new responsibility, a real teaching experience.

We had a heavy frost in the morning. The snow had melted, but it was still bitterly cold. In a way this was good, the semi-frozen ground wasn't muddy, but a horse tripping over a frozen rut was a real danger. In sunny spots, another dangerous condition occurred when the ground on top thawed with the frozen ground underneath. Grease.

It was official. Gillian told me, "My parents wrote. You are invited to my home for our Christmas break." Our holiday started on Boxing Day on December 26 after evening stables and included the whole day Wednesday and Thursday. We had to be back by Friday night to work and teach on Saturday.

Seniority and rank mattered in getting choice time off. Jeremy had not been here long enough for the extra time off.

Jeremy, Gillian, and I would be at the riding school for Christmas.

This would be my first Christmas away from my family ever. Our family had been to many strange places, but somehow, we were always together at Christmas.

On the Wednesday before Christmas, Mrs. Highstaff received an unexpected telephone call from a debutante from a leading foxhunting family in the county.

"Mrs. Highstaff? This is Enid Boswell. I am looking for another horse. Rodney told me about a young horse that would make an excellent hunter prospect. He couldn't remember the horse's name, but he suggested I call." Rodney, our farrier, was a great gossip.

Mrs. Highstaff patiently explained, "I always have several excellent young horses, although they are not really for sale. But, Enid, can you please be more specific?" After a lengthy conversation, it came down to one horse. If the horse would pass the vet check for soundness, which everyone believed it would, she agreed to pay the extravagant sum of five hundred guineas.

Horses and other important purchases were always paid for in guineas, not pounds.

On the first official day of winter, Dr. Amsley appeared at ten o'clock. This Thursday was my last half-day off before Christmas and I was glad Doc came in the morning. I watched the lengthy and thorough pre-purchase exam. Jeremy and Mr. Hobbs helped with the examination, which included Jeremy galloping Minstrel for several minutes to check for soundness of wind.

I skipped dinner at HDH and took the bus into Leicester with a clear mission in mind. The birthday money I received in late November had been in the form of personal checks. It took two weeks for them to clear the bank. Today I could collect the money.

My first stop after the bank was a post office. I mailed my tiny box of presents home to my family. Air postage was exorbitant, and I sent the parcel surface mail. I apologized for the additional delay in my letter.

I mailed a calendar of English horse breeds to the tack shop in Greenleaf to thank them for the help they gave me when I was preparing to go to Heels Down Hall.

Lately I had been feeling a lot like *Georgy Girl.* For the last several trips into Leicester, I had been eyeing a smashing dress displayed in the front window of the trendy Beat shop, a hip boutique in the town center.

The dress acquisition temporarily pre-empted my obsession with buying a leather coat, but, even so, the shop was a little expensive for my budget. My coveted dress was a gorgeous deep purple velvet, Edwardian-style shirtdress, mid-thigh length. A white lace ruffle cascaded down the front, and the white satin collar was embellished with round white pearl buttons. On the end of the long sleeves, white satin cuffs edged with lace and pearl buttons gave the outfit extra "pizzazz."

The dress was finally on sale.

My mother taught me never to pay full price for clothing because the markup on ready-made clothes was tremendous.

Cash in hand, I proudly stepped into the shop and asked to try on the dress. The Mod shop attendant frowned. "We only have the one in the window left. Would you like to try something else?"

My Christmas spirit wilted. "No, I would *not*."

The shop had racks of cool clothes. I resembled a stick figure topped with long hair. I could wear anything, but I had my heart set on *that dress* ever since I spotted it a month ago.

Just as I was about to leave, a woman with blond hair streaked with pink came into the shop. It turned out she was the manageress returning from her coffee break. In the Christmas spirit, she was wearing a red miniskirt and a green-checkered, long-sleeve jersey sweater, and a pin made of holly. She considered the problem for a moment. Business had been slow that day. She didn't want to lose a sale this close to Christmas. She looked at me and then she looked at the mannequin in the window. She asked the attendant to take the dummy out of the window and to allow me to try on the dress.

It fits! And because it was "shop soiled" the manageress offered me an additional discount on top of the sale price. Mom would have been proud.

When I said good night, I proudly showed Mrs. Highstaff my dress and I told her about my summer travel plans with my mother after I left Heels Down Hall. Mrs. Highstaff graciously said, "I will write to your mother and invite her to visit you at the Hall."

This was groovy. Mom would get to see where I lived, see what I was doing, and put faces to the people and horses mentioned in my letters.

A letter enclosed in a Christmas card from Greenleaf had news of my brother burning up the basketball courts in eastern North Carolina. In every game Richard was the high scorer.

Chapter 19

Revelers on Horseback

At ten o'clock on Friday morning, Boswell's horsebox drove into the yard. Minstrel left. He had never been advertised for sale, but the price offered was too good to turn down.

I wasn't sad to see him go. I never had ridden Minstrel; he was Denis's project.

Great, now there will be one less stabled horse to muck out this winter.

While I was walking Meteor to relieve his colic earlier in the week, Mrs. Highstaff had overheard me singing to him.

Mrs. Highstaff thought it would improve our Christmas spirit if we sang Christmas carols. At the beginning of our lesson, she informed us, "Caroling is a very old British tradition, and I believe there is not enough caroling these days." It was harder than you think to sing and ride at the same time, but it was fun and made us forget we were cold and homesick.

The Saturday before Christmas was our first time to teach our new children's rides. Of course, we had our proper lesson plans approved by Mrs. Highstaff the day before, but we had such fun singing the carols in our lesson, we ditched our approved lessons. We decided the kids should also keep British traditions alive and sing carols.

Gillian asked her tiny tots, "What songs do you know?"

"Jingle Bells," "Away in a Manger," and "We Wish You a Merry Christmas." Their repertoire was somewhat limited.

Gillian decided to teach them some new songs.

"We three kings of Orient are—
One in a taxi,
One in a car,
One on a scooter, blowing his hooter,
Following yonder star."

It was perfect for a stately extended walk. The howls of laughter almost made the children fall off the ponies. And then Gillian taught us another one.

"While shepherds washed their socks by night,
All seated on the ground.
An Angel of the Lord came down
And kicked them all around."

This carol was good for sitting trot and it produced more shrieks and giggles. Not to be outdone, I came up with an American parody.

"Jingle bells,
Santa smells,
Rudolph ran away.
Oh, what fun it is to ride—
In a brand-new Chevrolet."

Only a few kids knew what a Chevrolet was, but once I explained it was a car, they thought it was hilarious. In Europe, General de Gaulle and General Franco were big shots, but in the USA, General Motors ran the show. We even got into singing some rounds. "We Wish You a Merry Christmas" was a good song for rounds because there were so few words to remember.

We were quite a band of merry revelers on horseback.

On the drive home after the Saturday lessons, I was certain there would be quite a few confused parents listening to the fractured carols being sung by their tiny equestrians. I liked Christmas in England. It was celebrated at Christmas like we used to do when I was little. In the USA, the Christmas holiday was heavily commercialized starting in early November. On the church calendar, the month before Christmas is Advent, meaning "the coming of Christ," or in America, the buying of stuff. At our house, it was the making of Christmas cookies.

The Twelve Days of Christmas starts on Christmas Day and continues through January 6, the Epiphany, representing the day when the Wise Men came and presented Gifts to the Christ Child. In Greenleaf, they threw Christmas trees out the day after Christmas. I was a little disappointed; my promised package from home had not arrived in the afternoon post.

Christmas Eve fell on Sunday, and we had an easy day. In the morning, everyone who wanted to—in other words, Gillian, Ruth, and I—accompanied Mrs. Highstaff to the no-singing St. George's in Storkey. The service was austere with incense, candles, and lots of kneeling. We didn't miss the carols. We had been doing rather a lot of singing earlier in the week. Marion's and Ruth's holiday was supposed to start today, but Ruth's plans unexpectedly changed. Her parents couldn't collect her. I was sad that Ruth couldn't go home, but happy for us. Ruth's upbeat attitude would help make Christmas at HDH a jolly occasion. April and Cricket joined us in the dining hall for Christmas Eve lunch because there were so few of us and it felt more like a family.

After the evening feed, Mrs. Highstaff invited us to decorate the Christmas tree in her dining room. We had fun making paper chains and smothering the tree in tinsel. We drank cups of cocoa and ate little mince pies. On the way to bed, we placed our Christmas cards for the Highstaff's and Mr. Hobbs on the post counter.

The sun finally appeared after breakfast on Christmas Day. It was Monday, but for the stable, we kept the Sunday schedule. As a holiday bonus, mucking out and bedding down your horses was optional. Of course, there would be no riding. Only quartering and set fair had to be done for grooming.

It was dark by four o'clock in December.

After the horses were fed in the evening, we were invited for a candlelight Christmas dinner with the Highstaffs in their private formal dining room.

We changed into our finest clothes.

Compared to our rather spartan quarters, the enormous dining room dazzled.

Old Oriental rugs were scattered over the hardwood floor.

The walls were covered with faded maroon damask silk with a subtle floral pattern. Some large hunt prints and original paintings hung from the chains from the wooden dado rail around the walls. "This is my favorite painting," I said. A horse was nuzzling a hound surrounded by puppies. A little brass plaque on the bottom of the fame read SLADE INSTITUTE OF ART. STUDENT SHOW. FIRST PRIZE. The painting was signed *M M Carrington*. Mrs. Highstaff smiled.

A large yule log crackled on the andirons in the fireplace. The front of the mantel was draped with an evergreen garland. The top of the mantelpiece was dotted with black and white photographs in silver frames; horses at one end, and, at the other end, photographs of people. In one photo, a tall, dashing pilot with black hair was standing beside a WWII aeroplane, with his helmet in his hand. Another smaller frame contained a photo of a mounted Cavalry officer sitting on an Arabi-looking horse in front of a stone wall. In the bright desert sun, the rider was not quite distinguishable because the brim of his hat threw a shadow over his face. Christmas cards filled the space between the photos.

The moon and stars could be seen through the large, mullioned windows. Carefully arranged on a white sheet around the base of the glittering tree, beautifully wrapped presents decked with ribbons and bows sparkled in the moonlight.

Ruth and Gillian were not of legal drinking age, but Mrs. Highstaff said, "It is Christmas," and poured everyone a glass of sherry.

That warmed me up. I was wearing my new purple minidress, with heavy pantyhose called tights. Gillian wore a very smart skirt, blouse, and jumper. Ruth wore a midi-length gray wool dress that, combined with her short pixie haircut, made her look like a novice nun. We had enough makeup on to make Cleopatra proud.

Jeremy appeared wearing black trousers, a sports jacket, a long-sleeve white shirt, and a bow tie. He looked like a *maître d'.*

Without a doubt, Christmas dinner was the best meal I ever had at Heels Down Hall.

We had a name card on a silver holder to show us our place. Each end of the table was lit by long white, red, and green candles in silver candelabras. The centerpiece was an arrangement of holly and ivy in a porcelain bowl.

We sat on chairs with carved legs and arms and tapestry-covered padded seats and backs. We ate from china dishes laid out on red or green placemats on the white brocade tablecloth. We drank from crystal glasses.

For starters, we had a salad. Then Mr. Highstaff carved the roast turkey and Mrs. Highstaff filled our plates with side dishes of lumpy applesauce and bread dressing with chestnuts. We had real vegetables, parsnips and Brussels sprouts. Of course, there were mounds of roast potatoes.

I can't imagine how I thought parsnips and Brussels sprouts were a treat. In Greenleaf, I probably would not have eaten either of them.

Before the pudding, we pulled our brightly wrapped Christmas crackers. All sorts of things silly spilled out of them. We promptly put on our paper crowns. We took turns reading the jokes printed on little slips of paper and we laughed heartily at the ridiculous answers. We tried to make the tiny useless toys, like plastic tops, work properly.

The finale of the festive meal was the flaming plum pudding, properly molded and steamed, and served with brandy butter. More brandy was poured on the pudding before the serving was passed around.

I never had this before. It was strangely delicious.

Munch, munch, munch. Crunch.

What's this?

I had bitten into the lucky sixpence inserted in the pudding. I thought it would be lucky if you didn't break a tooth or choke. I wasn't superstitious, but just as a precaution, I kept the sixpence in a safe place.

After dinner, we cleared the table for games and stacked the dishes in the butler's pantry for April to wash tomorrow.

HAPPY
CHRISTMAS
Johnson

Chapter 20

Season to Be Jolly

Gillian and I were the Green team and Jeremy and Ruth were the Red team. Mr. Highstaff was the scorekeeper. After a few silly games, we had a quiz from the Pony Club book. It was Gillian's turn in the final round. This would be the deciding point; our Red and Green teams were tied.

Mrs. Highstaff turned toward Gillian with the last question. "Gillian, what does MFH stand for?"

This was a no-brainer. We were going to win. Gillian turned as blank as paper, then wrinkled her brow, deep in thought.

"Time's nearly up. Answer or forfeit," said Mr. Highstaff.

"*Hmmm*—many fat horses?"

What? My teammate said that?

"Oh, no!" Quickly correcting herself, Gillian exclaimed, "Master of Foxhounds!"

It was too late. The victorious Red team was awarded fat candy canes for being smarter than us. Still wearing his paper crown, Mr. Highstaff played Father Christmas and gave each of us a beautifully wrapped present from under the tree. The presents were perfect for each person.

Jeremy got a proper necktie in a quiet blue. *Thank God. He looks so silly wearing that bow tie. It makes his Adam's apple look huge.*

Ruth got a pair of warm string riding gloves. She needed new ones. I got a lovely book, *Anthology of Equine Literature*. Gillian's present was a sketch pad and a set of drawing pencils. Presents for April and Cricket were under the tree, but they would get their presents tomorrow.

Maybe April wouldn't feel quite so bad cleaning up the remains of our Christmas dinner when she got her presents. Our dinner tomorrow would be leftover Christmas, although there was not too much left. Helpings of extra potatoes and cabbage would fill the plates.

Not to worry, I will be eating a proper tea at Gillian's house tomorrow evening.

There is only one day of work tomorrow, and then we will be off to Gillian's. Hurray!

I got sad. I missed my parents and brother in Greenleaf. I silently wished them a Merry Christmas and hoped they liked their presents when they eventually got them.

It was the first and last time I ever opted to not muck out my stalls on a holiday. Throughout England, Boxing Day was a day off. For some, it might involve hunting, shooting, or a party, but at HDH the stalls were extra messy and there were only four of us to muck out all of them. Ruth and Jeremy cleaned their stalls on Christmas Day, but Gillian and I had not. Rob Roy was a real pig at the best of times. He twirled around in his stall and completely saturated every piece of straw with muck. His entire box had to be gutted. Every horse's box required extra trips to the muck heap and needed more bales of straw to bed down in the afternoon.

I learned a great lesson that Christmas: with animal care, there are no days off. The horses were exuberant from two days of no riding. Our riding was exciting, horses bucking and snorting. No one could relax for a moment. At least the day passed quickly.

In another part of Leicestershire, the Featherstone Foxhounds were holding their traditional Boxing Day Meet. Through his father's business connections, Denis managed to get himself invited by Lord Boswell, who had just invested heavily in Parkhurst Industries.

Everyone turns out for Boxing Day. Riders and horses were turned out to the nines. The field of riders was enormous. Grooms led the youngest riders. Several little tykes turned up in basket saddles on donkeys. Mobs of Pony Clubbers, riding equines of assorted sizes, milled around, telling each other what Father Christmas had brought them. The hunt members arrived on stately long-legged hunters, or on less grand but very capable horses. With this large of a turnout, it was highly unusual for a capper to ride.

It was a bustling scene. More horses and ponies kept arriving. Throngs of local families came to see the hunt off, and they would follow on foot or by car until the hounds would go out of view. Riders drank from stirrup cups handed to them from silver trays.

Elegantly turned-out Enid Boswell was mounted on a fine Thoroughbred. When she wasn't on a horse, Enid was pretty unremarkable—tall, skinny, and getting rather too old to keep coming out at tiresome balls in London every summer. She surveyed the crowd and spied the handsome newcomer at once.

She knew all the hunt members and most of the Pony Clubbers, but Enid knew nothing about her father arranging Denis's invitation to the hunt. She loved horses and cared nothing about business.

Denis was on a borrowed mount that more resembled a workhorse than a hunter but was reputed to be a good jumper. Denis was undeniably good-looking. Even if he had been riding a mule, Enid would have sought him out.

Enid waited until Denis made his proper greetings to the hunt staff, then she weaved her horse through the crowd, intending to make some funny remark about the horse Denis was riding. "That animal resembles Hercules," she was going to say. Hercules was the cart horse of Steptoe and Son, who were East End rag and bone men on a TV comedy series.

It was no wonder Enid wasn't engaged. She had a sharp wit but didn't realize how she could hurt people. A countryside rule she seemed to have forgotten was "To get along with others, never insult a man's horse or his dog."

Smitten at once, Enid forgot her rude remark and stammered, "I hope you will enjoy the hunt." Then she couldn't resist adding a challenge. "If you can keep up with me, I'll show you the best jumps in the county."

"Hounds, please! Hounds, Please!" The huntsman blew his horn and they moved off.

Gillian's father picked us up in the afternoon. Mr. Benson was short, a little stocky but not fat, and he was very friendly. He wore a smart camel-hair car coat, a trilby wool hat, and a plaid wool scarf around his neck.

He arrived before we finished tack cleaning, so April made him a cup of tea in the kitchen. We had already packed, and we were ready to go. In no time at all, we headed down the lane and off to Braefield in Mr. Benson's Ford Anglia, my favorite car.

On the way, we passed the site of the famous battle on Bosworth Field where Richard III reportedly cried out, "A Horse! A horse! My kingdom for a horse!" I hoped I could find the famous missing horseshoe on the battlefield, but it was dark and there was no time to stop.

A while later we drove by the monument for the Battle of Naseby on the fields of Broad Moor where Cromwell's Parliamentarian forces won a decisive battle over the main Royalist Army. "Gillian, when was the Battle of

Naseby?" She looked at her watch, and with a completely straight face, she said, "Three-quarters past four. I'm afraid we missed it."

It took me a while to figure out "three-quarters past four" would be written as 1645.

It took nearly two hours to get to Braefield. Now I realized why the Bensons didn't come for Gillian every week.

The tea waiting for us was worth the long drive. Mrs. Benson served some of Gillian's and her brother's favorites. We were famished and we devoured the delicious hot soup, cold salad, meats, fruit, cheese, pickles, and piccalilli.

Gillian's older brother Christopher looked quite intellectual dressed in blue jeans, a turtleneck, and a tweed sports jacket. He wore tortoiseshell eyeglasses. He had a mustache, much like the Beatles, to make himself look older and more distinguished.

Normally when he was up from London, Christopher would sleep in the little bedroom overlooking the back garden. He generously gave his room to me, and he opted to sleep in a loft under the eaves of the thatch roof in the attic.

I loved Gillian's Gran, who was living with them. Gran was a tiny, well-educated, and well-traveled woman. She dressed in a classically understated way.

Gillian bunked in with Gran. I had my own luxurious room with a soft bed that didn't sag and fluffy eiderdown duvet and soft pillow. This was heaven.

We had planned to take baths at Gillian's. Before we could bring the bath subject up, Gillian's mother suggested it, as soon as we finished eating. Mrs. Benson was going to suggest the baths upon our arrival, but it was late and everyone was hungry.

We carried boiling water in a kettle from the kitchen upstairs to add to the tepid water in the tub. Hot water was limited at the Bensons too, but with the aid of the kettle, we each had a bath and washed our hair. Afterward, to dry our hair we sat near the heater in the dining room.

I went to bed, full, clean, warm, and happy.

The house was interesting with small rooms that had doors that shut. Each room had a small, solid fuel heater inserted in the fireplace, which made it possible to warm the room to a livable temperature.

Even though Gillian was shorter than me, many of her clothes, especially jumpers and tops, fit me. We could trade clothes. This was wonderful—it increased my wardrobe tremendously. I was living out of my trunk with the few additions of clothes I had bought in England or were sent to me as presents. Gillian thought wearing things made in America was fun. American blue jeans were especially sought after by English teenagers.

The next morning, we had an amazing full English breakfast of eggs, toast with butter and marmalade, bacon, sausage, tomatoes, mushrooms, and baked beans. Mrs. Benson assured me they did not eat this menu every morning.

"Hold the baked beans on mine, please."

Gran surprised us with matinee tickets for the Pantomime at the Repertoire Theatre. I had never seen a Pantomime. Going to the theatre was a real occasion, an excuse to get dressed up. I could wear my new purple dress.

In the middle of getting dressed, I suddenly became concerned that I did not have any white gloves with me.

Gillian asked, "Why do you need them? Don't you have your black riding gloves with you?"

"I do, but I always wear *white* gloves to the theater."

In reality, the only time I ever went to live theater was in Addis Ababa, and we *did* have to wear hats and white gloves because the Emperor was attending the production.

I had seen photos of the British Royals wearing white gloves when they went here and there. I wondered if there would be any royalty in Northampton. Reluctantly, I stuck my black leather riding gloves in my coat pocket.

When Gillian's dad was heading out to get the car, Gran said, "Wait a moment, please, Edmund. I need something from upstairs." She came back in a few moments with a wonderful pair of white lace gloves.

"Thank you so much!" I wondered why no one else was wearing white gloves, but the borrowed ones looked great with my dress.

The pantomime was *Sinbad the Sailor*, more or less transformed into a bawdy slapstick musical comedy. Men played women's parts. The actors wore exaggerated clown-like makeup. The dialogue consisted of corny jokes and rude remarks. The audience was encouraged to shout "Boo" or "Hurrah" or advise the actors, "He's behind you!" It was fantastic, ridiculous, and completely silly. God Save the Queen.

On the way home, Gran explained how pantomime became popular. "Until 1843 in Britain, only a few theaters had a Royal Patent to have speaking parts in plays. Miming doesn't require speaking. But long after actors were allowed speaking parts, the pantomime remains a favorite English Christmas tradition."

The next day when we went shopping for groceries in the village with Mrs. Benson, we carried shopping bags and baskets. We walked to the butchers, the greengrocers, and the bakery, all within a few blocks of the house. The village also boasted a couple of pubs, a post office/stationery/newsstand, an off-license, a chemist, and a betting shop.

We bought horse magazines from the newsstand.

This was a much different way of shopping than in America where housewives would drive their station wagon to a chain grocery store for a weekly shopping trip. A teenage bag boy at the checkout counter would pack the groceries in large paper bags and put them in your car.

In Braefield the ladies walked to the shops, brought their shopping bags with them, and only bought one or two days of perishable food at a time.

Along one part of the main street, there was a long, solid brick wall that turned out to be the windowless backside of a shoe factory.

Less than a block away from the Bensons' house was a stone church with a square tower. The Saxons built the tower to keep an eye on the Normans. The watchtower was later attached to the church and converted to house the bells.

The village had almost everything you needed for day-to-day living, even a regular bus service to Northampton with a convenient stop on the corner.

The Bensons' house had a tiny galley kitchen and a minute refrigerator, but directly across from the kitchen, on the other side of a narrow driveway, was a two-story bakehouse. The upper floor had a large window/door with a hook, block, and tackle to lift the sacks of flour. The downstairs contained a variety of ovens built into the walls. Large wooden paddles with long handles that hung on the walls were used to put in or remove baked goods from the ovens.

Mrs. Benson explained, "In the 1800s most people could only cook things in their home in a pot hanging in the fireplace. The bakehouse provided bread for the village all week. On Sunday, the village ladies would bring their joints of meat to be roasted to the bakehouse's oven before they went to church. After church or a couple of hours at the pub, the ladies would come and collect their cooked Sunday dinner."

Christopher couldn't wait to add a gruesome bit of information. "In Victorian times there was a famous police case involving a bakehouse in London. A gang of criminals used the ovens to dispose of their murder victims' decomposing bodies."

After tea, Christopher, Gillian's boyfriend Arthur, and their friend Ian took us on a pub crawl. Arthur had a car, a little Hillman Imp. The plan was to start further afield and drink your way back home. Appropriately, we started at the World's End. We proceeded to the Tudor Rose, on to The Lion, and finally, we ended up back in Braefield, at The Shoe.

By the time we came in at eleven, the older generation of Bensons had gone to bed. We decided to play dominoes.

Christopher thought it would be an excellent idea if we drank some of Mr. Benson's banana liqueur. It was delicious. The liqueur glasses were tiny, so we drank another round. I started telling the guys that Brits were lucky. "You do not have to worry about getting drafted to fight in the Vietnam War."

We went to bed well after midnight.

Luxuriously, Mrs. Benson was allowing us to sleep in as late as we wanted.

I was just at that point of almost waking up, wondering if I could ignore the urge to pee and go back to sleep. I felt a little queasy, but I was having great dreams. I was winning a big class at White City on my show jumper Rob Roy when suddenly Sinbad the Sailor sailed in, and pirates swarmed the place. The whole place swayed, and pirates were running amok throughout the stadium.

Bong . . . Ding . . . Dong . . . Gonnnng . . . Gonnnng . . . Gonnnng.

It was loud yet melodic. It sounded like the "1812 Overture" exploding in my head. It went on and on.

Bong . . . Ding . . . Dong . . . Gonnnng . . . Gonnnng . . . Gonnnng.

They didn't let up.

The bell-ringing practice for the New Year's Service was being held this morning one block away from my window.

Ugh, time to get up. Man, do I have a headache.

As soon as I went downstairs, I asked Mrs. Benson, "May I have some aspirin and coffee, please?"

Christopher slept through the hubbub. He was used to hearing the bells. Braefield was quiet compared to noisy London.

The Bensons made me feel at ease and I was a little sad to leave the comfortable, warm, friendly home and head back to the riding school. Mr. Benson assured me on our next holiday, I was invited to come back.

He dropped us off and then had a few words with Mrs. Highstaff in her office.

My face brightened when I saw that I had a package and three cards waiting for me on the counter. The Christmas present from my parents was two sets of long underwear. Not very glamorous, I admit, but they were just the ticket. The cards contained checks. I was happy I would have some extra money in a couple of weeks.

Gillian and I went upstairs.

In the lounge, everyone was showing off their Christmas presents. Gillian got a useful jumper from her parents, a silk scarf from her brother, and a hunting crop with a silver collar from Gran. Ruth got a new pair of jodhpurs. Fiona got two warm riding shirts and a large tin of Drinking Chocolate. Marion had a smart new navy-blue helmet. Jeremy had his tie from Mrs. Highstaff, and Mr. Hobbs presented Jeremy with a proper dressage whip. It had been his own.

Heels Down Hall was fully staffed again.

I had fun teaching the kids on Saturday. A few days away from horses renewed all our spirits.

The New Year was almost here, but even so, what a year 1967 had been.

I had graduated from high school in a comfortable USA suburb and went to study horsemanship in a foreign land and live in spartan conditions.

On my birthday, the steamship RMS *Queen Mary* was decommissioned, and the Beatles released *Magical Mystery Tour.*

The pound devalued from \$2.80 to \$2.40.

At home, America was up to its eyeballs in race riots and the Vietnam War. Anti-American sentiment was growing in Europe. The world was in turmoil.

We were asleep by half past nine on New Year's Eve. We wanted to be ready for whatever the New Year had in store for us.

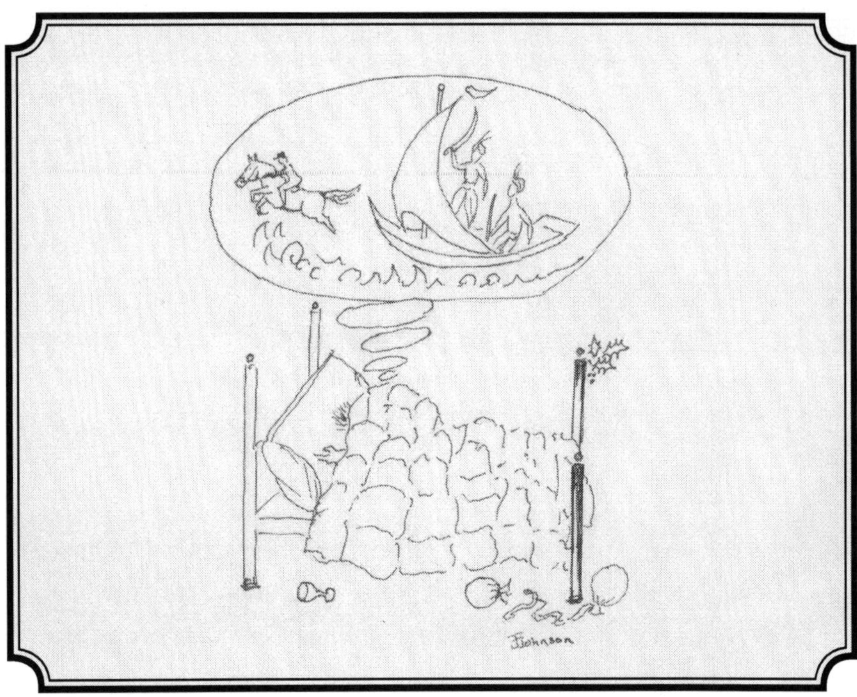

Chapter 21
Foot and Mouth

The New Year blew in with strong, cold winds and frigid weather. We were watching the evening TV news when Labour Prime Minister Harold Wilson gave a speech encouraging workers to work extra time without overtime pay or, whenever possible, to work without *any* pay. He called this his "I'm Backing Britain" policy. I thought the Labour Party was far behind the BHS on this idea. Mrs. Highstaff had implemented and perfected that policy long before the British Parliament thought of it. One way of looking at being a working pupil was that we paid for the privilege of being able to work.

I was relieved to find out that my family received their Christmas presents intact and with everything I sent still in the box.

The holidays were over. Things were back to normal at HDH—hard work and riding. Horses, horses, and horses.

In the *Horse and Hound* we bought in Braefield, we read the announcement for the Featherstone Foxhounds Ball to be held on Saturday, January 13. Since we were not members, had not been invited, and had no dates, no money, no clothes or any means of getting there, we did not give it a second thought.

Two days after the Hunt Ball, disturbing headlines on the radio, on TV, and in all the newspapers rocked the country. Foxhunting and all other forms of hunting, shooting, and all country sports were stopped nationwide, immediately, and until further notice.

Even though neither horses nor dogs (hounds, please) could catch foot and mouth disease, it was possible that they could spread the disease from farm to farm. People had been known to catch foot and mouth by drinking unpasteurized milk from infected cows, but this was rare. The disease was highly contagious and deadly to cloven-hoofed animals. Foot and mouth spread rapidly throughout the Midlands where there were thousands of cattle and sheep.

My hopes of foxhunting in England were dashed. The hunting season only went on until about the end of March.

On Tuesday afternoon, Gillian and I went to Leicester for our half-day off. We walked around aimlessly until we thought we were lost. We invented a saying, "You can't be lost if you don't know where you are going." Finally, when we really did have no idea of where we were, we spotted something that looked like a castle.

On further investigation, we discovered it was an ancient church, and next to it was the medieval Guild Hall built in 1450. By mistake, we had stumbled into the medieval center of the city. The Guild Hall was part museum, part disused old prison, and part mayor's chambers. There was an art exhibit on display inside, with no admission charge.

We were admiring some artwork when Penny, the Vicar's daughter, appeared. "If you have seen this exhibit, would you like to go with me to another museum?" On her suggestion, and because we didn't have anything else to do, we accompanied her. Our chance meeting resulted in a very cultural afternoon.

The second museum contained a display village with a row of shops that illustrated the vital role Leicester played in Britain's Industrial Revolution. The village was occupied by realistic life-size wax figures that were, at the same time, interesting and a little bit creepy.

When we got back to HDH, I was pleased that my friend and mentor, Betty, from my high school saddle club, sent me several photographs cut from American horse magazines portraying Tennessee Walking Horses, the Three and Five-Gaited American Saddlebreds, and Roadster Ponies. She even sent one of an American Quarter Horse pictured with its hindquarters closest to the camera. This was a huge help; I could use them to illustrate my talks on American horses. A picture really could be worth a thousand words and would save me a lot of prancing around.

New ponies arrived. Caesar was a dun gelding, only 14-1 hands. Julian had him on trial and was going to keep him at livery here if he was purchased. Except for a difference in the shade of coat, Caesar and Meteor looked and behaved identically. Frosty, a roan mare, 14-2 hands, was supposed to be purebred Arab but was probably part Arab/Welsh. She had been broken in for riding and then put in foal. She seemed very docile.

The British Horse Society published an official date for the next BHS Assistant Instructor Examination at Heels Down Hall: Thursday, 20 June, 1968. It stated that the number of exam participants was limited to eight. Mrs. Highstaff immediately reserved a place for me.

Because of the date, I had to get permission from my parents to stay at the school for an extra two weeks. My passport was stamped on June 9, 1967, departing the USA and arriving in England on June 10. My student visa was good for one year. I would have to get a visa extension, good for three months, and notify the local police. With Mom coming to visit, I would be in England longer than the extra two weeks. I would also have to get my open-ended *year-long* airline ticket extended. The ticket was expensive. It was questionable that the airline would refund the unused return fare. Getting the ticket straightened out might be harder than extending the student visa.

I hoped my parents would agree to let me stay longer. There were so many advantages to taking the exam at the place you trained. If my parents did not agree, Mrs. Highstaff would find another spot for me at another BHS examination center in another part of the country earlier in the spring. As far as my parents were concerned, the whole point of this trip was for me to achieve the BHSAI, an internationally recognized teaching qualification.

By taking the exam at HDH, the familiar surroundings would help to eliminate some of my nerves. I still had a nervous stomach, but less of it. The best reason to take the exam where I trained was that I would know the horses and the cross-country jumps.

As we previously planned, on the evening of Friday the thirteenth we held our Dressage and Jumping competition. It was much less grand than we'd hoped. None of the outsiders we invited could come because the foot and mouth restrictions now prevented the movement of *all* livestock.

In the dressage phase, Rob Roy and I placed third, only three points behind Topaz, the winner, ridden by Ruth. In jumping, Rob Roy acted like a goblin inhabited the brush jump, which he had jumped many times before, and he wouldn't go near it at all. We were eliminated. I still had faith in Rob Roy; he was just a baby. The other horses were all more experienced.

The next day a very official envelope arrived from the United States. At last, I had been accepted to Flatlander University in Greenleaf. The application process was pretty much a formality since I had already been accepted into Flatlander College, the same place, but the official letter was a great relief.

I mapped out a foolproof plan. *I will double major in English and psychology and after graduation, I will land a big-bucks job in advertising on Madison Avenue.*

It never occurred to me that there was a glass ceiling for women in America or that I would not be paid as much as my male co-workers.

Gillian was interested in what type of job opportunities there might be in America. Since I had had other requests along this line after coming to England, I asked my dad to send us the Help Wanted section of the Want Ads from the *Sunday Washington Post*, a national newspaper. The Help Wanted section was about fifty pages long.

My father decided not to send it. It would be expensive to mail, and the jobs would be out of date by the time the paper arrived. It was even questionable that English people could easily obtain work visas for the USA.

I was disconcerted by a letter from my parents. My grandfather had suffered a stroke. My portly, diabetic grandmother with a weak heart was not going to be able to take care of my grandfather by herself.

My grandparents were moving in with my family. The grandparents would have to live downstairs since they couldn't cope with the stairs. Many rooms would have to be changed around. With the moving and caregiving, it was doubtful that Mom was going to be able to come over at all. The growing anti-American sentiment in Europe added to the difficulty. Anti-American resentment was highest in France, from where we previously planned to ship the newly purchased car back to the USA. My dad nixed the car; he didn't want Mom and me driving around France.

The possibility of my mother not coming to England in the summer rattled me. I started making some alternate plans. Even though I was slowly freezing to death in England, I was in no particular hurry to go back to the South with its Ku Klux Klan rallies and church burnings.

If Mom couldn't come over, maybe Gillian and I could go on a summer holiday. Gillian had spent a summer on a kibbutz in Israel. I was certain we could have a great adventure. One small snag in this plan: Gillian's course ended in October, not June.

Gillian's parents usually go to Greece on their holidays; maybe I could go with them?

Monday was April's half-day off. She kept her standing appointment at the village hairdressers. Afterward she would pick up Cricket from primary school and they would walk home together. While she was at Styles, April perused the day-old Sunday paper. All of a sudden, she asked the proprietor if she could tear out the Society page. The other patrons wondered why, but they were too polite to ask. No one objected, but they were puzzled. April clearly did not travel in society circles.

Later in the afternoon while I was turning out horses, I saw April almost dragging Cricket down the drive. She intended to meet us for our tea break. When we trooped in for tea, a newspaper page was spread out on the dining table. On the top of the page, a black and white photo featured two horses and riders. We were curious. We crowded around to see it.

There was a tall lady on a magnificent horse.

"Is that Denis on Minstrel?" wailed Fiona.

The caption read, "Leicestershire residents, Ms. Enid Boswell, well-known socialite, and Mr. Denis Parkhurst, son of industry tycoon Phillip Parkhurst, are pleased to announce their recent engagement."

The wedding was set for the first Saturday in June. Fiona went silent, then pale. I swear I saw a black cloud form over her head. She left abruptly.

April couldn't contain herself any longer. The scuttlebutt at the hairdressers was that the pair had met at the Featherstone Foxhounds Boxing Day Meet and were engaged at the Hunt Ball.

When Enid realized Minstrel was the horse that Denis had trained at HDH, she gave Minstrel to him as an engagement present.

The ladies at the hairdressers had to give all the particulars. Denis, now twenty, was to become a full partner in his father's leisurewear factory in Leicester when he was twenty-one, but the Parkhurst Industries Company Charter required all board members to be married.

It was rumored throughout the county that when Enid turned twenty-one, she would inherit a vast sum of money from her mother's American side of the family.

When April headed back to her lodgings in the Gate House, she stopped in the yard to tell Gillian and me that there was even more to the story. "For Fiona's sake, I did not tell you at tea break. One of the ladies in Styles had a sister working at Parkhurst Industries. According to the sister, Mrs. Parkhurst is a terrible snob. The word on the factory floor was Mrs. Parkhurst was the one who had squashed Denis's romance with Fiona, "the pretty little thing at the riding school."

One day late in October, Mrs. Parkhurst hysterically ran onto the factory floor, looking for her husband, shouting, "*No* Parkhurst will ever marry an Irish Boyle, no matter if she is pretty, or how well she rides." Of course, there was an option. Mrs. Parkhurst generously told Denis he could feel free to marry Fiona and make his own way in the world."

Mrs. Highstaff posted a list of twenty lessons we had to prepare for the BHSAI examination. We could be asked to teach any of these to a group of four to six riders for fifteen to twenty minutes. My first four were: "Circles and Turns," "Transitions," "The Diagonals," "Position."

The announcement, big news, Heels Down Hall was holding a Riding Display with musical drills toward the end of March. The original plan was we would each be in two drills. I would ride Rob Roy. This made me happy. I hadn't been riding him so much. Jeremy was riding him in all the jumping lessons.

As fortune and fate would have it, Mrs. Highstaff's elderly aunt died. Of course, she had to attend the funeral on Friday. Mr. Hobbs put me down for Rob Roy for the lesson. Naturally, without Mrs. Highstaff there to watch us, we jumped perfectly. I am sure Jeremy's schooling had something to do with the improvement, but after all the disappointing jumping rounds in the competitions, it was satisfying to have him going well.

On Saturday the weather turned very nasty—freezing and rainy with fog. None of the kids wimped out and lessons went on as usual.

By lunchtime a rather battered mail package addressed to me from the Luther League in Greenleaf was waiting for me on the post counter. I thought it was intended to be a Christmas present. It turned out to be a *squashed* tin of cookies. After we pried the tin apart, we found it contained nothing but very delicious crumbs. I told everyone I would share the cookie crumbs at supper; please bring your spoon. I could just visualize the sack of US mail being dropped from a ship and the sack containing the cookies smashing onto the concrete dock.

It was Gillian's and my turn on the Rota for Squaring the Muck Heap. This task was even worse than Ducks—this job stank. The muck heap had to be a dense rectangular box at all times. When you had this duty, you kept the muck heap tidy all week. We stood on top of the heap trying not to choke on the aroma. We filled in the low spots and pounded to compact the straw. When the muck heap was wet, the ammonia smell of urine made your eyes water.

By the end of the week, the heap had to be in tip-top shape. We forked away and squared it in the freezing mist. Mushroom growers bought it when the pit was full. This muck was valuable stuff.

Chapter 22

Winter of Discontent

It was Gillian's day on the Bath Rota. Lucky for her. As smelly as we usually were with only one bath per week, the muck heap reeked, and we reeked.

Arthur, Gillian's boyfriend, was driving down from Braefield tomorrow, Sunday, and bringing Ian with him. I was distraught. Ian had only ever seen me clean.

We planned to take the bus and meet them in Leicester in the afternoon. Ian and I had hit it off over my Christmas visit to Gillian's. We had written a few letters to each other. Using the telephone was out of the question.

Of course, I would wash and wear clean clothes, but I was filthy. Gillian had a brainstorm. "I won't empty the tub. Be standing by the door when I come out in ten minutes and just take a bath anyway. The water will still be warm." It would have been foolish to drain out the gray water left from Gillian's bath. Fresh water would have been ice cold *and* people would hear the water running. It was the fastest bath I ever took. At least the worst of the dirt came off.

We doused ourselves with a cheap scent and went into Leicester. Arthur and Ian met us at the Clock Tower. The weather was miserable, so the cinema seemed the best choice of activity. We watched *Will Penny*, starring Charleston Heston as a lonely cowboy, a real he-man. After the movie, we headed to the nearby Wimpy Bar. We munched and chatted until it was time for us to catch the bus. We were having a good time, and Arthur generously decided he would drive us back to the riding school. Petrol was expensive and it would add a lot of extra time and miles to take us to the opposite side of Leicestershire.

In the winter night, the countryside was completely dark. There was only farm traffic past the Hall. You could see any lights coming down the drive, or indeed coming out of Brickton, from any room in the front of the house.

When we got to the Hall, Arthur drove to the parking area by the stables.

Mr. Hobbs was outside, greeted us, and said, "Lads, you have to go around to the front of the house and meet Mrs. Highstaff."

While Mrs. Highstaff grilled them, Arthur and Ian were quaking in their shoes. Fortunately our dates were neatly dressed and well-mannered. They passed inspection. They were known to and approved of by Gillian's parents. Thank God. I liked Ian.

The next day Gillian and I got told off by Mrs. Highstaff in no uncertain terms. "In the future, all boyfriends who are taking you off the property must meet me and be approved *before* you leave the premises. A return time will be predetermined. No exceptions."

In our flatwork lessons, we worked on drill rides nonstop. We had to learn a whole new set of military parade commands. "Dress right. Keep your spacing. Half a horse length. Whole horse length. Catch up. Slow down. Trot, trot, trot." To dress right meant to look at and line up on the horse to your right. "Half sections. Sections. Down the center in pairs."

It was our regular half-day off and my day for the Bath Rota. Gillian and I were going to Leicester. We planned to have dinner at the school to save money. I would take a bath immediately after dinner. The water was warmest when the big AGA stove was hot. Then we would rush to the bus stop to catch the two o'clock bus.

Gillian asked me to save my bath water for her. *This was a great plan! Now we could take one and a half baths per week!* There was only one flaw in our plan. Fiona popped up to her room to get a pullover, and saw Gillian coming out of the bathroom with her bathrobe. We didn't see Fiona, and she didn't say anything to us.

We went to town. I collected my £12 Christmas cash. We did our usual roaming around, ate an omelet supper in the Swiss Chalet, and headed back to Brickton.

The Vicar had invited us to attend the Confirmation classes. Ruth had become interested in the Church and she was meeting us there. Gillian and

I were both already confirmed but we went for moral support for Ruth and the comfortable surroundings.

Vicar Hanleigh put a question to us all: "Who is Jesus Christ?"

Some scrawny teenage boy immediately piped up. "My dad says Jesus never lived and it's all a bunch of stories." I thought I had the upper hand on that point because, while we lived in East Africa, my parents had taken me on a trip to the Holy Land. I had been to Bethlehem, Jerusalem, the Garden of Gethsemane, the Holy Sepulcher, and the Dead Sea. Ours was not a luxury tour. We stayed inside the Walls of the Old City of Jerusalem in a pensione with no screens and only wooden shutters on the windows and a lazy ceiling fan to keep the warm air moving. The front door of the pensione opened onto a narrow cobblestone street that Jesus may have walked on. There was nothing modern in the Holy Land except running water and electricity, and cars *outside* the city.

I told the boy, in no uncertain terms, "The Holy Land is a small place, and everything is pretty close together. Remember, Jesus and his disciples walked everywhere in sandals. Whatever you believe about the Trinity, the Man Jesus lived without a doubt. When He was crucified by the Romans, His death changed the world forever." The boy looked a little taken aback.

Gillian chimed in. "I was in kibbutz on a working holiday, and Alexa is right!"

I continued, "In 1961, the walls of the City of Jerusalem were patrolled by heavily armed United Nations soldiers. We saw bags of grain, stamped US FOREIGN AID, being distributed in the ancient market squares and carried away on the backs of donkeys." At this point Vicar Hanleigh took over and we had a lively debate.

We walked back to the Hall in good time, in the dark, quietly, with our little minds reeling with the mysteries of the universe. We cheerfully popped in to say our "good night" to Mrs. Highstaff.

Mrs. Highstaff wasn't as elated as we were. "The sharing of bathwater is unsanitary and is forbidden. Use sponge baths when it is not your turn."

Fiona had ratted us out.

When we got up to the lounge, Fiona and Mr. Hobbs were watching television, as happy as magpies. Jeremy was at the table, diligently working on his twenty lessons. As soon as she saw us, Fiona started in on her woe-is-me act. She whined, "I am so tired. Could you please make me some cocoa?"

She flaunted her Drinking Chocolate tin like a queen with a scepter. I thought for a moment she would offer us some, but she didn't. Even though Fiona was a real bossy-boots, we felt sorry for her after the newspaper article about Denis.

We went back down to the kitchen to sit on the AGA to get warm while we waited for the kettle to boil. We took Fiona her blasted hot chocolate. This was a mistake.

The next week, I received a letter from Ian. He said, "I have never been as terrified as when I was being cross-examined by Mrs. Highstaff." I could sympathize completely.

The days gradually grew a little longer. The sun rose at eight o'clock and set by half past six. If it was possible, the weather in February was worse than that of January. It was even colder, freezing with rain which was not quite ice. We frequently rode out in the fog. The dense fog made it gloomy and even darker. It was too foul to jump cross-country. In general I was wet, cold, and discouraged.

It was terribly cold in the early mornings. The coal fire in the boiler would be almost out by dawn. We could expertly get dressed while still in bed. This was made easier because the beds sagged and there was room enough in your hammock to maneuver a little bit. I kept at least a layer or two of clothes in the bottom of the bed so they would be warmer when I put them on. We left our work jeans outside of the covers. They were practically stiff and could almost stand up at the foot of the bed by themselves.

The sun looked more like a white pearl than a blazing ball of fire. The sky was an unhealthy shade of gray. I started thinking about the crystal-clear blue sky of North Carolina, such a special blue it had a name, Carolina Blue. This English sky must be the hazy shade that Simon and Garfunkel were singing about.

I loved folk music. Often, the melancholy and sometimes defiant lyrics matched my moods.

My mind jumped to another winter song, and I started to hum "California Dreaming."

The sunny warmth of California would have made a pleasant change from freezing Leicestershire, but when I thought about it, I realized when I was in California, four years ago, I didn't like it.

To me California equaled opulent consumption.

The first bad impression I had of California was flying into the Los Angeles International Airport. It was daytime, but the sky was black as night. Hazy balls of light would appear and fade. A voice came over the plane's loudspeaker, "This is Pilot McCoy. May I have your attention, please? There is nothing to be alarmed about."

This immediately got everyone's attention.

"Due to the thick smog, we are landing using an automatic pilot."

The smog was thicker than fog; it was fog mixed with factory and automobile pollution. *Automatic pilot?* I hope that worked.

California was a beautiful place with great scenery and weather, but by now I realized there were a great many places in the world that fit that criteria. *There were way too many roads and cars, too many houses, and too many people rushing around showing off their clothes and cars. Every suburban house had a swimming pool.* This made me feel guilty. Every day, kids in Africa had to walk miles carrying heavy jugs of water for their family. Kids in California regarded precious water as something to play in.

Our family went to Disneyland, every kid's dream. We had a great time, but I didn't see the point of it all. The real world was much more exciting.

Right now, I had to forget about California and carry two heavy water buckets across the slippery stone stable yard without tipping the icy cold water down the top of my workman's wellies.

Mrs. Highstaff sensed low morale. She posted a Programme of Upcoming Events for the next five months on the tack room wall.

HDH 1968 Spring Programme of Events	
13 February	*Jumping Competition for Everyone*
23 February	*Children's Competition*
27 February	*Dressage Tests to be judged by Archibald Swithwick, Esquire*
23 March	*RIDING DISPLAY*
1–5 April	*BHSAI Preparation Course Mrs. MM Highstaff, IIH*
8–12 April	*BHSAI Preparation Course Mrs. MM Highstaff, IIH*
22–27 April	*Children's Holiday Course*
3–7 June	*Horsemanship Course Mrs. Leda Ainsworth, FBHS*
20 June	*BHSAI EXAMINATION AT HDH*
Subject to additions or changes, Mrs. MM Highstaff, IIH	

Only Mr. Hobbs was privy to information this far in advance. Fiona would find out a week or so before we did. The rest of us were informed on a need-to-know basis. By working part-time in the house, Ruth overheard many pertinent conversations, so we often found out things as quickly, or before Fiona.

In the evening we watched the news and saw the first immigrants from what turned out to be a tidal wave of Indians and Pakistanis that were being deported from Kenya. The British Parliament was embroiled in fierce and heated debates. Many were worried this major influx of immigrants would ruin the country.

I wonder if the Indian tailor who made my jodhpurs in Nairobi will be able to escape to England. If he could only get to Leicestershire, I naively thought, *he certainly would get a job sewing made-to-order hunt clothing.* In reality, the Leicestershire tailors would not have welcomed the competition, nor would the riders have given him much trade.

I was genuinely distressed by the situation in Africa. I loved the ancient, austere beauty of Africa. I was sorry that once again politics was ruining everything.

In Greenleaf, if you tried to converse about Africa, people would start talking about Tarzan. Southerners were not interested in Africa.

On Monday night, Ruth, Gillian, and I were invited to the Vicarage for tea. There had been a heavy snowfall that day, but because it was a working day the roads had been partially plowed. It was worth the long walk to the other end of the village to get a real meal.

When we got back from the Vicars', Gillian flopped onto her bed by the window. *Bwonng.* The bed shook like a mini trampoline. Ruth decided to have a go. She trotted across the large room and flopped down. *Bwonng!* The bed bounced up and down.

"Hey, stop that!" cried Gillian. We had this silly habit of plopping down on Gillian's bed when we came in from outside. Gillian's bed occupied the favorable position by the window, and it was a straight shot from the open door to the bed. We were like the Three Musketeers. I was not to be left out. I zoomed over and piled onto the bed with them.

Instead of *bwonng*, the bed went *cra-a-c-c-k-k-k* and caved in completely.

Downstairs Lord Daffy barked. *"Wufff!"*

"Oh, dear!"

"Bloody hell."

"What are we going to do?"

It wasn't easy for us to get out of that caved-in, broken bed. We were horrified and laughing at the same time. Mrs. Highstaff, who was reading in her sitting room directly under us, heard all this commotion.

A few moments later, Lord Daffy came into the room followed by Mrs. Highstaff. "How did this bed get broken?"

Silence.

We were terrified. Gillian started to explain, "The bed was wobbly when we sat down on it and it broke. It collapsed."

Well, almost.

"This bed didn't break itself. Young people today have no regard for property. I may have to bill your parents for this bed, Gillian. But now, you will have to take the sheets off that one and make up another for tonight. We will discuss it in the morning."

Bill her parents? This was catastrophic. These beds were prehistoric, but not valuable antiques. They sagged so much in the middle that when you pulled the covers over yourself, no one could tell the bed was occupied.

To top it off, we three lived in a room for six people. Take the broken bed out and there were still spares. I was certain there were loads more beds of a similar age in the attic.

Ruth and I felt terrible that Gillian's bed broke and she was in trouble. Actually, we all were. We wrote an apology letter to Mrs. Highstaff. "We are very sorry we broke the bed," and all three of us signed it. We put it on the post counter downstairs so Mrs. Highstaff would find it in the morning. The next day, April told us she carried the broken wooden slats down to the boiler room to be burned. The wood slats were completely riddled with woodworm, and she could snap them with her hands.

The Bensons never received a bill or even heard about the incident. We were only reprimanded. "Do try to conduct yourselves with more ladylike behavior and do not behave like ruffians." We didn't flop on the beds anymore, mostly out of fear that another one would break.

Chapter 23
Rag Doll

It was Fiona's week on Breakfast on the Rota. We noticed the tea was especially strong every morning. We drank so much tea that we could tell how many scoops in the pot made the tea strong or weak. This was builders' tea, a strong, black loose tea made palatable by the addition of milk and sugar.

A large tin with a scoop was kept in the kitchen. The number of scoops to go in the teapot for each meal or break was rationed. There was a chart.

We were pleasantly surprised to get raspberry jam in the pots on the table at breakfast. Usually we had plum jam.

In the stable Fiona started to nag us about inconsequential details every minute. She could find fault with anything. If we got complimentary remarks in our riding lessons, she got pickier.

She developed a demerit system, and the loser (high marks) every evening had to make her cocoa. Demerits were awarded for infractions like being the last one out to the yard in the morning was one demerit. This was ridiculous; someone always had to be last. The only reason we went along with this treatment was that Fiona was Head Girl and had Mrs. Highstaff's ear.

The instrumental version of "Love Is Blue" played on the radio when we turned it on after dinner. We were melancholy enough without it. One thing was for sure, the sky was gray—*le ciel is gris*. While Princess Margaret was carousing in the sunny Caribbean, we were just miserable.

Even with the £12 I received for Christmas, I was nowhere near having enough money to buy the leather coat I so desperately wanted. My tall black riding boots were really in a deplorable state. I think the polish was holding them together. I had to be as frugal as possible.

At lunchtime, after an intense morning of drills, I made a remark to the effect, "While all this drill team riding is interesting and undoubtedly good schooling for the horses, my real ambition in life is to be an international show jumper."

This is the first time I voiced my secret. I had a little confidence now that I had won one jumping competition on Wizard, even if Rob Roy was not brilliant.

All the other WPs, even Fiona, agreed that Show Jumping was a worthy pursuit.

Mr. Hobbs kept eating, looked thoughtful, and did not comment.

The big Whole School Jumping Competition was coming up soon and we jumped more often, frequently riding different horses.

One afternoon when I was carrying my tack for the lesson up to the stables, Mr. Hobbs stopped me. "I would like to ask you a few questions, if I may?" He seemed concerned.

"Of course." I couldn't think of anything that Mr. Hobbs would want to know from me.

"Does your family own a stable in America?"

"Noooo . . ." *Is he asking me for a job?*

"Are either of your parents horse people?"

"No." I didn't even own a horse at this moment in time. The horse I leased in Greenleaf was returned to its owner before I left for Heels Down Hall.

"Are your parents millionaires?"

"No." I wasn't happy about the way this conversation was headed. I wasn't expecting questions about my parents.

"Give up the thought of becoming an international show jumper." Mr. Hobbs said this very calmly and matter-of-factly.

"*Why*? I can do it. I am not afraid of big jumps or going fast. I love it." I watched show jumping on TV and saw photographs of the top riders in magazines. I knew I could do it.

"That is not the point. Riding ability has little to do with it. It costs millions of pounds to get to an international level in show jumping."

"I'll get a sponsor." All the top show jumpers had sponsors. They had the logos and advertising on their horseboxes and even in part of the horse's name, Window World's Clear View, for example.

"You won't get a sponsor until you are already winning at the top level. You'd be far better off to forget about it. Study and pass your exam. Go into Horse Trials. You only need one good horse."

After "you won't," I had already tuned out. I politely listened to the end of the sentence, and I stomped off in my worn-out riding boots to saddle up Sword of Justice for the jumping lesson.

Mr. Hobbs just does not realize I am going to be a New York advertising executive in a few years. I will easily be able to get a sponsor. After all, I read Kit Hunter, International Show Jumper *and watched the Disney movie* The Horse with the Flying Tail. *Well, I will just prove them wrong. I'll show Hobbs.*

Justice was a sensitive old Thoroughbred and he knew that I was upset. He could feel the tension in the reins, indeed in my whole body, and he put forth a feeble effort. He could literally fly over the solid cross-country jumps, which were three feet six inches or bigger. In today's lesson, he jumped like a kangaroo, up and down, propping every two-foot-six-inch jump. Now, I was demoralized. *I can't even get a steeplechaser to jump cavalletti properly. Maybe Mr. Hobbs is right.*

Justice was still in my care, and I got along with him fairly well, but I preferred the less temperamental horses.

After exercise every day, we did the main grooming called strapping. Each horse had its own grooming kit that included a hoof pick, dandy brush, body brush, curry comb, water brush, two different colored stable sponges, wisp, and stable rubber. The stable rubber was a white woven tea towel with a red stripe down the center with the words Stable Rubber woven into the stripe. It cost twice the price of an ordinary tea towel.

Fiona delighted in making us recite the grooming procedure from the *BHS Manual.* Grooming had to be done in an exact order, which we had to be able to recite like Bible verses. We also had to demonstrate the techniques and be able teach to our students.

When Fiona grilled us, Gillian would start by reciting in a sing-song voice, "Collect the grooming kit, and put the headstall on the horse. Tie the horse on the short rack using a quick-release knot. Then, pick out the feet. Use the dandy brush to remove any caked mud, avoid the use of the dandy brush on sensitive areas of the horse."

"What's next, Ruth?" scowled Fiona.

Ruth replied with a bored look on her face, "Use the body brush, flip the mane over, start at the bottom of the mane, and brush out a few wisps of mane at a time. Next use the body brush on the whole horse in short, circular strokes and clean the body brush on the curry comb. Knock the scurfy curry comb on the floor to get rid of the dirt. Wisp the horse in a rhythmic massage. Brush the face."

Then Fiona looked at me. "Alexa, how do you finish?"

"Sponge off the eyes, nose, and dock with the different colored sponges. Lay the mane with a damp water brush. Wash the feet. After the feet are dry, apply hoof oil. Finish by wiping whole horse with the stable rubber, replace the rugs, and put on a tail bandage on the horse."

"That's good," Fiona said snottily. "What about saving the mane and hair tails that get pulled out and putting the mutton tallow on the hooves? Get it right and don't forget it." She marched off.

She never asked Jeremy these questions.

An experienced groom with a not too filthy horse could strap a horse in a half-hour. It took me three-quarters of an hour, an improvement over the hour it took when I first came to Heels Down Hall. Now we each had three horses to groom every day.

Occasionally, without notice, while we were strapping our horses, Mrs. Highstaff would come through the yard and wipe a silk handkerchief over your horse. Then she would inspect the handkerchief carefully to see if there was any scurf present.

In my never-going-to-be-a-show-jumper mood, I forgot to collect the headcollar and lead rope when I gathered my grooming kit. Hastily, I decided to just get on with it. I still had two more horses to groom before bedding down. During the lesson, Justice had splashed up some dirt under his belly. Ignoring the entire grooming routine, I went straight for the mud.

I'll just knock this off first.

Facing his hindquarters, I gave the dandy brush a few vigorous swipes. The neurotic old horse had had enough of me for one day. I had literally rubbed him the wrong way. While I was bent over, brushing his belly,

Sword of Justice swung his long neck right around. *Snap!* He grabbed me with his teeth, picked me up by the hip, and threw me eight feet across the stall as if I were a rag doll. I hit the wall with a loud thud.

Once the untied Justice removed his annoyance, he casually resumed munching his hay.

Jeremy was the first one over to the box. "Heavens! Gillian! Get a head-collar and lead rope."

Jeremy was a good egg. He never lowered himself by getting involved with the petty squabbles in the Yard or Hall. Jeremy helped me up and escorted me out of the stall. I was literally shaking in my boots, so he whispered, "I'll see Mrs. Highstaff this evening and see if I can take over caring for Justice."

Mr. Hobbs arrived next. "Take it on the chin. Keep a stiff upper lip. Quit crying."

I wasn't blubbering, but a tear rolled down my cheek.

"Go inside and make sure you are alright. When you come back, finish up your other two horses. We'll take care of Justice."

My winter clothing saved me from a serious injury. Even so, my breeches and long underwear were torn. I had a great bruise on my hip, but the skin was not broken. I was stiff, especially my shoulder, which hit the wall first.

The grumpy old horse could not be entirely faulted. I made two major errors: not tying up Justice, and using the wrong brush with excessive force. One of the reasons for short racking a horse when grooming, as well as generally restricting the horse's movement, was so the horse could not bite you.

If Fiona starts in with the demerits today, I might punch her.

The most unsettling shock for me was discovering that my beloved horses could intentionally hurt me. Thankfully, Jeremy and I swapped horses and I resumed taking care of Rob Roy. Even though he was a filthy pig and Justice was extremely tidy, Rob Roy was a happy horse. He was born here, and he lived a very pleasant life.

Chapter 24

The Price of Tea

It was my week on the Rota for Watering the Indoor School. The school was watered down during morning stables. A long hose pipe was attached to a faucet near the duck pen. The hose had a twirling sprinkler attached to the other end. If it was too cold, the hose froze, and we couldn't water the school, and the arena dust would choke us and the horses. The sprinkler couldn't stay for more than ten or fifteen minutes on any spot, or it made puddles. The real trick to all of this was to time your stable chores to be able to sprint down to the indoor school. Once there, you gauged the rhythm of the twirls and nipped in to pick up the sprinkler head without getting soaked. Then you dragged the hose over the new spot, put the sprinkler head down, and dashed out, trying not to get a shower.

On my first day, the whole procedure went well, and I even stayed pretty dry.

My second day was the morning of the Whole School Jumping Competition. I started watering the school without a hitch, but then, one of the ponies came in with a cut on its leg and I was summoned to help. *Poor little Dinky, how does he manage to get into trouble?*

"A long way from his heart," Mr. Hobbs said. "Go and get the wound care kit."

I did as I was requested and gave the box of first aid supplies to Mr. Hobbs and resumed my regular morning routine. I completely forgot about the sprinkler. When I did remember that I'd left the twirling water fountain on in the school, I ran, even though running was forbidden, down to the arena. It looked like an African desert mirage. I was horrified.

I couldn't leave it like this. I skipped breakfast and raked dirt into my man-made lake. *Nobody can jump in this slop!*

We would be setting up the courses for the competition after the morning ride. The competition was going to start as soon as the kids could get here from school.

Luckily for me, it was Gillian's turn on for "Breakfast" on the Rota. When I hurried in to change from morning work clothes into my riding kit, I was grateful she saved me a few pieces of toast to eat. I swilled down a cup of lukewarm tea.

In the morning lesson, I rode Heathcliff, the Irish wild man. At least he did not cart me around like he did the last time.

After our lesson we set up the jumping courses for the competition with all the standards in place and flags (red on right) on the wings. We had extra jump poles handy, and everything necessary to change the courses quickly. We set a cavalletti course for the little kids on the tiny Welsh ponies. Everyone, except the tiniest of tots, would be competing in two different classes and have a high jump at the end. Courses were posted in the tack room and stable and outside the school.

We were getting the tack laid out and organized and suddenly I was sick to my stomach. The same queasy feeling I had every morning when I first arrived at HDH suddenly returned. I told Mrs. Highstaff I was scratching from the competition. I would forfeit my entry fees for the Young Horse and School Horse classes.

Mr. Hobbs asked me if I would like to be the ringmaster and the announcer for the competition.

We sat on ladders in the still not completed viewing area so we could see over the kickboards and avoid getting run over.

The competition went off without a hiccup. The footing in the arena survived the dousing.

Little kids, beaming from ear to ear, jockeyed the ponies around the courses with ease. I swear, if the ponies could read diagrams, they could have jumped the courses without the kids.

Julie, Caroline, and Julian's group, a half dozen riders in all, was quite competitive. Julian won on Caesar, quite a handy pony, after Caroline and

Mango had the last rail down in the jump-off. Julie, who was usually as cool as a cucumber, uncharacteristically went off-course on Marigold.

In the second class, Julie recovered her composure. Marigold and Julie won while Mango finished second and Caesar third. The other kids had at least one clear round.

The High Jump course was set like a Puissance: one vertical jump, one oxer, and then onto a big vertical jump, which got higher every round. Mango won the Pony High Jump at four feet three inches—not too shabby for an under 14-2 hand pony.

In the WP's section, Gillian rode Frosty in Young Horse. Frosty was very green; she didn't get past the first round. Because I scratched, Jeremy rode both Rob Roy and Heathcliff, and both horses went clear in the first round. In the first jump-off, Heathcliff and Rob Roy each had one rail down on different fences, but no refusals. In the second jump-off, it came down to Topaz with Ruth and Fiona with Jazzy. Topaz refused.

Jazzy won. Fiona was gloating.

The School Horses were the main event of the evening. Gillian drew Attila. She jumped clear, but not fast. Ruth and Meteor knocked a rail down in the first jump-off. Fiona should have been riding Justice, but because I scratched, she had Wizard. Jeremy rode Justice, and at least he got him over both courses, but he intentionally did not enter the high jump.

As usual, Wizard laid out a flawless performance, and Fiona won hands down.

Meteor came back to win the School Horse High Jump at 4'6". The ponies could jump as high as the horses, maybe higher.

Fiona was over the moon with her two wins.

Mrs. Highstaff purchased tiny rosettes for this competition—first place red and second place blue, the opposite colors of the USA.

Mr. Hobbs and I stayed behind to collect the flags and other things left in the arena. "It's too bad you don't feel well. If you had ridden Wizard, you would have won that." This made me feel sicker than before.

The kids' parents saw the Programme of Events posted on the tack room wall. By popular demand we added children's rides to our musical display. The children were happy that they would be riding an additional time per week.

"I think we should add jumping to the display," said Mr. Hobbs confidently, and the children cheered.

The next morning I was ecstatic when I saw The Red Book. As a reward for all of our hard work, Mrs. Highstaff was sending us on hacks. What a lovely Valentine's Day present to us all.

The restrictions on foot and mouth had eased a little bit in our area. Horses were now allowed on bridle paths and lanes through any property without livestock. The farms adjoining HDH were arable land, not grazing. There were no longer any sheep dotting the steep fields near the village.

I was in the first group on Wizard, Gillian rode Attila, and Mr. Hobbs accompanied us on Justice.

We went down the drive, turned left, and rode past the farmhouse lane, onto a long bit of track, wide enough for one car or tractor, but not really a road. About a mile later we got to a small village, a hamlet. There were no shops, only some empty tiny brick houses with thatch roofs, some with caved-in roofs. "Deserted clay pit," Mr. Hobbs explained as we passed by. "Clay is essential for Leicestershire bricks."

We looped around the hamlet and caught a bridle path. We walked, trotted, and had one short canter, and we returned to HDH an hour and a half later. Horses and riders were much more relaxed when they came back than when they started. I thought the change of scenery was good for Mr. Hobbs.

The hacks continued every morning all week. Every horse was scheduled to go at least once. Drill practice and learning new drill movements filled every afternoon lesson.

By Thursday Gillian realized the tea caddy was getting low. The tin was not due to be filled again until Sunday before April went home. On Friday when Gillian made the pots of tea weaker, to stretch out the remaining loose tea, everyone complained. By Saturday morning there really was no choice; she had to go to Mrs. Highstaff and ask for more tea.

Even though the shortage of whatever it was would always be replenished, we always felt like Oliver Twist when he held up his empty bowl of gruel and said, "Please, sir, may I have some more?" when we had to ask for more supplies.

"More tea? If you wouldn't heap the scoops there would be enough tea to last the whole week." Gillian meekly showed Mrs. Highstaff the nearly empty caddy. "Alright, come with me."

Mrs. Highstaff went to the pantry and opened a large tin and measured out enough loose tea for the next two days. "Do try not to be wasteful in the future."

Gillian replied meekly, "Thank you," and went back to laying the table for breakfast.

"Rats, the jam pots need filling," she said to Artemis under the table. "Back to the pantry."

"Hmmm." Things were supposed to be used in the order they were placed on the shelves. Mysteriously, the lid had been removed from the next tin in line, and carelessly replaced. This should have been a new, sealed container.

On another shelf, Gillian discovered a nearly empty jar of raspberry jam. The raspberry jam Fiona gave us was not intended for us, but for the holiday kids.

Gillian had the three-kilo plum jam tin down from the high shelf and was pondering what to do when I walked by the pantry door on my way to the coat rack. Gillian whispered, "*Psssst*, come in here."

I popped into the pantry and shut the door quietly. She showed me the tin of jam. "What should I do?" The jam in the tin had turned into a slushy version of Polish plum liqueur. "Let's get a spoon and eat some first." It was weird but tasty. Gillian refused to taste her spoonful.

"Better tell Mrs. Highstaff. We have to use a new tin." I stated the obvious, but not the desired advice. If we didn't report this, Gillian would be questioned. Throwing out the offending condiment and taking the next tin was not an option.

How old is all of this jam? How did this tin get opened?

Mrs. Highstaff couldn't believe it when she saw the jam. "How did this happen? I have never had students as wasteful as this class." Nonetheless, she gave Gillian a new tin of jam and went off to the kitchen with the sweet-turned-sour jam, and she tipped the rancid slush into the ducks' swill.

Tomorrow was Gillian's full Sunday off, and her father was coming to pick her up this evening. She would be back tomorrow evening. I was grateful she was taking some of my underwear home with her to have her mother wash in the washing machine.

Gillian seemed quite relieved to get away from the series of unfortunate domestic events at HDH.

She picked a great time to go home.

All the regular Saturday kids would start coming Saturday evenings from six until eight, from now until the Riding Display. Eighteen riders and ponies were simultaneously learning drill team riding. The kids loved it. We didn't finish the evening stables until half past eight.

Sunday wasn't quiet either. Featherstone Pony Club hired the use of the indoor school. Every Sunday for the next month, Instructional Rallies were being held at Heels Down Hall. Rides were scheduled all day. The Pony Clubbers had their own mounts, but there was constant traffic through the stable courtyard. To get from the parking area in the paddock, they had to pass through the carriage house arch and cross the yard.

Invariably someone would need to borrow something. We had to make sure whatever it was was returned, cleaned, and put away properly. "A place for everything and everything in its place" was our mantra at Heels Down Hall.

Kids needed to use the loo. "Please, Miss, where is the WC?" followed quickly by, "Can you please hold my pony for a few minutes?" The kids were nice but pesky.

Ruth observed the upper-level classes and took notes. She would be testing for her Pony Club B this spring.

As soon as the first ride was safely deposited in the school and the group in the paddock by the horseboxes started saddling up, Mr. Hobbs and Jeremy prepared Rob Roy and Heathcliff for their hack. Usually there was no riding on Sunday, but due to changes during the week, these two horses missed their scheduled hack.

It was Rob Roy's first time off the property.

Chapter 25
What Horses Eat

Heathcliff had supposedly hunted in Ireland before he came to HDH, but Mr. Hobbs told us this didn't mean much. Since his arrival, Heathcliff had run away with everyone, except Jeremy, in the indoor school at least once. I asked Mr. Hobbs what training hunters in Ireland received.

"Training?" Mr. Hobbs looked at me like I was from another planet. "I knew a Major who exported Hunters from Ireland to England and sold them for excellent prices. He told me, 'I just saddle the horse and hack to the meet. As soon as the hounds start running, the horse follows along. At the end of the day, I've have had some fun, and I have an experienced hunter to sell.'" Mr. Hobbs winked. "In Ireland they jump anything, even wire fences." I thought that was dangerous.

After Mr. Hobbs on Heathcliff and Jeremy on Rob Roy set off down our drive, I noticed the ducks staggering around. I had never seen a drunk duck before. I wondered what proof that jam would have registered.

About forty-five minutes after the dashing duo set off on their pleasure ride, they came back. Mr. Hobbs was still mounted on Heathcliff, but Jeremy was leading Rob Roy.

In the deserted clay pit hamlet, a stray dog ran at Rob Roy and tried to bite his legs. Rob Roy kicked out at the dog, slipped, and lost his hind end. Mr. Hobbs cracked his hunting whip at the dog and the startled dog ran away.

In spite of the cracking whip and the other terrified horse, Mr. Hobbs managed to keep Heathcliff under control. Rob Roy was limping a bit. He was badly bruised and there was a lot of swelling. Rob Roy had never come to any harm before, and he was a frightened big baby. I helped unsaddle him. Jeremy went straight to cold hosing his legs.

This unfortunate turn of events made me miss my favorite TV show, *The Avengers*. I idolized Mrs. Peel. She was beautiful, stylish, sexy, and skilled in judo and shooting. She and Mr. Steed saved the world from evil masterminds week after week. The Avengers drank expensive champagne, drove luxury sports cars, and wore impeccable clothes. In the Avengers' version of England, the sun was always shining.

Gillian looked sad when she returned, much cleaner than she left, from her day at home. She told me, "Driving home last evening, we could see bonfires burning in the distance across the fields. The stench was so overpowering we had to close the car windows. Even tonight, on the way back, and the fires were out, the smell of burnt animal carcasses was sickening." Burning was the official, and the only practical way, of disposing of the carcasses from the deadly foot and mouth disease.

While Gillian put her things away, I gave her the bad news about Rob Roy and everything else she had missed in the last twenty-four hours. She gave me my washing, all neatly folded, and she placed a brown paper bag under her bed.

We went into the lounge to watch *Top of the Pops* with the others. Marvin Gaye's "I Heard It Through the Grapevine" was blaring out of the TV. I immediately loved it. Fiona listened to about half the song. She got up, sniffled, and went into her room, and closed the door.

I thought Fiona's reaction to this song might be useful and I mentally filed the information away. I was learning a lot about psychology from watching TV spy shows.

The sports came on the TV. The Winter Olympics in Grenoble were over. Zero medals for Great Britain—this was disappointing.

A handsome, dashing French skier, Jean-Claude Killy, won three alpine events and retired a millionaire at age twenty-four. Everyone loved him. He was the poster boy of the jet-setter lifestyle.

A Children's competition was scheduled just a few days before our Dressage competition to be judged by the honorable Archibald Smithwick, Esquire.

Mr. Hobbs said, "Riding before a prominent judge at a schooling show is an excellent way to get a good critique." Mrs. Highstaff invited a few outsiders. Competition would be stiffer than usual. I was happy I would be riding my favorites, Rob Roy and Wizard.

Julian bought Caesar and was keeping him at livery at Heels Down Hall. He would ride Caesar in the Display.

Brownie, who came for two weeks of training, was sold and gone. Merrylegs, a silver dappled Welsh pony, 12-2 hands, arrived to be schooled for showing. I was far too big to ride her. Frosty was still here.

I had seen Ian a few more times, but it was complicated. He had to take a bus and change buses in Northampton, and then onto Leicester. The trip was expensive, and we could only spend a few hours together. I hoped to see Ian again the next time I visited Gillian's family.

I liked Ian, but I wasn't looking for a long-term English boyfriend. In September I would be in Greenleaf at the University.

Practice for the Dressage competition became intense. "Rhythm is the foundation of dressage," Mrs. Highstaff would proclaim at the beginning of a session. To emphasize this point, we had to recite nursery rhymes while we rode.

Dang, Fiona took my poem.

She shouted while trotting around, "Twinkle, twinkle little star, How I wonder what you are. Up above the world so high, Like a diamond in the sky."

"A tisket, a tasket—," said Ruth.

Gillian rattled off, "Hickory dickory dock, the mouse went up the clock."

Jeremy came up with "Georgie Porgie, pudding and pie, kissed the girls and made them cry." He shot a sideways look at Fiona.

Now it was my turn. I couldn't think of anything. I knew hundreds of these childish rhymes, but I couldn't think of any. *Quick, think!* Or I was going to have to recite the Lord's Prayer. Suddenly, I thought of something and set off trotting. "Peter, Peter, pumpkin eater, had a wife and couldn't keep her, put her in a pumpkin shell, and there he kept her very well."

No one had ever heard it before. It was truly a unique American nursery rhyme. Mrs. Highstaff said, "That is very amusing, Alexa. Please teach it to everyone." There we all were trotting school figures, chanting "Peter, Peter, pumpkin eater." We found out that "Row, Row, Row Your Boat" was perfect for cantering.

Then followed the more monotonous lessons like, "How many strides are there in each quarter of the circle?" at all three paces.

Fewer than you may think, depending on the size of the horse's stride.

"Keep the bend. Use your outside leg to keep the quarters from falling out. Inside leg to outside rein. Lighten the contact on the inside rein."

One evening we watched a new comedian, John Cleese, in a television docu-comedy, *How to Be Annoying by Being Considerate.* It was absolutely *brilliant.* This show had to be worth a three-credit course in applied psychology. Maybe I could write a paper on it.

The Children's Competition, composed of Pony Club dressage tests, went off well.

The Want Ads I asked for hadn't arrived from Greenleaf, and Jennifer disappointed us all by never sending the photos she took before going home in September. None of us owned a camera. "I'd really like to see those photos before I leave in April. Maybe I could make some copies." Ruth sighed.

Wait a minute, is Ruth leaving here in April? She had been planning to take the exam in June. Ruth was my rock here at the Hall. It would be sad to have her leave.

It was still hideously cold. The sun was shining but it was snowing. April was upstairs giving the bedrooms the weekly cleaning. Lord Daffy followed her everywhere. Mrs. Highstaff was in her study, busy with details for the Display.

"It smells in here, doesn't it, Daffy?" April asked the happy dog. His tail wagged in acknowledgment. She opened the window at the foot of Gillian's bed. "I'll just let some fresh air in here while I clean." She set about vacuuming and changing the sheets.

Meanwhile, Lord Daffy sniffed the room a mile a minute. April did not notice when the fat dog wiggled under Gillian's bed and retrieved a brown paper bag. Proudly carrying the bag in his mouth, Daffy trotted off, through the lounge and down the hallway to seek out Mrs. Highstaff, who was downstairs in her office choosing the final music for our rides.

When Lord Daffy appeared with a bag in his mouth, Mrs. Highstaff quizzed him. "What's this, Daffy? A present?" He sat in front of her wagging his tail until she patted him on the head. He dropped the parcel at her feet.

She turned the military march off and picked up the dog's rumpled offering. When she opened the paper bag, she couldn't believe her eyes. She was stunned. "Daffy, this is the missing tea! Where did you find it?"

She went into the hallway and rang the bell on the post counter.

"April! Come down here at once."

April went downstairs straightaway and forgot to close the window.

After Mrs. Highstaff filled her in, April went into the kitchen. Artemis and Apollo were sitting under the table. April complained to the attentive cats. "It's just like *Casa Blanca* around here! Mrs. Highstaff is just like the French Police captain, ordering me to 'Go round up the usual suspects!'"

❧

Gillian was in charge of Boiling the Linseed this week, another task on the Rota. A heavy oval cast iron pot, specifically for this purpose, sat on the boiler. There was a long wooden spoon to stir it, so it didn't stick to the pot. Linseed had to be stirred frequently.

The mysterious recipe was a lot of water to a fair measure of linseeds. At a certain point, a measure of barley was added to the boiling goo. The linseed was boiled on Saturdays when the horses ate a mash of bran, hot water, topped with the boiled linseed and barley, freshly chopped carrots, or other root vegetables, and with a dash of Epsom salts, if necessary. The mash looked and smelled delicious.

When feed was delivered to the Hall, Mrs. Highstaff always tasted it to make certain it was of good quantity. Mr. Hobbs taught us to be aware of dusty or moldy feed, as these things made horses sick, and he added, "Horses will eat almost anything. In Palestine, they ate dates and oranges."

One of our required textbooks, *Animal Management*, from the Veterinary Department of the War Office, listed the acceptable foods for horses as

"Oats, maize, barley, rye, unhusked rice, wheat, bran, beans, peas, and linseed. From India: Kulfi, moth, mung, urad, millet, Lathyrus satius, Vicia sativa (all types of peas), and Ratti seeds, and gruel and rice water."

"Mr. Hobbs, I saw horses eating dates, oranges, bananas, and other odd fruits in Ethiopia. The old Italian man, who owned the farm where we took riding lessons, fed his horses and cattle the leftover mash from the local beer brewery. My horse in North Carolina got fat and shiny on a diet of peanut hay and dried corn on the cob, like they feed cattle."

Mr. Hobbs smiled. "Alexa, the *BHS Manual* won't list any of those particular equine edibles."

On Saturday evening, Gillian helped a young rider prepare for the drill practice. The child couldn't find the right size girth. Finding a girth was harder to do than usual because every pony was in use at the same time. Gillian set off purposefully in search of a diminutive girth.

Naturally, the linseed started to merrily bubble away at that very moment. The child and the correctly girthed pony headed off to the indoor school, in time for their class, while the slimy mess bubbled over the pot. Boiled linseed flowed down the front of the smoking boiler, covering the stone floor, and was advancing toward the door into the passageway. Gillian was in despair. "Alexa, please help me! How are we going to get this slimy linseed off the stone floor? Mr. Hobbs is waiting in the feed room to make the mash."

We salvaged as much of the slimy linseed mixture as we could by spooning it off the floor and back into the pot. When we took it to Mr. Hobbs, he was less than thrilled. "Go back and boil enough water to make up the difference."

We were careful that we didn't slip and fall while we mopped the slime off the stone floor of the boiler room with rags. We threw the slimy rags into the boiler, which made it smoke. I wondered why Mrs. Highstaff just didn't buy linseed oil in a can.

After evening stables were finally over on Saturday, we bolted after our spaghetti on toast so we wouldn't have to make Fiona's cocoa. There would be demerits galore for boiling over the linseed.

We rushed upstairs only to find the window of our room wide open, a gale blowing through the room, and a nice clean layer of snow coating Gillian's bed.

This was it! I couldn't believe it! "I'm going to have it out with April!" April was always nattering on about the benefits of fresh air. We didn't need fresh air when we came inside. We were outside fourteen hours a day. I wanted warm (I had forgotten what hot was like), stuffy air when we came inside.

Sunday morning while we were at breakfast, Mrs. Highstaff appeared with a plain brown paper bag. She questioned each of us. "Does this bag belong to you?" I couldn't believe that even an errant paper bag was noticed at Heels Down Hall.

"Not mine."

"Not mine."

"Not mine."

"Not mine."

Gillian had not realized the bag was missing, and her face went white. Mrs. Highstaff turned to Gillian. "Lord Daffy brought me this. Gillian, why are you hoarding the tea?"

When she was at home on Sunday, Gran had given Gillian the tea, so that when it was her *next* turn to do breakfast, she wouldn't have to be embarrassed and ask for more.

After a long but suitable explanation, and me throwing in the part about the snow on the bed, Mrs. Highstaff sternly reminded us, "No food of any kind is to be kept in the bedrooms." She left the dining room.

Fiona was not as easily satisfied. She gleefully pounced on the situation. "Hoarding tea! Demerits, demerits, demerits. Make my cocoa this evening!" she demanded.

I saw a strange glint in Gillian's eye. She sweetly smiled. "Of *course*."

Mr. Hobbs mused aloud while munching his toast. "Except for Jeremy." He paused while he swallowed another bite. "I think the lot of you would be better off working at Woolworths."

Chapter 26

Bowler Hats and Smelly Socks

Julian pleaded with Mrs. Highstaff to allow Gillian to ride his new pony in the Dressage competition. He couldn't get to the riding school on Tuesday evening and the competition would be good schooling for his pony. Julian believed Caesar stood a good chance of winning.

As a result of this impassioned plea, Gillian was diligently practicing with Caesar.

Before breakfast on the morning of the competition, Mrs. Lockhart rang Mrs. Highstaff and scratched Caesar. "We will forfeit the entry fee and we are deeply sorry for your trouble. Julian sends his apologies to Gillian."

Mrs. Lockhart did not supply a reason.

The decision to scratch made no sense to me. Gillian really clicked with Caesar.

At tea break Gillian discovered her mount had been switched to Marigold, and now there was no time to practice. Marigold was not originally scheduled to be in the show and had been used in lessons earlier in the day.

The three outside riders came from a nearby event yard and had ridden in the clinic with D'Endrody, and they each did a different test. They came for the critique and did not compete.

My biggest surprise was realizing that my riding improved by reciting silly nursery rhymes and endlessly counting strides.

I won the Dressage competition. I was especially pleased because the judge, Mr. Archibald Smithwick, was a noted judge of Hacks and Children's Ponies and had countless wins at White City.

Results (out of 110 possible marks):

1. *Wizard and me (score 88).*
2. *Mango and Ruth.*
3. *Frosty and Jeremy.*
4. *Meteor and Gillian.*
5. *Rob Roy and me (75).*
6. *Topaz and Ruth.*
7. *Jasper and Grace Edwards.*
8. *Justice and Jeremy.*
9. *Heathcliff and Fiona (he didn't run away).*
10. *Jazzy and Fiona.*
11. *Marigold and Gillian (68).*

The lack of practice made Gillian's result slightly less disappointing.

My confidence was returning. At least I could do this Dressage even if it wasn't exciting.

The comments on Wizard's test read, "Extremely good, only spoiled by a slight inclination to poke," which meant the horse pokes his nose out. Rob Roy's main problem was "unsteady in the head." This was not surprising; Rob Roy was teething.

We were never allowed to fiddle with the bit to get a horse to drop his nose. We were taught to maintain steady contact with the mouth and use half-halts, not "play the piano." We had to hold our hands correctly, never flat, or crooked inwards.

Mr. Hobbs would preach to us. "Get the rhythm, bend, and impulsion, and the horse will carry himself correctly," and "Lighter contact on the inside rein. Leave the horse's mouth alone—you're not riding his head."

After the competition, I overheard Mr. Smithwick tell Fiona, "You are riding rather stiffly, Fiona. If you would relax, sink into the saddle, and not perch, your horses will go more freely forward."

The Dressage competition was behind us, and Mrs. Highstaff had a surprise for us the next day. She popped into the dining hall while we were eating. "Girls, come upstairs after you eat your dinner."

A massive steamer trunk, big enough to hide a body, stood in the middle of the sitting room floor. Mrs. Highstaff smiled wistfully as she carefully opened the trunk. It reeked of mothballs. She gently removed a big hat box and untied the ribbons holding it shut. The opened box revealed layers of faded crinkled silk rosettes, mostly red or tricolored. "Days gone by." She sighed. She closed the hatbox and placed it on the writing table.

She knelt down to lean over the trunk. She began pulling out jackets and funny-looking skirts and vests of canary or Tattersall check. She laid about a half-dozen different ensembles on the threadbare rug. "Yes, yes, these will do nicely. I believe young ladies should learn how to ride side-saddle. We are adding side-saddle riding to our Musical Display."

I knew from reading the horse magazines that side-saddle classes for ponies and horses were popular in England.

Mrs. Highstaff explained the articles of clothing. It wasn't a skirt; it was an apron. The apron looked like a wrap-around skirt when you were dismounted. It wasn't a vest; it was a waistcoat. We were crowned with, not derbies, but bowler hats.

We resembled Twiggy at different heights, and Mrs. Highstaff easily found us each a lovely habit.

Mine was solid navy blue, Fiona's was mossy green houndstooth check, and Gillian's was gray herringbone tweed. We looked very elegant.

For our first side-saddle lesson, Mr. Hobbs assigned us the saddles. "A side-saddle must fit the horse properly." Ever since I arrived at Heels Down Hall, except for a monthly cleaning, the side-saddles sat on racks high on the tack room wall.

First, we learned how to saddle up with the extra girth, a balancing strap, and how to adjust the funny stirrup leather followed by mounting, not from the ground, but with a leg up from a groom. This was a little tricky as you had to pop straight up and not bend over the saddle as in astride riding. The less graceful way to mount was using the millstone mounting block.

I was riding Wizard (hurrah), Fiona had Jazzy, and Gillian was on Atlanta.

It felt odd with both legs on the left side of the horse, but strangely enough, when we got used to it, we found the grip aside was more secure than in a cross saddle.

Mr. Hobbs enlightened us. "In the old days, all the dealers kept a side-saddle in their yard. The stable lads would use it when they had to correct recalcitrant horses, buckers, and balkers. The scissors grip makes it harder to get the rider off."

Santini's book, the one I made my mother send me, contained charming photographs of women riding aside sailing over huge cross-country and show jumps.

This could be interesting. We loved our habits.

When Julian arrived for his lessons on the Saturday after the Dressage competition, he confided in us the reason his mother scratched Caesar. "When I entered, my mom did not realize who was judging. Last year Mr. Smithwick promised I could qualify for White City, if we bought one of his overpriced ponies." Julian wasn't remotely interested in a show career, and he preferred the all-around training taught at Heels Down Hall. "My mom did not want Smithwick to find out we bought a pony from Mrs. Highstaff."

Early Sunday morning Colonel Jameison arrived in his jaunty two-seater green MG to teach the Pony Club Instructional Rally. On the previous Sundays, the rally was taught by local instructors who volunteered their time.

The Colonel told me, "Alexa, I would like you to ride as the leading file for one of the sessions." Mrs. Highstaff told me to have Rob Roy ready. I was happy to ride, even if it meant missing my afternoon off. An extra lesson with the Colonel was invaluable, just what Rob Roy needed, low-level gymnastic jumping. There was a bonus. If I went upstairs as soon as I could after the lesson and made notes while I still remembered it all, I would have a good lesson plan for the "Set of Progressive Jumping Lessons" that we had to prepare for the exam.

Late on Sunday afternoon, a newish top-of-the-line Land Rover crunched up the gravel drive and parked in the circle by the front door of the Hall.

A small, plump, sweet-looking lady, with mousy, slightly frizzy hair and a generous smile, jumped down from the driver's seat, marched up to the front door, and rang the bell. "Good afternoon, Mary Margaret. Where's Harold?"

"Lillian, it's so nice to see you again. Please come into the foyer and put down your bag. The Colonel is still teaching in the school. The lesson should be finished soon."

Ruth was upstairs at the airing cupboard, located at that strategic place in the upstairs hallway where, because of the vents and the open gallery, one could hear almost every conversation in the Hall.

"Well! I have been better. Harold was supposed to drive the Land Rover and leave me the MG. He knows I don't like to drive the Land Rover on the motorway! And it uses so much petrol! I can hardly show up at my brother's son's sixteenth birthday driving a farm vehicle!" She sounded exasperated. "Thank you for inviting me to stay; otherwise, I would have to drive home again and come past here tomorrow on my way—an extra ninety miles in all."

"Nonsense. Do calm down, dear," Mrs. Highstaff said authoritatively. She ushered Lillian into the drawing room, asked her to sit down, and poured her a sherry. "Don't worry about dinner. There will be plenty. We're having a lovely ham. In fact, I've invited Mr. Hobbs to join us. Lilian, remember when we did musical drills? We're doing a display here late in March. Your input will be invaluable."

The following morning, Lillian would swap the Land Rover for the MG and head off to the birthday celebration. Tonight, she was having dinner and staying at the Hall.

Mrs. Highstaff had asked the Colonel to stay on to give us a three-day course that was not originally posted on the tack room schedule, and he agreed.

Mr. Hobbs suggested, "The Colonel may have agreed to teach the course by bartering for the hire of the Indoor School for the Pony Club."

While we were walking together down the stone pathway to the back door of the Hall, Colonel Jamieson re-invited me to his show jumping yard, but this time, after I finished my course.

He looked astonished when he strode into the Hall and spotted his wife in the lobby. He started waffling. "Good God! Lillian, you're here! I completely forgot—the car—bloody birthday party." He disappeared upstairs to the guest rooms to change for dinner. Lillian was right behind him.

I was chuffed to be invited to the Colonel's. Maybe I did have a future in show jumping.

Maybe I will pretend I am trying a horse to purchase and take back home to America. I know my father would never agree to that, but the Colonel won't know it.

It was an ingenious scheme.

Little did I know, but the girls working in the Colonel's show jumping yard never competed. They did a lot of jumping, at home, schooling the horses. His teenage sons competed at the shows where the girls had the privilege of being the designated groom, horse holder, and gopher. (Go for this, go for that . . .)

To fit the Colonel's course into our already busy schedule, we had to forgo our half-day off this week. I hoped he didn't notice my boots were about to fall apart. Not only were my riding boots falling to bits, but I also managed to poke a hole in the toe of my Wellington boots. In February, I stabbed my Clarabelle the Clown rubber boot with a pitchfork tine while I was still in charge of Sword of Justice.

In the dark mornings, it wasn't difficult to stab your boot while trying to muck out the box and simultaneously dodge the grumpy horse. The only reason I didn't stab my toe was my rubber boots were men's boots and too large in the foot. I was lucky. I escaped a tetanus shot.

Over time, the puncture ripped into a pretty big tear on the top of the foot, until I could just barely keep it on my foot. Water and muck would seep into the boot and my sock would get wet, freezing my foot.

With no money to buy new Wellingtons, I came up with a temporary solution. I would wear multiple layers of socks. After a while, the outer layers of socks stiffened like a plaster of Paris shell inside the boot. I could insert my foot with a clean sock into the hard shell.

I was using up socks at an amazing rate. Gillian offered to help. "I'll ask my dad if he has any old socks for your collection."

Downstairs in the dining room where we ate our Christmas dinner, the group of old friends were having a jolly time eating, drinking, and chatting.

We were upstairs watching TV and/or studying. Somehow we thought we could do both activities simultaneously.

Noses around the dining room table began to crinkle. Lillian's handkerchief appeared and she politely covered her nose. Lord Daffy pushed the door from the hallway into the dining room open and the odor became more powerful.

"Bloody hell, what's that smell? Smells like that damn bloody awful cabbage and turnip stuff the Koreans ate. *Kimchi*—that's the stuff!" The Colonel was quite animated about the smell because he had served in the Korean Conflict.

"Rotten fish?" offered Mr. Hobbs. "Where did you get a fish, Daffy? Been in the village again?"

Mr. Highstaff chimed in, "He's found a dead mole, or something dug up out of the garden."

Daffy cheerfully trotted over to Mrs. Highstaff and dropped an indistinguishable mass of rotting stench down at her feet and plopped down on the carpet. Lord Daffy wagged his tail and gazed adoringly at Mrs. Highstaff, looking for praise.

"What's this?"

Mrs. Highstaff gingerly picked up the offending damp, black object with her linen napkin. Upon closer examination, she exclaimed, "Oh dear, oh dear, oh dear, I believe these may have been socks! Harold! Open the window!"

The Colonel jumped up from his seat and pushed the heavy window open and yelled, "Fire at will!"

Mrs. Highstaff hurled the offending socks well over the hydrangea bush and the Colonel slammed the window down.

"Excellent throw, Mary Margaret! You should have played cricket," the Colonel exclaimed. Everyone burst out in hearty laughter. Mrs. Highstaff laughed so hard she had tears in her eyes. The dinner resumed.

"Let's have some more wine and wash down this ham," the Colonel added. The salty ham was enormous.

There was no denying the stinking socks were mine. Interrogation or the process of elimination would have netted the same results.

Who would have imagined Lord Daffy would extricate the reeking socks from the boot and deliver them to Mrs. Highstaff the very moment she was entertaining dinner guests? This dog, Lord Daffy, was like a dog Sherlock Holmes, with impeccable timing and appearing with a quintessential clue to embarrass the culprit in front of assembled witnesses. Daffy should have worked at MI5 or Scotland Yard.

I was mortified that the Colonel had seen my filthy socks. He never mentioned the incident. He had survived combat and wasn't the least bit fazed by dirty socks.

When I showed her the state of my Wellingtons, Mrs. Highstaff said, "I will agree to loan you the money to buy another pair. Just pay the money back when your father's quarterly allowance check arrives."

On Monday, the Colonel's course was not his usual format. The focus on this course was "How to Instruct," a good follow-up after watching the instructional rallies. We had two hours of riding in the morning, two hours of riding in the afternoon, and lectures after supper. After all the drill team riding, the course was refreshing.

Again, Fiona was getting the "too stiff" comments. "Looks like you have a broomstick down your back," bellowed the Colonel. "Sink down into the saddle. *Re-lax*!"

At the command, "Relax," we all stiffened.

In addition to the clinic riding sessions on Monday, in the late afternoon, we had a thirty-minute side-saddle lesson. It took us as much time to tack up as the time we spent riding. Our horse's muscles and our own muscles had to adjust to the new feeling.

Mrs. Highstaff frequently corrected our posture. "Sit square with the horse's shoulders and do not twist toward the pommels. Keep your weight off your left seat bone."

After supper, when the others went upstairs, Ruth revealed, "I found out that Fiona is topping up her cocoa tin every time she goes home. I saw the top of the tin sticking out of her carry-all when her father picked her up."

I wondered how Fiona's Christmas present could last into March at the rate she was drinking it. The never-empty tin was something like the miracle of the Hebrews and the lamp oil that never ran out. Every evening, Fiona enjoyed her special mug of cocoa, delivered to her by the daily demerits loser—a human mug.

Ruth continued to grouse. "Fiona's bullying is one of the reasons I want to leave in April." This really steamed us.

Ruth had planned to stay through June and take the exam with me. In an effort to keep Ruth at HDH until June, Mrs. Highstaff promised Ruth she could compete this spring. Mrs. Highstaff also thought Ruth would benefit from more teaching experience.

Several intensive courses, designed to have us thoroughly prepared, were scheduled after the Display.

"I considered leaving this month, but I am determined to ride in the Display. I want my parents and grandparents to see me ride!" said Ruth defiantly.

Sometimes I pitied Ruth. She came from a large family that was only marginally interested in her life. At the Hall, Ruth was at the mercy of Mrs. Highstaff and April in the house, Mr. Hobbs in the yard (although he never bothered her), and Fiona with her stupid demerits.

We went upstairs to watch a little TV before we went to bed.

This evening it was Ruth's designated turn to make the prima donna's chocolate drink.

"Any time now would be nice," Fiona whimpered. "A lovely hot drink relaxes me before I go to bed."

Ruth made no indication of getting off her chair.

Gillian jumped off the settee. "I'll make it!" She snatched the tin from Fiona and disappeared downstairs.

While we were engaged in the hot chocolate cold war upstairs, the Colonel enjoyed cold ham sandwiches with English mustard, pickled onions, Leicester stilton, and red cheddar cheese for his tea. "Good ploughman's. Nice of the farmer to sell you the ham."

He downed a lager.

Chapter 27

Ham, Ham, Ham

The next afternoon, Lillian unexpectedly stopped back at HDH on her way home from the birthday party with a black Labrador Retriever puppy sitting in the passenger seat of the MG. The Featherstone Pony Club presented Mrs. Highstaff with Sir Yawnberry Dawdle, a pedigreed puppy, as a thank-you present.

The surprise was pre-planned at the dinner party, after the socks episode, when Mrs. Highstaff left the room to get another bottle of wine. She considered getting Daffy a companion ever since he wandered into the village. Dawdle was given to Lilian by one of the Colonel's shooting companions because the dog was gun shy and worthless at the shoots.

Mrs. Highstaff was as pleased as punch. Lord Daffy was delighted. The two dogs became inseparable companions. The guests were served cold ham slices, bread, and vegetable soup for lunch.

We were still holding our jumping competition tonight because it was planned long before the course. The Colonel was going to judge and give us marks for form, as well as the usual faults and time.

To celebrate her birthday and her present, Mrs. Highstaff decided to hold an impromptu supper party for the Jamiesons after the competition. She invited Mr. Hobbs to join them. April suggested serving ham and pea croquettes, which she could make up before she left. This way supper would be ready right after the jumping competition. A birthday celebration or not, supper would be late.

I was very disappointed with the jumping competition.

I put a lot of pressure on myself to impress the Colonel and did not pay enough attention to Atlanta, and I allowed her to get lazy. Atlanta balked at the third jump, a big X with a pole across the middle like a bow tie. I didn't even place in my class.

Lillian watched the competition, and afterward ate the ham croquettes for supper, then stayed the night. She privately told Mrs. Highstaff, "I'm grateful to have a few days away from our farm. Usually, I am left behind, running the whole place at home, while the Colonel travels around teaching, examining, and going to shows."

Mrs. Highstaff was grateful for the adult company.

The supper party ensemble worked out the final Programme for the Display, including a side-saddle mime, a skit, and a little dance on horseback. Ruth (we were short one adult male), Mr. Hobbs, and Jeremy would wear tailcoats and top hats.

At breakfast on Wednesday morning, Colonel muttered wistfully over his cornflakes and coffee, "I do hope we are having something different for dinner today."

Mr. Highstaff, who was reading the paper, was grateful the Colonel brought up the subject first. "The ham was good, Mary Margaret, but don't we have a chicken to roast?"

On her way into our dining room on Wednesday morning, Mrs. Highstaff stopped April. "Take the ham from the butler's pantry and put it in the riding school pantry."

Daffy and Dawdle appeared in our dining room. The two dogs served as an early alert system for "Mrs. Highstaff in the area."

We were greedily munching toast when Mrs. Highstaff interrupted our breakfast. "We are pleased to have finalized the Programme for the Riding Display." Mr. Hobbs had not said a peep about this.

The Display was only three weeks away. Mrs. Highstaff had our complete attention.

"Opening Remarks.
The Children's Ride: 18 ponies.

Children's Jumping.
Side-saddle.
Intermission.
Intermediate Jumping . . ."

Without warning, Fiona shoved her chair away from the table with that terrible screech of wood grating on stone. She stood up like she had received an electric shock.

"Excuse me, ma'am. Can't wait." Fiona dashed out of the room, ran upstairs to the bathroom, and slammed the door.

We were stunned.

I shot a glance at Gillian. *Do I detect a trace of a smile?*

Mrs. Highstaff barely missed a beat:

"Oh dear, how undignified. To continue with the Programme:

Senior Jumping.
Ride of Eight.
Senior Ride – Quadrille.
Finale –"'God Save the Queen.'"

"For the finale, all of the horses, ponies, and riders will parade around and line up in the school."

We all thought the Programme was marvelous and Mrs. Highstaff left.

A few minutes later we heard the Crapper's noisy flush, and Fiona did not reappear until it was time to go out to the yard.

To thank the Pony Club's volunteer instructors, they were invited to bring their horses and join us for the last day of our course.

In general, English riding instructors knew little about some of the American breeds of horses. After breakfast, the Colonel asked me to give another talk on American breeds. I thought he was trying to have some fun at my expense. I was rejoicing that Betty sent me those magazine photographs. I would not have to prance about imitating Tennessee Walking Horses or Five-Gaited American Saddlebreds.

In the morning ride, Colonel Jamieson complimented Fiona. "You're sitting trot is better today, Fiona. Eh, wot?" I swear he was chuckling under his mustache. Mr. Hobbs had clued him in on Fiona's sprint to the loo.

Fiona blushed.

I gave my talk after lunch using all the magazine photographs and the PC instructors thought it was great, but the Colonel looked disappointed.

In the afternoon we had a boring lesson.

The course was over. Colonel Jamieson left.

By Thursday we were in Display overdrive.

There was no time for me to write home. *I wonder how my brother's basketball team is doing. It should be playoff time about now.*

Mom had not given up on her idea to tour Europe this summer. She was planning the summer trip around visiting our old friends living on the Continent.

I wondered if the worldwide economic turmoil was going to squash our travel plans entirely. There was a gold pool crisis and money was devaluing everywhere. I remembered my dad lecturing us about the problems that would result from having paper money with nothing of value to back it.

I also wondered what type of questions I would be asked in a college interview. I wasn't very up on recent American politics. We rarely saw the newspaper and often missed the TV news. The English news didn't have too much about the States anyway.

It was probably just as well that I was unaware of the turmoil in America. I tended to take social injustice personally.

I couldn't afford to dwell on these unanswerable questions for long because I had a lot to memorize in preparation for the Riding Display.

Luckily for me, we had different leading files for all these rides. The Leading File directed the exact moment to turn or circle, trot, canter, or halt. Leading File would change a few times within a drill due to reversing direction or dividing the ride, or a million other things. There was a lot to memorize. I had to draw the movements out over and over again. I am better at learning patterns than learning lists of letters.

In addition to Saturday night, now on Thursday nights, starting today, all eighteen kids came to practice. By now we had all the tack down exactly, so that part went smoothly. But the kids never seemed to put everything away; brushes might turn up in hay racks or mangers. It was easy to mistake one black velvet cap for another. At least one hardhat would end up on the wrong child's head for a moment until that got sorted out.

Some of our junior show riders were in three musical rides as well as jumping. It amazed me how easily the kids remembered these drills.

Now there were eighteen ponies to get ready every Thursday evening. *Oh well,* I thought, *there are only a few more weeks.*

Starting next week, we would be riding all the drills with the music. We wondered what music Mrs. Highstaff had picked. We knew our side-saddle skit "While Strolling through the Park" was cute. Mrs. Highstaff was good at this.

Late Friday morning, after the dinner was in the oven, April was going to empty the dustbins. Being very methodical, she started in the kitchen since that is where she was. In the little bin under the sink, a two-inch square, waxy, bright pink wrapper appeared among the tissues and other bits. Anything of color blazed like a beacon in our drab student accommodation.

April's curiosity was aroused. "That's interesting." Gingerly she picked the little paper out of the bin. "It's a wrapper."

She tucked the wrapper into her dust coat pocket and finished emptying the rest of the bins.

When we were seated around the dining table and had started to eat, April walked into the dining hall. Breakfast and dinner were the two times a day when we could all be guaranteed to be in the same place at the same time.

April produced the pink wrapper out of her pocket.

She looked very solemn. "Has anyone seen this before?"

Keeping a straight face, she added, "I found it today, "

Jeremy sprang up and snatched the waxy pink wrapper from April's hand.

In his most Colonel Jamieson-like voice, Jeremy carefully read the label out loud, "Coco–Lax. Chocolate-flavour Laxative. New and Improved. Overnight Results." He turned it over and squinted to read the tiny writing. "Dissolve with boiling water. When cool, drink it all. Coco equals go-go."

For a moment, we sat there with wide-eyed silence.

Then the room filled with howls of laughter.

"Not me!"

"Not me!"

"Not me!"

"Not me!"

Mr. Hobbs laughed so hard he held his sides. April ran back into the kitchen, laughing hysterically.

Fiona turned bright red, snatched up her dinner plate, stomped up to her room, and closed the door.

On Friday night, Fiona sheepishly went downstairs to say good night.

Mrs. Highstaff was sitting in her study by the fireplace reading the latest *Horse and Hound.* She peered up over the top of the magazine and said, "Do come in, Fiona, and shut the door."

Fiona meekly complied.

There was a long silent pause. "I understand you have been making the girls serve you cocoa every evening. First, may I remind you that keeping food in your room is forbidden, even for the Head Girl. Second, and more importantly, your position here is to build a team, not to have people wait on you. When you started your demerit system, it was little more than marks on paper and was intended to be a way to get everyone to sharpen up a bit."

Mrs. Highstaff paused again. "No more *demerits* and no more cocoa." This statement was followed by a shorter pause. "Let's concentrate on presenting the best Riding Display we possibly can," and then she smiled and added, "Especially now that your sitting trot has improved."

Mrs. Highstaff could hardly keep a straight face and raised the magazine to hide her giggle. "Good night, Fiona."

"Yes, Mrs. Highstaff. I am sorry, Mrs. Highstaff. Good night." Fiona pulled the big collar of her Irish fisherman's sweater up over her face until only her eyes appeared, and she vanished down the hallway.

Fiona had barely closed the door when Mrs. Highstaff tossed the magazine in the air, laughed, and got up to hug Daffy and Dawdle.

Cricket could not believe her good fortune when Fiona gave her a nearly full tin of Drinking Chocolate on Saturday morning. "It isn't my birthday or anything." Little Cricket came to the Hall on Saturdays and Sundays with her mother. There was no childcare nearby, and even if there was, April wouldn't have been able to afford it.

At breakfast Fiona tapped her water glass with her knife. "Please be quiet." She gave us a little pep talk. "We must all try to get along better. We need to work together as a team. With our Riding Display, we have a good opportunity to show the world what good riders and what great horses we have here at Heels Down Hall."

I thought it was a bit over the top, the "show the world" part, but we all gave her a "hear, hear" and a "hip, hip, hooray" and zeroed in the day's lessons and evening practice.

Chapter 28

The Ginger Mare

Today, the kids were practicing the jumping course they would do for the display. This evening, they would practice the musical rides.

Many of the parents asked if their children could stay for lunch. This was more practical than driving back and forth to the riding school twice in one day. Supper wasn't a worry; the parents could deliver sandwiches for the children when they came back to watch them ride.

Parents were permitted to watch the practice, but *never* allowed to comment on the child's riding. Calling out or waving to a rider was absolutely forbidden in the school. With the precision and concentration necessary for the drills, distractions would be disastrous.

April wondered what she was going to feed all these extra people. Then she remembered the remains of the ham on the porcelain platter in the big pantry. She went to check it. *Wow, there's still a lot left.* There was one small problem; a super hardy fly somehow survived the frigid climate of the pantry and deposited some eggs on the ham rind. The eggs were starting to hatch into larvae.

"Good grief!" April chopped off the offending pieces and threw them into the boiler before anyone saw it. "Whew!"

April sliced the ageing ham and put it in the oven. She had read an article in a ladies' magazine that claimed extreme heat kills bacteria.

At lunch Gillian gave me the leave-it sign when the ham was doled out. Gillian was in the pantry earlier checking on the tea supply and saw the ham on the sideboard.

We'd been eating a lot of mutton, and everyone dived into the ham, except Mr. Hobbs, who commented, "This ham is like boot leather." Gillian and I claimed we weren't hungry and only ate potatoes and cabbage.

Fortunately, everyone survived with no ill effects. We, of course, said nothing about maggots. Thank God that meal finished off the ham.

Julian told me about a zany children's television show. "I think you will like *Do Not Adjust Your Set* with Terry Gilliam, Eric Idle, Terry Jones, and Michael Palin, plus they have an outlandish musical group named the Bonzo Dog Doo-Dah Band." We watched it on Saturday night. The irreverent, intellectual humor mocked all parts of society. The silly show provided what we needed—some comic relief.

On Monday morning, we were hacking out on the horses we would be performing on in the skit. The three side-saddle ladies were to ride in full attire.

"You will never develop a true seat if you only ride in a school on level ground." Mrs. Highstaff smiled as the six of us disappeared through the carriage house arch. "Remember to behave like ladies and gentlemen."

Instead of turning left and going around the Farm, we turned right and went past the bus stop and through the hillside village. Wherever possible, we rode in pairs and practiced various ways of dropping back into single file. The villagers who saw us smiled and waved and cheerily called out to greet us.

"Good morning," we replied with a nod of our head.

Toddlers pointed at us. "Mummy, Mummy, Neddies! Neddies!"

We felt very grand. We stopped in front of the Church Hall in an orderly three pairs. The Vicar was just coming out, and Mr. Hobbs tipped his hat. After exchanging pleasantries, he asked Vicar Hanleigh if we could put a poster announcing the Riding Display on the Church Hall Notice Board.

"Why yes, certainly. Jolly good fun! An evening out! I'll bring Mrs. Hanleigh and Penny." The Vicar nodded enthusiastically. After all, three of his teen group would be riding and some of the other children in the Display occasionally attended St. Cuthbert's.

The practice continued seriously all week. WPs hummed and walked around in zigzags and circles. I used the grassy yard in the walled garden to learn my drills. I would be out there running around, saying, "Canter, canter, trot, turn across the school as a ride and change the rein, leg yield across the diagonal . . . and canter . . . circle in the corner."

We probably looked like looneys to anyone from the real world.

I asked Gillian, "How do you remember all these drills?"

"It's easier for us, we learned these country dances at school," Gillian explained.

The music Mrs. Highstaff picked was brilliant.

In our riding lessons we perfected the Scissors at trot and canter, the Comb, Spirals, and Pinwheels, and turning down the center in half sections, sections, and eight abreast. We were good. I thought we would be able to give the Royal Canadian Mounted Police Drill Team, the Mounties, a run for their money.

My good friend Gillian's eighteenth birthday was Friday. We managed to get the half-day off together. With the Colonel's course and the practices, time off was completely rearranged or nonexistent. We walked down to the village hoping to get a bite to eat, but the only places open were pubs that did not serve food.

"Hey! What's that?" A hand-painted sign on the lawn by the Church Hall caught our attention. JUMBLE SALE.

"Let's go," said Gillian gleefully. "Now we have something interesting to do."

We wandered in tentatively. "Oh, dear! Look at the time. Girls, you will have to hurry. We're about to close," said the kind but tired-looking lady at the door. "I'll give you a few minutes."

We zipped over to the tea stand in the corner to buy some broken-crusted pork pies, slightly stale bacon buns, and a cup of lukewarm tea.

"Half price on the refreshments." The lady was probably thinking, *They look like they are from the riding school.* The Vicar would have told her how we always polished off the food at the youth group gatherings.

We were already lucky. We found a cheap non-riding school meal.

"If you find anything you would like to buy, just let me know." She started packing up a box of dishes that hadn't sold. The goods in the place were well picked over and the room was quite untidy.

I was good at noticing anything out of the usual. I spotted something that might have been easily mistaken for a yak. "Hey! What's that?"

"Wow!" The yak turned out to be an Afghan coat—creamy white leather outside and shaggy white hair on the inside just like the Beatles wore.

We couldn't believe our luck; under the first furry coat was another one. The second one was brown suede leather outside with thick wooly hair inside.

The coats fastened with wooden toggles. The white coat had probably once been a Himalayan goat. The brown one resembled a poorly sheared sheep. They reeked of patchouli oil and country sheep market.

I was sure we couldn't afford them.

The lady watched us trying them on. The coats were at least two sizes too big.

"Do you like those?" she asked quizzically.

Like them? We are crazy about them. We had a quick discussion. "How much are they?"

The lady couldn't believe that anyone would be interested in those coats. They smelled so badly that they might go directly to the dustbin and not to the missionary barrel.

She thought back to early this morning when Mrs. Townsend of Storkey dropped off her donation.

At the Church Hall, Mrs. Townsend recalled why she didn't like her sister-in-law. "Frieda was out of her mind giving those stinking goatskins to our children for Christmas. My kids are now safely back at boarding school, and I am here to donate the coats to your Jumble Sale I saw listed in the local paper."

When the donation arrived at the Church Hall, it was quickly removed to the far end of the large room, away from the door and the food. None of the volunteer helpers wanted to stand near the stinky coats.

On High Street, high-quality Afghan coats sold for £100 or more, but these were cheap knockoffs with leather hides cured in horse pee.

No shoppers had even looked at the smelly heaps all day.

"How does a pound apiece sound?" the lady asked hopefully. She knew we wouldn't have much money.

After another swap, we tried on the coats again, and we agreed.

I started over to the table to pay for both coats and the refreshments. I was buying the brown coat as Gillian's birthday present. I didn't have any time to go shopping anywhere else, and this was, after all, a perfect gift.

I spotted a leather jerkin on a pile of work clothes. It was similar to the one I owned, but this one was falling to bits. "How much is this, please?" I inquired.

I could almost read the lady's mind. *Another thing for the dustbin. Why do people drop off such rubbish at the Jumble when they should burn it or throw it away?*

Even Gillian asked, "Why do you want that tattered thing?"

"You'll see." The coats gave me a great idea. I would cut the leather jerkin into long v's, cut the outer seam of my jeans with the hole in the knee that I couldn't wear to work, sew the v's in, and make bell bottoms.

Glad to be rid of it, the nice lady said, "You can just have it."

"That's terrific! Wow! Thank you ever so much."

I paid for our new coats, and we put them on at once.

The lady clicked off the light and locked the door behind us. "I'll finish clearing this up in the morning," she said, and she started to walk home. At the next Parish Council meeting, she was going to bring up the subject of people donating unsellable tat to the Jumble.

We looked like a moth-eaten polar bear and a molting brown bear wearing these coats, but we imagined we were hip and trendy.

We set off to the pub. The Brave Grenadier was by far the nicer of the two village pubs, but it was directly across from the church and, therefore, quite easy to be spotted.

We started toward the Queen's Head to celebrate Gillian's eighteenth birthday and to congratulate ourselves on our incredibly good fortune.

"Whose head is it?" I wanted to know. I was always badgering Gillian with impossible questions. "Anne Boleyn's or Mary Queen of Scots'?"

Being Queen, historically speaking, wasn't always a cushy job. It was safer now that the practice of chopping off heads was abolished.

When we walked into the pub, the farm lads, who were regular patrons, looked at us and moved away to the darts area. Some of the older patrons sidled up to the bar.

We couldn't believe it. We walked in and got a table to ourselves on Friday evening, and we weren't regulars. By now I had learned that British people like to sit in the same seat, every time, and every place: church, dining room, sitting room, or pub.

We drank whiskey and fizzy Dry Ginger, which came in nifty little glass bottles. Of course, it was served warm. We could only afford one drink after buying the food and coats at the Jumble Sale.

We walked back to the Hall warm as toast.

On Saturday, practices were in full swing.

The choreography matched the music. The horses and ponies danced to the rhythm of the music and kept time with the beat.

Fortunately, on Sunday, the seventeenth of March, we missed the evening news. We were busy downstairs at the dining room table making posters for the Riding Display, blissfully unaware of the turmoil in the City.

Only Mr. Hobbs watched the breaking news report, which interrupted his favorite program. In London, ten thousand "Stop the War" demonstrators headed by Pakistani leftie Tarq Ali and actress Vanessa Redgrave were protesting against the US involvement in Vietnam. A mob surrounded the US Embassy, and they threw bricks and smoke bombs at police armed only with nightsticks.

The mounted police, being used for crowd control, were accused of purposely knocking people over with their horses. In the end, ninety-one police officers were injured and two hundred demonstrators were arrested.

The Home Secretary was in an uproar.

Mr. Hobbs never told us about the riot when we came upstairs. He knew it would upset me terribly.

Mrs. Stapleford was coming in the morning to collect and distribute the posters. April said Styles in Brickton would put one in the front window. The kids got permission to put them up in Ashby de la Zouch, Storkey, and Crowsville.

We were only six days away and counting down.

On Monday afternoon we looked smashing while we rehearsed our side-saddle skit. At one point, the gents tip their hats and the pairs circle around each other in a kind of do-si-do. Then the ladies leave the gents, by coyly cantering off to the other side of the school. Cantering off had to be done in unison.

Wizard was a pleasure to ride; he knew the whole skit already. Jazzy and Fiona were right on the mark.

Atlanta was not in the mood. Gillian asked her to canter nicely. Nothing happened. Gillian quickly followed the seat and leg aid with a tap of the whip and confidently said, "Canter!"

No result.

Then Gillian hit the horse hard.

Whack!

At *whack*, instead of cantering off, the ginger mare put her head down and threw a buck that would have made a rodeo bronc proud.

Gillian flew straight up, like a levitator hung in the air, then slammed to the ground, flat on her back. The footing had some give in it, but it was still hard.

Gillian did not move. I thought she was dead.

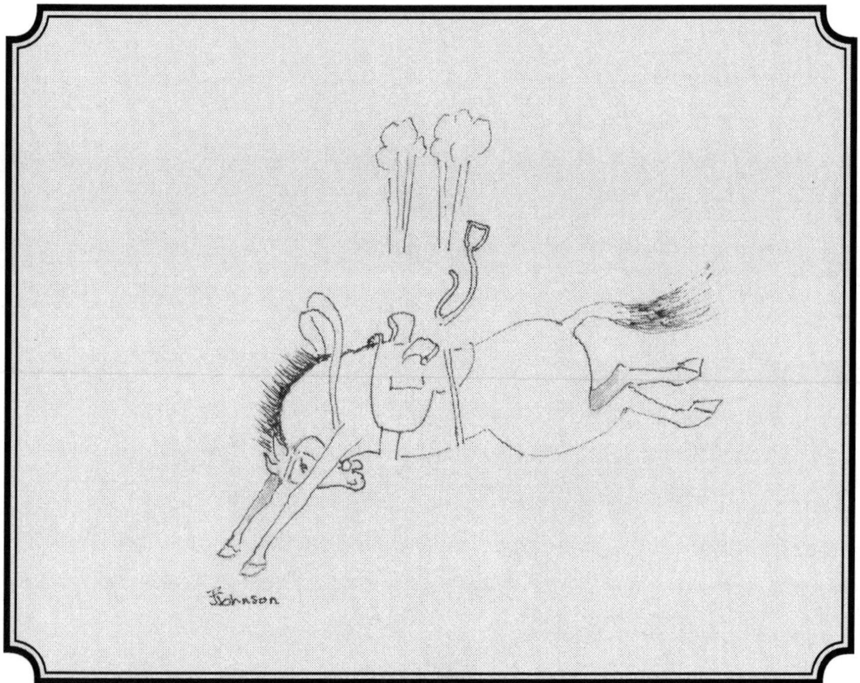

Chapter 29
Jolly Good

Mr. Hobbs and Jeremy hopped off their horses and handed us their reins. After Mrs. Highstaff loosened Gillian's tie and shirt collar, the men carried her, chair style, up to a guest room in the Hall. Mrs. Highstaff gave us instructions to take care of all the horses and hurried along after them. I looked at Gillian's imprint in the footing. *No wonder I call that chestnut nag Attila. The horrible horse killed my friend, who just turned eighteen.*

Upstairs, Mrs. Highstaff, well trained in first aid, determined that nothing obvious was broken.

"Jeremy, fetch a cool water bottle to put under her head."

There wasn't any ice at Heels Down Hall.

Mr. Hobbs phoned the doctor in Crowsville.

The doctor advised, "Undoubtedly it is a concussion. Keep her quiet and awake for a couple of hours. If she takes a turn for the worse, you'll have to move her to Leicester to the hospital." There were no ambulances out in the countryside.

"Gillian! Stay awake! You must not fall asleep, dear. Here, let's read this book together and take your mind off it." Mrs. Highstaff produced a complete set of Beatrix Potter stories, and one by one, they read the charming stories until it was safe to allow Gillian to sleep.

Mrs. Highstaff held a vigil in the big chair by Gillian's bedside all night. Lord Daffy, Sir Dawdle, and Apollo and Artemis, the orange tiger cats, all lay by the bed and kept watch.

In our own ways, we prayed for her recovery.

I began to question if side-saddle really was safer than riding astride. I had heard stories of horses falling and accidentally crushing their riders. It would be easy for an unbalanced rider to pull a horse over while scrambling out of a ditch or charging down a bank.

The next morning when Gillian woke up, she was groggy. Mrs. Highstaff was dozing in the big chair beside the bed.

Gillian was puzzled. "Why am I in this room? I don't remember what happened."

She was unconscious for a few minutes after the fall, and the events were blurry in her mind.

"Don't try to think about it. You fell off Atlanta."

"Oh dear, I hope Atlanta is alright." Strangely enough, Gillian adored Attila.

"She's fine. Don't worry about her. Stay inside and soak in the bath with Epsom salts for a while after the others go out to the yard. Let me know how you feel after that. You should stay inside and study today."

An extra bath? Take one when you can. Stay inside? No riding? Good grief! It is already Tuesday and the Display is Saturday.

That afternoon Mr. Hobbs schooled Atlanta.

Except for a splitting headache eased by aspirin, Gillian suffered no long-lasting effects from the fall, but on the doctor's orders, Gillian had been taken out of the Senior Jumping, which disappointed her.

Mrs. Highstaff wondered if Gillian felt up to riding in everything else. Gillian insisted that she should be allowed to ride in the side-saddle skit. Reluctantly Mrs. Highstaff agreed the skit only worked with six riders. She smiled, but spoke with authority, "Gillian, you will, of course, ride in the Grand Finale."

Gillian and I were especially proud that Biscuit was making his public debut at the Display. Biscuit was spindly when he arrived at HDH in October, but he filled out quite a bit after he received regular meals and proper care. We trained Biscuit to lunge, long rein, and we started him under saddle. Caroline, Julie, and the other girls continued his mounted training.

Mrs. Highstaff recorded the entire musical programme in order on reel-to-reel tape. Each piece of music was timed precisely to end when the drill ended.

Mr. Highstaff and Mr. Hobbs were in the indoor school setting up the stereo system with the reel-to-reel tape recorder and speakers from the sitting room. With their ladders leaning precariously against the kickboards, the men climbed up and down to locate places for the speakers on the steel arches.

"One up here and one over there should work." Mr. Hobbs hung them up. Mr. Highstaff went into the gallery and turned on the music.

Mr. Hobbs walked around the school. "The riders won't hear it."

He climbed up the ladder and took the speakers down. "Let's try them in opposite corners."

Mr. Hobbs moved the ladder, climbed up again, and secured the speaker. He climbed down. "Sound check."

"I can't hear it in the gallery."

The process repeated itself several times.

Mr. Highstaff was beginning to think his new top-secret project on something called Concorde was going to be easier than getting this sound system right.

We prayed it wouldn't rain. If it rained, the sound system probably wouldn't work, and the sound of the rain on the metal roof could drown out a wailing banshee.

Thursday evening was the Dress Rehearsal. As soon as the parents arrived with the riders, they were met by Mrs. Highstaff with pen and pad in hand. She recruited fathers for jump crew and parking attendants. Two fathers would collect admission at the gate; and ushers would hand out programmes and escort people to their straw bale seats. The general admission was half a crown (two shillings six pence per person), and children under eight were free.

Mrs. Highstaff was a woman of many talents. She typed out the entire Programme without a single error.

The Dress Rehearsal went perfectly except at the very end. We lined up to salute the flag, and there was complete silence. Mrs. Highstaff was standing in the viewing area and gave a loud "Hemm. Hemm." More silence. Some of the little ponies started to fidget. "Hemm! Clive! Push the play button!"

"Oh yes, of course, dear."

"God Save the Queen" came on loud and clear.

Just for a moment, Mr. Highstaff appeared to be thinking about the Concorde and not the Grand Finale of the Riding Display. Mr. Highstaff was always very detached. The only student's name he could remember was Ruth, who had been here for nearly two years and whom he saw in the house every day.

The weather on the evening for the Riding Display was chilly but clear.

The Programme was starting promptly at six. Cars started rolling up the drive at five o'clock. People streamed through the yard and the ushers herded the spectators to the stands. The adults wanted to stop to ask questions and the children wanted to see the horses. It was starting to make us nervous.

Two hundred and forty people came to watch us ride. We knew quite a few of them. Colonel and Mrs. Jamieson, the Vicar, Mrs. Hanleigh, and Penny, the children's parents, the riders whom we competed against, and curious villagers all crammed together, shoulder to shoulder, in the viewing area.

April and Cricket were guests of Mrs. Highstaff. Cricket was sternly warned not to call out to us when she saw us riding. She was especially excited because Mrs. Highstaff promised to give her riding lessons for her next birthday.

It was a full house.

"Ten minutes!" We were ready. The eighteen kids were mounted and standing in order on the lane down to the Indoor School.

Mrs. Highstaff gave brief opening remarks, thanking the helpers and everyone for coming. She made it quite clear. "I ask you to please hold all applause to the end of the performance."

As soon as she was seated, she blew her silver whistle.

The Display opened with "Tiptoe Through the Tulips," with Tiny Tim singing his heart out, and the ponies prancing perfectly to strains of the ukulele.

A collective "*Ahhhh*" rippled through the audience and we knew the crowd was ours.

Gillian was fully restored to the Display, except for jumping. She, Ruth, and our six junior show riders performed the lively Scottish "Schottische" to fiddle music.

I noticed Julian, riding Caesar, was making eyes at Liza on Frosty every time they met in pairs. Liza was an attractive blond with long plaits, a clear complexion, a pleasant smile, and huge blue eyes.

With guidance from Mr. Hobbs, the jump crew fathers expertly arranged the cavalletti and crossrails for the smallest ponies. Violet Stapleford was ecstatic to be jumping Dinky, our littlest pony. All six kids and ponies, including Biscuit, had clear rounds, but we didn't get to watch.

When we were getting outfitted for the side-saddle ride, Gillian told me, "My Gran has photos of herself riding side-saddle as a young lady. My whole family wanted to come tonight to see us ride, but my dad was unable to get off work early enough to make the long drive to Leicestershire for the six o'clock start."

The side-saddle mime to "Strolling Through the Park" was adorable. Attila behaved perfectly.

When we went back to the stables to change outfits and tack for the jumping, Fiona's father popped into the yard. He gave her a rose. In a broad brogue, he said, "Fiona, you remind me of my own dear sweet mother back in the Old Country." He kissed her on the cheek.

"Thank you, Dad, but you will have to hold onto that rose for a while. We still have a lot to do."

The Honorable Mr. Chugwig, secretary of the Animal Health Trust, gave a short talk during the Interval, while the jumps were being set up for the next courses.

Mr. Chugwig was thrilled. "Heels Down Hall has raised £50 for the new Veterinary Equine Research Center at Newmarket! In 1939, the Animal Health Trust was endowed by a veterinarian to improve the lives of dogs, cats, and horses through improved veterinary care."

The audience started to clap. Mrs. Highstaff was very firm. "Please, please, all applause should be held to the end."

The Junior Jumping was an exciting relay race of two teams. Each round was timed, and the scores were added together. The Red Team: Ruth on Topaz, Caroline on Mango, and Jessica on Meteor won by a few seconds over the Blue Team: Julian on Caesar, Julie on Marigold, and Liza on Frosty. Around the stables, we were hoping that Liza could persuade her parents to buy Frosty.

We couldn't do a relay race in the Senior Jumping with five riders, so we each jumped one round at 3'6". Ruth jumped two horses, Topaz as planned and Wizard for Gillian. It would have been negligent to leave out one of our best jumpers.

We all went clear. I had been a little worried about Rob Roy, but he had improved light-years.

The fathers expertly cleared the arena.

We quickly transitioned to "The Pride of the Regiment." Fiona, Ruth, and Jeremy, and I stayed on our same mounts. Caroline, Julie, and Julian were waiting for us at the gate. We transformed the indoor school into a lively military parade ground.

For the Students Ride, the music was a stately "Radetzky March." This drill included lots of cantering, and half-passes (or leg-yields, depending on the horse). The music was perfect.

In the Grand Finale, twenty-three horses and ponies and their riders marched into and around the arena to the strains of "Pomp and Circumstance" and lined up nose-to-tail across the arena.

"Ride! Right quarter turn. Ride, turn!" In unison we did a quarter turn on the haunches, to face the audience for the final salute.

Mr. Hobbs carried in the Union Jack and Mr. Highstaff, right on cue, switched on "God Save the Queen."

The audience stood up and we all saluted.

As the last note of the national anthem faded, Colonel Jamieson called out, "Jolly good show!"

The audience could no longer contain itself. An explosion of applause and cheering broke out.

Ponies and riders whizzed around the arena like wasps flying out of a nest.

Amazingly no one fell off.

"Hold your applause, please! Please!" Mrs. Highstaff blew her whistle. "Riders, line up!" We did so quickly, and we left in an orderly and dignified manner.

Mrs. Highstaff, as proud as a peacock, was mobbed with happy parents. Hearty congratulations, handshakes, and uncustomary hugs were given all around.

While we had biscuits and coffee for refreshments in the student dining hall, the Colonel presented Mrs. Highstaff with a bouquet of flowers.

Mr. Hobbs said, "Well done, well done!" which was remarkably high praise coming from him, a man whose best compliment would be "that's better" and never "that's good."

The Heels Down Hall Riding Display was a smash hit.

Chapter 30

The Horse-Trading Major

Toward the end of March, a second Clean Air Act was passed in Britain, phasing out the use of solid fossil fuels for heating. This was good news for everyone, except the Midland coal miners who were now permanently unemployed.

My financial situation was also bleak. I was down to my last £6. Bus fares, birthday presents, meals, and entry fees didn't leave room for any discretionary spending. I needed new boots. *Rats! I might have to take this bloody exam barefoot!*

When my father's letter arrived in the post with my last quarter's tuition, it did not contain an allowance check for me. I needed £2 to join the BHS and the £7 exam fee, plus I was taking Wizard to the hunter trials. I had no idea how those fees would add up.

At dinner on March 29, a minute after he laid down his pudding spoon, Mr. Hobbs informed us, "I'll be back in an hour. I'm not scheduled to teach until half past two." He dashed to the car park and drove off in his rickety car.

It was very strange indeed to leave the premises during the week without scheduled time off. *This is odd. If this was official business, Hobbs would take the Land Rover.*

The weather brightened. It was sunny after all the rainstorms, gale winds, freezing snow, and dreary fog.

Even though the weather was better, my mood darkened. Dr. Martin Luther King was shot dead, in cold blood, at a motel in Memphis, Tennessee.

What is going to happen in America without Dr. King heading the civil rights movement?

I couldn't understand hatred.

By permission, Ruth took her Easter holiday early, the week before Easter. No one minded. She got gypped at Christmas, and, in any case, we couldn't all have the same days off.

Ruth wore street clothes when she disappeared with her dad on Friday afternoon. She took an overnight bag, but mysteriously, she also took her best riding clothes, hat, stick, and gloves. Everything was cleaned, pressed, and polished ahead of time, a perk of working inside.

Ruth did not return on Saturday evening as we expected. Instead, she appeared early Sunday morning, just in time to throw her overnight bag upstairs and join us for a cup of tea before starting work.

Bursting with news, Ruth grinned from ear to ear while she danced around. "I'm a Horsemaster at last!" She jumped up and down and spilled some tea. "This is my last day at Heels Down Hall. I'm packing up tonight and leaving tomorrow."

Yesterday, at an exam in the east of England, Ruth passed the BHS Horsemaster's Certification. "I had more than enough overall marks but missed the Assistant Instructor by *one* mark in the Powers of Instruction phase."

She proceeded to tell us that she had accepted a job offer from Major Everett to work with show jumpers starting next week and she would be working with Marion. Marion was quickly promoted to Head Girl after she returned to the Major's yard in February.

I thought the two of them would be a great team. Marion would run the yard without Rachael's haughty attitudes or Fiona's moody airs. Ruth could calm the most excitable ponies. I had noticed the graduates of HDH were holding good jobs in the local horse world.

Of course, Mrs. Highstaff knew Ruth was going to sit the exam at Bit and Spur School. Using her considerable connections, Mrs. Highstaff found a vacant exam spot on short notice, paid the late fees, and arranged accommodations for Ruth and her father at a bed and breakfast.

Ruth had been a WP since she left school at fifteen. She came from a large and rather poor family. For the past two years, Ruth worked in the

Hall to pay off her board and in the stable to pay for tuition. Ruth groomed Mrs. Highstaff's favorite horses, and she was the only WP allowed to exercise Topaz.

Mrs. Highstaff tried to persuade Ruth to stay until the exam in June, only ten weeks away, but the task proved to be impossible. Mrs. Highstaff particularly wanted Ruth to end her training at HDH on a good note. She thought of Ruth as an adopted daughter.

During the relatively short time I had been here, I realized Mrs. Highstaff's motivation came from her love of her horses and a true desire to educate students for successful careers.

The Major's motivation in life seemed to be promoting himself. He was something of a flash and dash sort of guy.

Ruth enthusiastically continued. "Major Everett promised me that I can take the Pony Club B test the next time it is offered."

She could stay in Pony Club until she was twenty-one and she wanted to get the Pony Club A. "The Major promised me a young pony to train and show." Training a pony or horse to competition standard was a requirement of the Pony Club A level.

At this point in Ruth's exciting narrative, Mr. Hobbs, who had been silent through the whole story, put his tea mug down on the kitchen table. Without a word, he walked up to the stables. I said, "Good luck, Ruth," and followed Mr. Hobbs up to the yard.

The next evening after Ruth left, Mr. Hobbs told us, "Ruth's arrangement might be a good deal *if* the horse-trading Major doesn't sell the pony Ruth trains the first time it goes to a show. And there is a good chance Ruth might not stick it out long. Major Everett can be difficult to work for . . ."

Before Marion worked for the Major, there was always a steady turnover of staff at his stable.

Mr. Hobbs continued, "Major Everett will have to keep his promise to allow Ruth to take the B test this spring. Colonel Jamieson will be one of the examiners. And Mrs. Highstaff will check to see if Ruth participates."

If Ruth would have stayed at HDH, she could have pursued her A level with plenty of opportunities to compete. Mrs. Highstaff could guarantee the pony would not be sold because the pony would be one of her home-breds, which she intended to keep. A successful riding school needs quality, well-trained ponies.

I was secretly worried. *Ruth is a brilliant rider, and yet she missed getting the AI by one mark! Granted it was one mark short in Instruction, not Equitation. I wonder if Ruth stayed until June if she would have passed the AI.*

I vowed to start studying with renewed vigor. It was easy for me to get sidetracked reading *Animal Management.*

Wow, did you know there are seven distinct breeds of camels in Sudan alone?

April and Cricket were installed in the drafty Gate House before Christmas and Jeremy lived in an attic garret, next to Mr. Hobbs, with a school desk and lamp so he could study undisturbed. He was intent on passing on the first try with six months of intensive training. With the men living in the attic, they were out of the way when the onslaught of holiday children, mostly girls, arrived.

With Ruth's departure, Gillian and I were removed from the enormous front corner room with six beds that we inhabited ever since we arrived. We moved to the tiny pink room, previously occupied by April and Cricket. From the window we could see the stable car park, paddocks, and road beyond. It was a more cheerful room, being pink, than our former depressing, dried mud-colored room. This room was more private and there was a door that opened directly onto stone steps, without a landing or handrails, which went down into the kitchen.

With access to the AGA in the kitchen, you could fill your hot water bottle, if you owned one, which Gillian and I did not. Before coming to HDH, I had never heard of putting a hot water bottle in your bed. I didn't have any extra cash to buy one.

The steps saved precious time in the mornings when every minute counted, and they could serve as a possible escape route. Where we would go if we had *time* to escape was yet to be determined.

As hungry as we usually were, the kitchen steps would have not proved useful for raiding the larder, something we never did. Everything was stored in tins and the food was kept in the big pantry at the base of the stairwell in the main hallway.

The other door of our room opened directly into the student lounge. No one would keep you awake late. Lights out at ten o'clock meant just that. Most times, especially in the winter, everyone was in bed well before lights out.

There were other perks to occupying this little room. At night, when you were wearing pajamas, it was a shorter trip to the loo, crossing a carpeted floor, instead of trotting down the long, chilly, creaky hallway. The best perk of all was that the pink room was not directly above the Highstaff's sitting room like our old room.

Artemis and Apollo moved their sleeping accommodation from the front room to the pink room with us. As cats go, they were very gregarious. Since I was without a hot water bottle, I encouraged the cuddly, fluffy kitties to sleep on my bed. They were good hand and feet warmers. Sometimes when I was studying, I would put a cat on my head or drape one around my neck to keep warm. I would say, "I'm wearing my living hat." I justified this by saying Daniel Boone and Davy Crockett were cool and they wore dead raccoons on their heads.

Gillian and I went to bed in our new room, feeling like we had moved up in the world.

We shut the wooden plank door to the kitchen steps and latched it. It was a hook and eye latch, more to keep the door from blowing open in the drafts than for security. The door to the lounge, like the other student bedrooms' doors, could not be locked.

Well after lights out, a piteous cry started to seep into my consciousness. At first, I thought I was dreaming. But as I started to wake up, it sounded like it was coming from the kitchen.

"*Woooooo.*"

Silence for a minute.

"*Woooooo.*"

What the heck is that? It didn't sound like the owl that took up permanent residence in the cedar tree in front of our bedroom after Halloween.

This was not an owl.

Is Heels Down Hall haunted? This place is centuries old. No one has ever mentioned seeing or hearing spirits, but then again not everyone has extra sensory perception. I was interested in ESP. It was the latest thing in psychology.

Is a ghostly kitchen girl who broke the duck eggs getting whipped? Did a stable boy's spirit have a terrible stomachache after being poisoned by arsenic while feeding the ponies?

The baleful moaning resumed, softly at first, and then getting louder and more persistent.

"*Ooohow-o-o-o.*"

"*Psssst*, Gillian, did you hear that?"

"Yes," she whispered.

I turned on the light. From my bed in the corner of the room by the door, I could reach the light switch without getting up. I wasn't worried about lights out. *Everyone else is fast asleep, and should stay that way, unless this phantom wreaks havoc and destroys us all.*

Cold as it was, I got out of bed. I carefully unlatched and cracked open the door to the steps, trying not to make any noise. It was hard to see with only a little starlight coming through the curtainless window.

Gillian handed me the little torch without speaking a word. Cautiously, I shined the little beam of light around the kitchen, and it flashed on the cat's eyes. Sir Yawnberry Dawdle, the black puppy, was just barely visible under the table.

Apollo and Artemis were opposite each other, circling the base of the table like the Indians in western movies circled the wagon trains.

Dawdle was cowering under the big table. Whenever he would try to come out, one of the cats would soundly swat him. Then Dawdle would pitifully yelp and hastily retreat, back under his shelter.

Earlier in the evening, Lord Daffy had been taking his protégé, Sir Dawdle, on a walkabout. After his humans were safely in bed, Daffy roamed throughout the Hall. Like a dog version of Mrs. Highstaff, he checked everything. When Daffy was satisfied, he signed off, and retired to his bed outside the Highstaff's bedroom door.

Before the dogs reached the kitchen, Apollo and Artemis were carefully stalking the mice that lived in the drain under the table. The cats played a waiting game. Crouching motionless, they were within moments of making their fatal attack. The bravest mouse just popped his head out of the drain grate when the nosy puppy wandered into the kitchen to have a closer look.

Lord Daffy spied the cats, stopped short, and did not enter the kitchen. Daffy respected the orange tigers and gave them a wide berth whenever possible, or if he was forced to be in close quarters, he completely ignored them.

Dawdle had not mastered Daffy's cat survival plan.

The mouse used the puppy's arrival as a diversion and scurried back into the pipe, spoiling the cats' late-night recreation and snack, but now Dawdle was stranded under the table and separated from his protector.

The cats decided to have some fun.

As soon as the cats saw the crack of light emerge from our slightly open door, they bounded up the stone steps, sprang through the opening, and nearly knocked us down. They leaped onto my bed and curled up as if nothing had happened. If they couldn't hunt, they might as well be comfortable.

Dawdle looked up and gave me a grateful wag of his tail. He left the kitchen with as much swagger as he could muster. Only his pride had been injured, but he learned a valuable lesson to leave cats well alone. He and Lord Daffy left to retire in a more civilized part of the house.

After sorting out the ghost, we went back to bed.

From now on, I need to make sure I check on the whereabouts of cats before I latch our door to the kitchen.

Chapter 31

Mods and Rockers

As promised, Mrs. Highstaff began the first of her two scheduled ABHSAI Examination prep courses on Monday morning. She gave us a preview of the next two weeks of our lives. There would be lectures on minor ailments, lectures on stable management, and, for some variety, demonstrations in stable management. Riding for the course included flat work and jumping equitation. "How to Teach" practices were scheduled every day. We were going through all twenty of the possible lessons, intensely covering two of them each day. The first week we would be jumping in the school. The second week would be devoted to the cross-country course.

All of us were participating in the two-week course and we would be joined by two other girls coming as day students for the second week. They worked at a riding school near the city, which was a lesson mill and did not have cross-country jumps.

Mrs. Highstaff's course was truly intensive. We were required to take notes on every subject and hand them in to be corrected. Loosely interpreting the curriculum was not an accepted part of the BHS training.

For one moment I thought how these two weeks might have changed things for Ruth, but there was no time to worry about what might have been.

With Ruth gone we were back to taking our half-days off separately. My half-day off was to be Tuesday and Gillian's on Wednesday, but we were required to get notes for the classes we missed.

Time off was good for morale, and people had errands to do.

Until another unsuspecting serf could be found, we had more work to do without Ruth. For Easter, we were getting only one night away, and we had to be back the next evening.

I was in serious money-saving mode. My upcoming expenditures exceeded my worldly wealth. On Tuesday I had dinner at the Hall and then zoomed down to the bus stop in Brickton. As poverty-stricken as I was, I needed to get away from the riding school for a while.

In Leicester I went straight to the tack shop. This was the third time this spring that I wistfully tried on several pairs of tall black dress boots at Lewes Equestrian Emporium. Of course, I took time to admire everything else in the shop. I confidently told the chatty clerk, "I will be back for the boots soon," but unless I met Robin Hood or a fairy godmother, I didn't see how this was going to happen. Fully lined dress boots cost seventeen guineas, more than three times the amount of my dwindling cash reserve.

Around tea time I had a meal at my favorite restaurant, the Swiss Chalet, where everything was fresh and light. I enjoyed a fluffy cheese omelet and fresh garden peas and a pot of tea.

It was a beautiful day. I didn't want to spend more money in town, so I headed to the bus station located a few blocks away. I planned to go back to school early, study for a bit, grab a late supper with the others, and hear about the day.

At the bus station, I had to search for the correct shelter because this was an earlier bus than I usually took. This bus followed a circuitous route with a million stops and it required a change to get back to Brickton.

The bus station shelters were on cement islands between the bus lanes. They had a roof, clear Plexiglas sides, and on each side, wide, open doors. If the rain was blowing, you would be cold and get wet.

Because today was beautiful, the usual groups of unsavory young people that perpetually congregated and hung around in the station were there. During the winter, there weren't too many of them. The worse the weather, the fewer of them there would be.

The two groups never mixed. Mods huddled in one shelter and Rocker types grouped in another one. These kids were scruffy versions of the glamorous people in fashion magazines. Some of them looked a bit deranged from the influence of alcohol or drugs.

These working-class teenagers were apprentices or factory workers who lived at home, and sometimes made more money than their parents. With money to spend, they spent it on clothes and drugs.

In America, our counterculture youth groups were the lazy, long-haired, flower power hippies and the frightful Hells Angels motorcycle gangs.

I stayed well away from all of them, at home and here.

The Mods wore modern, hip, tailor-made clothes copied from Continental styles from Paris and Milan, or trendy New York. If it was cold, they wore bright-colored parkas. If they could afford one, they owned a motor scooter, just the thing to pull a bird.

These bus stop Mods looked scruffy and slightly dowdy.

Mod girls with pixie or page-boy hairstyles wore tons of Mary Quant makeup, big earrings, and wild print dresses with colorful flat shoes or mini-skirts and tall boots.

The boys were peacocks, fussier about their short hair and close-fitting clothes than the girls. They favored chinos with the crease down the front of the pants leg.

Mods smoked a lot of cigarettes, and sometimes an unusual odor wafted through the clouds of smoke. They loved music by the Small Faces like "Itchycoo Park," a place to go and get high on drugs, and "Lazy Sunday," a completely foreign idea to our way of life.

I liked the Mod clothes. Carnaby Street had all the fashions.

I loved one of the Mods' favorite songs, "Green Tambourine," but it was about begging. Today the Mods had a transistor radio cranked up to the loudest, tinniest-sounding setting, and were playing "Incense & Peppermints." I liked the sound of it, but what about the words?

These people were without hope. I did not buy into the Mod philosophy. I tried to think carefully about the choices I made because I had everything to win.

The Rockers just scared me. I thought the boys looked ridiculous with high pompadour hairstyles and tight blue jeans ripped at the knees and the cuffs turned up. Black leather jackets covered their dirty white T-shirts, and they wore motorcycle boots or colorful suede brothel creepers.

The Rockers dressed like motorcycle riders, but I thought most of these teenagers would never touch a motorcycle unless they stole it. Motorcycles were expensive.

The Rockers' girlfriends had bouffant hairdos and garish makeup and chewed gum. They wore nasty dog-collar studded necklaces and platform shoes.

They all drank beer out in the open with the bottles in brown paper bags while they smoked cigarettes and listened to rockabilly music. They loved Elvis Presley.

Elvis Presley's greasy hair made me want to puke. My idea of a good-looking man was a tall, tan cowboy.

The Mods and Rockers sometimes had fights with each other. Both groups were considered to be violent, unruly troublemakers.

Usually, when we came to the station later in the evening, the unsavory teens would be drifting off to go home to be disagreeable to their parents or to take some easily obtained prescribed amphetamines and go dancing all night.

We tried to make a habit of standing near the nicest-dressed, most normal-looking people we could find while we waited for our bus. But, today, on a Tuesday mid-afternoon, there weren't too many normal people heading out of town.

I sized up the situation and made a snap decision.

Rather than wasting time hanging around, waiting for the next bus, and being noticed by one of the motley crews, I would walk out to the edge of town. Bus fares were paid on a zone system. By catching the bus to Brickton at the Black Horse Inn, the beginning of the next cheaper zone, I could recoup half the cash I'd squandered at the Swiss Chalet.

I loved the Black Horse Inn. In Elizabethan times, the inn was strategically built on the main route to London. The coaching inn was two stories high with a whitewashed exterior and black half-timbers.

You entered via a cobblestone passage under a large arch wide enough for a coach and a team of six horses to pass through, and tall enough so that the people on top of the coach would not get knocked off.

The square courtyard was paved with bricks. On two sides of the square, stables had been converted into offices. A row of shops filled another side, and the fourth side included the bus ticket office. A large tea room occupied the ground floor of the former coach stop hotel.

I loved the cozy tea room. It glittered with hundreds of horse brasses hanging on the black martingale straps that decorated the exposed timbers.

Large horseshoes, with the open side up for good luck, were nailed over the doorways. When it was cold, the giant fireplace had a cheery fire in the grate. In the old days, the coach passengers would sit on benches *inside* the fireplace to warm themselves.

Every bus that passed by the Black Horse stopped there so passengers could change buses. The drivers took their breaks in the tea room.

The tea room was popular, open early and late, and sold a few sundries, but the most important thing was that it had a clean, public two-penny loo. When we went to town together and used these coin-operated loos, the person coming out would hold the door open for the next person and reduce the cost by one penny. I hated to waste money by paying to pee.

I set off at a brisk pace. From the bus station it was only two miles. I knew the route. There might have been a shorter or better one, but I did not have a map and the bus went this way every time.

The further I got from the bus station, the grungier the buildings looked. I noticed the shops had accordion-style bars that could be pulled across the storefronts. *I never thought this area looked so shabby when I was on the bus. Maybe I'll hitchhike. It looks so easy on TV.*

I noticed there was less traffic in Britain than in America. Therefore, I stupidly concluded that only respectable people owned cars. The cars containing respectable people did not give me a second glance. They didn't want to take a chance by stopping in this neighborhood.

Being unsuccessful, I forgot hitchhiking and went back to my original plan, walking.

I passed signs on walls with arrows pointing up smelly staircases: THE PINK PUSSY CLUB, FEATURING TOPLESS GO-GO GIRLS, MEMBERS ONLY; and, THE OWL AND THE PUSSY CAT, LIVE MUSIC ON WEEKENDS, DJ ON THURSDAYS, COVER CHARGE. The Owl and the Pussy Cat was a notorious Mod nightclub. The sign was nice, though, from the nursery rhyme. Fortunately for me, the clubs were not open in the afternoon.

I hurried past alleys that led to clothing factory loading docks. A little sign pointed to PARKHURST INDUSTRIES, FINE SPORTSWEAR FOR LADIES AND GENTS, MAIN ENTRANCE, CLERMONT ROAD.

Damn, if I had taken the other fork, I would be on the respectable side of the factories, but I didn't know where Clermont Road went. No one was about. I looked sideways down the alleys to make sure no winos were lurking around.

I could hear a stupid Elvis song, "Adam and Evil," getting louder. A car pulled up to the curb, behind me, but did not turn off the engine. This area was marked No Parking. I knew it wasn't going to be Robin Hood coming to give me money for my boots. Instinctively, I moved closer to the buildings.

"Do you want a lift, dolly?" The driver shouted to be heard over the music and sniggering. "We're going your way." The others in the car laughed like hyenas.

I saw them out of the corner of my eye; the driver was just keeping pace with me. I did not want to turn my head to look at them.

"Hop in and we'll show you the town."

"And a good time . . . ," another taunted.

Four Rockers were stalking me, with their heads hanging out of the windows like dogs. The guy in the back seat started rapping his hand on the outside of the banged-up car door.

Don't engage. Don't show them you're frightened. Don't look at them. Lengthen your stride. Walk faster, but don't run. I felt like I was fleeing a pack of wild animals.

Why do I have to see one of those dopey To Let signs on an empty storefront now?

When I was riding the bus, I always found these signs amusing in a childish way.

To Let. They forgot the I, toilet. Ha, ha, ha, toilet. Not funny now.

Now I was starting to have to pee. I had drunk a whole pot of tea at the Swiss Chalet.

I hope these hoods don't get out of the car.

In a one-to-one fight, I thought I could have probably beaten the daylights out of *one* of the pasty-faced city kids. I knew I was as physically fit as I had ever been in my life, but I couldn't take on four of them.

Where is Emma Peel when I need her?

My heart began to pound, and my palms were sweating. *There's the sign for the Black Horse. Only a few more blocks to go.*

A patrolling police car whizzed around the roundabout in front of the inn and slowed down abruptly as it approached us. The policemen gave the beat-up car and its rough occupants a good look and blasted the siren.

At once, the curb crawlers lost interest in baiting me. The aged Citroën pulled into the driving lane and sped away.

Whew, that was close. Now I have to pop into the tea room and use the two-penny loo. While I'm here I might as well get a cup of tea before I find my bus. Tea was the standard British cure for practically anything; in this case, my badly frayed nerves. *There goes more of my money.*

As luck would have it, Harold Dingby, the friendly bus driver who drove the evening Brickton route, was at the counter. He looked puzzled when he saw me.

"I know ye. Yur from the Hall, aren't you? I didn't see ye on the bus."

"No, I wasn't on the bus," I mumbled while I sipped the hot, soothing tea.

I didn't feel like getting involved in a conversation with Mr. Dingby just now. It was fine when you were the only person riding the bus. Harold (his name was on his badge) would natter on about his kids, football, or something. To top it off, I had seen him in the church in Storkey with his wife.

"How on earth did ye get here? You didn't walk out from the town centre, did you?"

Damn, he figured it out. It was hardly a case for Sherlock Holmes and Watson. He wasn't going to let up until he knew.

I nodded. "Yes."

He looked stunned. "Don't be daft, lass! A proper young lady like yourself should niver walk through that neighborhood, especially alone. I wouldn't walk there meself. It isn't safe. Mrs. Highstaff wouldn't like it."

He sounded just like a parent, well-meaning but irritating. John Cleese was right. You could be annoying while being helpful. I hoped old Dingby didn't tell Mrs. Highstaff he'd spotted me at the Black Horse Inn. In my favor, it was a long way until Sunday, and he probably would forget about it.

I decided that the next time I wanted to save money on bus fare, I would ride the bus out to the Black Horse Inn, get off there, and hitchhike through the pleasant countryside where the nice people lived.

A stupid kids' song, "The Wheels on the Bus," started playing in my head. Once I was on the boring but safe bus, I started to think about how important buses were in England and how many songs there were about buses.

I did not want to think about how foolish I had been. Just for a moment, I had a vision of the plainclothes police officer from Crowsville saying he needed my photo, "in case you go missing."

Simon and Garfunkel may have just set out to discover America in a bus, but I wouldn't have wanted to ride the long-distance buses. You were quite likely to get fleas or lice included with your fare.

The bus song craze had been revived with the Beatles' "Ticket to Ride," although that song could have been about a bus, a train, drugs, or even other less savory meanings. The Hollies fell in love at a "Bus Stop," and the Who traveled on a hallucinogenic "Magic Bus."

I usually confided my adventures to Gillian, but I thought I would keep this episode to myself.

Chapter 32

Red Alligator

Fortunately, the dreadful foot and mouth disease was nearly at an end. The news sickened me. Nearly 434,000 animals, cows, sheep, and pigs had been slaughtered and their carcasses immediately burned. For every confirmed case, more than two hundred other animals were slaughtered.

Horse competition schedules were filled to the max. Many organizations were trying to cram canceled events into the already busy spring and summer schedule.

I was very happy when Mrs. Highstaff announced that we would be competing in horse trials, in turns. Fiona and Jeremy as the most advanced students were going to *two* horse trials. They would have gone hunting, had it not been stopped. I would be competing in a hunter trial at the end of the month, and Gillian would compete in the summer. Mrs. Highstaff also told us several of the ponies would be going to horse shows. These competitions were added to the schedule on our HDH calendar.

I was going to be very embarrassed at the Featherstone Pony Club Hunter Trials wearing my boots with the soles flopping off.

Miraculously, an Easter card arrived from home containing a certified bank check, not a personal one, from my parents. I could cash it on my next half-day off and have my new boots in time for the competition and my exam.

Now Mom was definitely coming in May and planned to visit HDH for a few days. The rest of the time, she would stay with Sareena in her fashionable London flat. Sareena reported the Arabic news for BBC International radio. She was one of the nice people who expertly escorted Jennifer and me through London when we arrived last summer.

With Mom coming I felt under even more pressure to pass. Failing an exam with your parents two thousand-plus miles away across the ocean was one thing, but having to face your mother a mere two days after the results would be quite another.

My parents were never thrilled with my decision to become a professional horsewoman. They would have much rather I became a teacher or a lawyer, but their philosophy was, "If that is what you are determined to do, do it to the best of your ability."

Mrs. Highstaff decided to visit her sister over Easter. She left Thursday evening and put Mr. Hobbs in charge of our course on Friday.

Because it was Good Friday, no outsiders were coming in for lessons. After lunch, Mr. Hobbs had us go out to the jumping paddock and assemble a proper show jumping course. We had been jumping in the indoor school most of the winter. We set the fences around three feet high, including a double and a hog's back that could be jumped from both directions, and a wide triple-bar spread. Mr. Hobbs frequently told us, "Make the jump wider before raising the rails. The horse jumps higher when it jumps wider." We practiced walking the course and measuring off the distances.

When we saddled up and came back to the paddock a short time later, Mr. Hobbs had cranked the show jumps right up. This was more like it. We had a blast; I was riding Rob Roy and he flew over the jumps. The course could be jumped in many different ways, and we each had to think up our own courses.

Mr. Hobbs had been in a good mood for the past week, humming and smiling for no apparent reason.

While we cleaned the tack, Mr. Hobbs walked in and started scrutinizing the cleaning chart on the wall. Had we forgotten something? I didn't want to have a great day spoiled by getting a telling-off.

Mr. Hobbs turned around. "It isn't Christian to eat beans on toast on Good Friday. Don't make your suppers. Come on, Jeremy, come with me. We'll be back in a jiffy."

We looked at Jeremy, questioning.

Jeremy was as clueless as we were, and he shrugged his shoulders.

Mr. Hobbs insisted, "No time to change clothes. Let's go."

Off they went, in Mr. Hobbs's rickety Mini. The rest of us went inside and changed clothes as always, and waited impatiently for something—but exactly what, we did not know. Mr. Hobbs was never very revealing, and this caper had an air of mystery about it.

They arrived back about an hour later laden with large bags. We hungrily assembled in the dining hall and were delighted by giant portions of fish and chips for all of us. Mr. Hobbs had purchased a beer for himself and Jeremy and lemonades for us. This extravagance was uncharacteristic. Fish was fairly expensive; we were far from the sea.

Mr. Hobbs spread his chips out on the newspaper they were wrapped in and doused them with malt vinegar. Then he explained why he'd disappeared last Friday. "I knew I could never get away from the Hall on a busy Saturday morning, so I nipped into Crowsville and placed a bet on the Grand National at Honest Joe's. Mrs. Highstaff doesn't approve of betting, so I said I needed to send a telegram."

The Grand National was held at Aintree on Saturday, March 30.

Mr. Hobbs was not getting to the point. He enjoyed talking about racing.

He started by telling us, "In last year's Grand National a long shot won by avoiding an enormous pileup at the twenty-third fence. Foinavon, an Irish horse, ridden by John Buckingham, literally ran away with the race, winning by a hundred yards. The favorite, Honey End, finished second. Coming in third, a horse named Red Alligator was closing fast on the leaders, but even before the big wreck, Red Alligator, jockeyed by young Brian Fletcher, was solidly in the race."

Mr. Hobbs paused to eat some fish and then continued, "This year forty-five horses started the Grand National over good ground. Twenty-eight never finished, including Foinavon, the Irish Black Beauty, who won last year. As it turned out, Brian Fletcher was able to ride Red Alligator and the pair won by twenty lengths."

The Grand National was notoriously grueling. I wasn't sure if I liked steeplechase racing. It was exciting, but there were always a lot of falls.

"Red Alligator paid 100-to-7 odds." Mr. Hobbs smiled. Mr. Hobbs won a packet. Seven pounds would have been an enormous sum for Mr. Hobbs to lash out on a bet, but he liked Red Alligator and he thought Brian Fletcher was extremely competent for a young lad, a real up-and-comer.

Mr. Hobbs explained why the odds were so high. "The day before the Grand National, Brian fell off another horse and it wasn't certain if he would be able to ride Red Alligator."

Mr. Hobbs finished his story with a bit of a high note. "My old friend, Tim Durant, sixty-eight years old, riding Highlandie, who came in fifteenth out of the seventeen finishers, was the oldest jockey to finish the race."

Mr. Hobbs took a sip of beer.

I wondered if the daring, handsome, famous, and now rich Brian Fletcher had a girlfriend.

With Mrs. Highstaff away and all kids off school, the Saturday lessons were packed. Fiona, with Gillian assisting, was teaching in the indoor school. Jeremy had the big kids out in the show jumping paddock. I was in the yard alone.

Mr. Hobbs came marching over. "I've just added a lesson this afternoon. Please have Frosty and Biscuit ready for half two. A lady is coming to try Frosty for her granddaughter. She is bringing her friend, a teacher from a local school, who wants a half-hour private lesson, which you will have to teach."

Hmm, I thought. *No problem with saddling up two ponies—they're already in and groomed—but now I am teaching a private lesson to an adult, and a teacher on top of that? On Biscuit? The pony Gillian and I trained last fall?* I had only taught children up to this point, and often with an assistant.

Mr. Hobbs read my mind. "You know, Mrs. Highstaff wants to sell Frosty, and you are the only person available to teach. The lady said she could ride a bit, and you know Biscuit very well. It will be good practice for you."

He went on, "This is a good opportunity."

Liza's parents said "no" on buying her Frosty. Lessons, musical rides, and holiday courses were as involved with horses as Liza's parents wanted to be.

It was true. Biscuit was very gentle, as sweet as could be, and quite cooperative, but he was only rising four and therefore slightly unpredictable. The real reason Biscuit was chosen for the lesson was the lady was short and he was the only other school pony not being used.

"Could ride a bit" could mean anything—an expert horseman being modest, a rank beginner with bravado, or simply ignorance, as it quickly turned out to be.

At quarter past two, the ladies arrived perfectly turned out head-to-toe in Lewes Equestrian Emporium's latest fashions. The older lady, who was trying out Frosty, had ridden quite a bit as a *teenager*. Agatha Chesham was well over fifty now.

The younger lady, in her late twenties, was physically fit but a little nervous. Diane Archer was a sports teacher at a local boy's school. The boys she taught were eight to twelve years old. I thought no wonder this lady is nervous after dealing with young boys all day. As it turned out, she loved horses but had only "ridden donkeys at the seaside."

Well, that would make things easier on me. Mounting, position, the aids, walking, halting, turning, and dismounting was about all you could teach a beginner in half an hour. Without any trotting or cantering involved, Biscuit would be fine.

Because every other space suitable for a beginner was being used, my lesson was assigned to the small paddock where we had trained Biscuit much of the time. The grass was pretty munched down, but the edges of the paddock were slightly overgrown. The weather had only recently turned nice enough to mow, and this paddock didn't make the first round.

Across the driveway from the little paddock was the large show jumping paddock.

Biscuit behaved admirably. I was proud of him. Even though we were only walking, I had him on a lunge line, and he wore a neck strap, required for all horses or ponies in a lesson. At HDH, intentionally or *accidentally* pulling on or yanking a horse's mouth was a mortal sin. Beginners of any age were never allowed to ride free until they acquired a balanced seat at rising and sitting trot with quiet hands.

Miss Archer seemed to be enjoying the lesson. Being athletic, she had good posture and coordination, but, of course, no riding legs or riders' instincts.

We did not notice a silly bird pecking around in the bushes. The doves recently moved into the old dovecote, and this one was collecting twigs for her nest.

I glanced at my watch; only ten minutes to go. Nine really, including dismounting, running up the stirrups, and loosening the girth.

Without warning the white dove launched out from under a bush, and like a perfectly aimed soccer kick, hit the pony squarely in the forehead. The stupid bird bounced off the pony's head, hit the ground, shook itself, and noisily fluttered back to the top of the carriage house.

Startled and stunned, Biscuit jumped backward and, while maintaining a good position, the lady went off the pony sideways smack onto her arm, which went "*crack*."

"I think I broke my arm," Miss Archer said nonchalantly.

We had all been trained in first aid. An American Red Cross or St. John's Ambulance advanced first aid certificate was a prerequisite for enrolling in the exam. I did my course in Greenleaf.

"Lie still for a minute, please. Breathe deep, take slow breaths."

Biscuit curiously walked over to the lady still laying on the ground, still in shock, and he sniffed her thoroughly.

Miss Archer thought this was amusing. "He is worried," she said sweetly.

No one had ever fallen off him before this, and Biscuit couldn't figure out why somebody who was supposed to be on top of him was lying on the ground.

Observing the scenario from the show jumping paddock, Jeremy instantly directed Julian to "jump off Caesar and go school Biscuit." It was important for Biscuit to be ridden immediately, so he would not lose *his* confidence or realize if someone fell off, riding was finished.

Julian flipped his reins to Caroline and hurried over to our paddock. After checking the tack, he hopped on Biscuit without using the stirrups.

Peter Stapleford aboard trusty Ghost was told to *ride* under the carriage house arch and through the stable yard, trot down the path, past the indoor school, out into the big field, and find Mr. Hobbs.

Out in the field, the older lady was "just loving" Frosty.

"Isn't she darling?" Mrs. Chesham asked Mr. Hobbs.

Mr. Hobbs replied by saying, "Frosty, walk on!"

Ten-year-old Peter trotted up, halted squarely, and with his reins in one hand, saluted smartly. Peter enjoyed being a messenger and made his report with military authority. "Sorry, sir, to interrupt. Mr. Hobbs, there's been an accident. The lady riding Biscuit fell off and was hurt."

"Thank you, Peter. We'll be along directly. Have them take Miss Archer into the dining hall and give her some tea."

By the time Peter got back to us, Miss Archer, was already sitting in the dining hall, still in shock. She sipped tea with her sound arm, and her other arm was in a sling I'd made out of a kitchen towel and blanket pins. "Directly" turned out to be at least another twenty minutes. To keep Miss Archer's mind occupied, I discussed the virtues of riding as a sport. Since most of the Royals rode, horseback riding was popular, especially among girls and women. I was a little surprised that there was no fuss or flap over Miss Archer sitting there with her arm in a homemade sling. Everyone calmly pitched in and went on as normally as possible.

Mrs. Chesham beamed when she came back from her lesson. "I *just love* Frosty. Doesn't Frosty have the most beautiful eyes and long eyelashes?" I thought the pony's eyes resembled a deer's.

Mr. Hobbs was standing behind her. He said nothing and looked up to heaven. Mrs. Chesham confirmed, "I'll know something definite by next week." Then she became concerned about her friend. "I'll take Miss Archer directly to the Surgery in Storkey."

I was alarmed. "Surgery?"

"Don't be worried, dear, a surgery is a doctor's office, not a hospital operating theater. The doctor in Storkey has open hours on Saturday, and it is on our way home."

I was outwardly polite, gracious, and self-assured. I had not lived in the honey-coated, genteel Old South for nothing, but inwardly I trembled in my tattered boots.

The ladies drove away. Mr. Hobbs told me, "Alexa, don't worry," but how could I not? While we filled out the accident report, Mr. Hobbs told me, "The first thing you always write is 'The rider lost their balance and fell off.'" Then he tried to reassure me. "The British Horse Society and the Association of British Riding Schools' insurances cover any accidents at Heels Down Hall. Miss Archer's healthcare costs will be covered by the National Health System."

That's good, but what about me? The "suing-for-accidents" craze had begun in America.

Mr. Hobbs could see I was still worried. "You are covered too. You are a member of the BHS in career training."

The iconic blue and silver enameled badge was pinned on the lapel of my hacking jacket. *Thank God Mrs. Highstaff sent in my membership as soon as the exam date was fixed. Now I am covered by insurance, plus I can compete in Horse Trials.*

Chapter 33
Never Caught a Tiger

Since he purchased Caesar, Julian often stayed on weekends. He told me his mother thought it was good for him, whatever that meant. Julian watered, groomed, cleaned tack, and helped sweep the yard. It was a big help.

When the latest issue of *Horse and Hound* arrived in the afternoon post, he grabbed it off the counter and proudly opened it to the article he had written about our Musical Display. He kept writing it a secret from us, even after the magazine had accepted the article for publication.

Including two large photographs, Julian's article filled a full page. A large headline congratulated us on raising £50, quite a tidy sum, for the Animal Trust's new equine operating theater at Newmarket. All of our names were mentioned. This was exciting—we had made the big time.

Every *Horse and Hound* subscriber in Britain, so pretty much anyone who rode, would see us. This particularly pleased Fiona. She knew Enid and Denis would see her on Jazzy in "Pride of the Regiment." Although we looked very smart, I thought the photograph made us look a little dazed. We wore nearly white pancake makeup with dark eyes, which made us look ghoulish, and the flash gleamed in the horse's eyeballs, making them look a little crazed. Behind us, you could see the crowd packed like sardines in the visitors' gallery.

On Sunday it was hard to believe it was Easter. We watched the sunrise over the clock tower in the stable yard.

On Easter in Greenleaf, clad in a new dress, hat, and shoes, I would accompany my family to the Sunrise Service. Afterward, the congregation would have coffee and doughnuts in the church hall and secretly compare

Easter outfits. At home, we would eat Mom's homemade chocolate-covered fondant eggs while we read the Sunday papers, trying not to mess up the sections before Dad read it.

Later, still dressed in our best clothes, we would eat a traditional dinner, ham baked with pineapple, mashed potatoes, asparagus, and fresh green beans, followed by my father's favorite dessert, strawberry shortcake. After dinner, we would leisurely walk around the neighborhood with the family dog.

There weren't any delicious doughnuts or homemade candies this morning with our pre-dawn cup of tea.

If Mrs. Highstaff had been home, we might have gone to the later church service, but there weren't very many of us to do the work.

In our smelly jeans, Jeremy, Gillian, and I did all the mucking. Julian helped with chores he was allowed to do. Mr. Hobbs made the feeds and supervised.

Just before lunch, Mr. Hobbs drove off. He said he didn't fancy the menu, leftovers made into a shepherd's pie. There were only a few of us and April had her half Sunday off.

I was grateful we didn't have ham. I had gone off ham.

I was invited to the Bensons, but due to the drastic staff shortage, Gillian and I couldn't go together. Very kindly, Mr. Benson said they would come and fetch me anyway. The Bensons were becoming my adopted English family. Gillian had the Saturday after Easter off, and my day off was on the following weekend.

I did have one great consolation. The money for the new boots had arrived in time so I would be able to wear my new boots at the horse trials.

That is, I could wear the boots at the horse trials if I didn't get sent home over the incident of the broken arm. Lazy Linda was banished for not shutting a gate and allowing the ponies to escape; and even though he was a qualified instructor, a good worker, and an excellent rider, just two months before the end of his course, Denis got the sack for being a Romeo.

Fiona would be back tonight for Mrs. Highstaff's course, which would start tomorrow. Fiona was feeling the pressure. This would be her third attempt at the exam.

Mrs. Highstaff would be returning in time to make the evening feed.

Temporarily, April was the adult on the premises, although she lived in the Gate House, did not have a telephone, and knew practically nothing about horses.

After lunch, Jeremy went up to the attic to study.

Julian's mother picked him up at three o'clock on Sundays, so she did not have to feed him lunch. I saw him walking to the end of the drive to meet his mom.

Without a bunch of busybodies around, I liked being in the stable yard with the horses. After all, horses were the reason I wanted to come to England in the first place.

We were listening to Radio Caroline's rock countdown on Gillian's transistor radio. Considered to be a dangerous distraction, radios were banned in the yard Monday through Saturday. Eventually, we convinced Mrs. Highstaff to allow us to play classical music in the yard on Sundays after I told her how dairy farmers used music to soothe their cows.

Gillian and I were merrily going about our chores. I volunteered to fill hay-nets and throw down the straw.

I entered the hayloft through a trap door above St. Christopher's corner stall using the ladder, which started about three feet off the ground and was embedded in the brick wall. The smooth wooden rungs were thin and worn from age. The ladder only protruded a few inches from the wall, so only the ball of your boot caught on the rungs. It was easy to slip. Fiona didn't like it.

To get into the loft, I had to push the heavy door open while still standing on the last rung of the ladder, and then once the door was open, I had to bend over and lie on my belly on the loft floor and scoot in.

After I got into the loft, I usually sat up there for a minute and looked out to the road through the front window. I thought it was also amusing to look down at the horses. Horses are quite a funny shape when viewed from above.

I climbed up to the loft and was sitting on the ledge, looking at St. Christopher and his very swayed back and beautifully shaped but lopping ears. Ever since Ruth left, Gillian had been taking care of him.

Old Chris was standing near his water bucket, head down, half asleep. Under his head, a circle of red droplets spotted the floor. A trail of red drops went from the water bucket and across the golden straw to the hayrack, where there were quite a few more drops of red. Red was not a good color.

Gillian was across the courtyard.

"Hey, Gillian, come over here."

"Now what?" she asked but she came anyway. We didn't frivolously ask people to do things.

"Better look at Chris." After Gillian had a headcollar and lead line on Chris and turned him so he could see me descending, I came down the ladder. He was used to people climbing up and down the wall.

Our sainted horse had a tiny but steady stream of blood running out of his nostril. The blood pooled on the edge of his nostril and then a big drop would fall onto the floor.

Good God! Is this horse going to die with us in charge of the stable? How could we explain to Mrs. Highstaff that her favorite horse slowly bled to death? We better hope we are lifted into heaven. If this horse dies, I do not want to stay on earth and face Mrs. Highstaff.

First, we tried sponging the blood off Chris' muzzle with water, but that created more mess and turned his white sock pink. We tried damming the blood by sealing it with Vaseline, which worked for a minute. Because we couldn't really see where the blood was coming from, we couldn't use direct pressure.

The only other thing we could think of was that people with nosebleeds sometimes put cotton in their nose and tilt their head upward. We could not very well rip up the gamgee for the bandages and we had no other cotton. Gillian reached in her pocket and balled up the new white handkerchief trimmed in lace her Gran had sent her for Easter, and she stuffed it up the horse's nostril. We tried holding Chris's heavy head up. I wondered if he could breathe properly like this. I hoped he wouldn't choke.

Mr. Hobbs' favorite adage, "it's a long way from the heart," didn't apply in this situation. Blood comes from the heart.

Christopher seemed very nonplussed that he was slowly bleeding to death. We hoped for the best. The handkerchief was turning bright red.

Using muck sacks to mop up, we cleaned the blood-tinged water off the floor and washed the pink sock clean using a little bluing. We picked up all the straws that had blood on them and placed them under dirty straw in the muck heap.

I gave the old horse a pep talk. "Come on, Christopher, don't die until after Mrs. Highstaff does the evening stable check." I already had a broken rider to my credit, and now, possibly, a dying horse.

I resumed filling the hay-nets, weighing each one.

Gillian kept checking on Chris. The color of the handkerchief eventually changed from red to brown, and we knew the bleeding had stopped. Gingerly, Gillian removed her once beautiful handkerchief from the old Saint's nose. There was a crusty, red-brown, flaky lining sticking to his velvet nostril. She gently brushed the brown flake off his nose. She stuffed the blood-covered handkerchief in her pocket. It would have to be washed in secret.

We had just switched off the radio and were heading to the kitchen for our tea break when two black Labs came bounding around the corner.

Like a pair of angels, we said, "Happy Easter, Mrs. Highstaff!"

"Happy Easter, Alexa and Gillian. I trust everything was in order while I was away."

"Oh yes! It is nice to have you back."

Mrs. Highstaff smiled.

I was quite sincere but very worried. There was no mention of broken arms or horses that bled to death when we said good night, only a reminder to be ready for the course in the morning.

The second week of Mrs. Highstaff's course went by quickly. The girls from Pelham Riding School were impressed with our horses and jumps. They were fun to have around. It was nice that somebody else appreciated our school. They thought it was interesting that all our horses went in snaffle bits. They were also pleased that many of our cross-country jumps had smaller versions, which were mostly the ones they jumped.

They were especially intimidated by the tiger trap. "We have never caught a tiger yet," Mrs. Highstaff drolly joked, "but you could become the bait if you look down into it. Just get your blood up, throw your heart over the jump, and go and get it."

Cross-country jumping was not scrambling pell-mell through hedges and over ditches, but very much about keeping the rhythm of the gallop, keeping the impulsion or energy, not getting ahead, and staying in balance.

We joked, "Get ahead and you're dead," but it was not funny. Going over the horse's head into a solid log could be a fatal mistake. We were taught a jump begins when you start for it. We practiced how to slip our reins at all paces if we did get left behind and how to shorten the reins.

It was thought a correctly balanced horse would be the best judge of where to take off in front of the jump. We practiced seeing the spot, counting the strides backward to the take-off.

We rode forward over the drops and down the slides, keeping our heels down and legs locked on, like in the European cavalry schools. By staying forward, the rider did not waste one or more strides on landing, correcting his position, rein length, and direction as happened in the leaning back method. A mistake was never the horse's fault; the rider should have done something different.

Fiona rode Wizard in every cross-country session, which secretly pissed me off. She was competing with him twice in the next two weeks. Jeremy rode Heathcliff the whole week for the same reason, but Gillian and I did not mind. Heathcliff hadn't done it for a while, but he could be a tear away. Gillian and I and the other two girls rode different horses every day. In the exam, you did not know which horses you would have to jump.

Chapter 34

A Lot of Flap

On my half-day off I took the bus to Leicester, cashed the check, bought my boots, ate at the Swiss Chalet, and rode the boring old bus all the way back to Brickton. The cuff-lined dress boots cost £9/9s or nine guineas. The fully lined ones I had my heart set on cost seventeen guineas, more money than I had to last me for the rest of my term. I couldn't wait to get back and polish my boots; they were full-grain calfskin and could be scratched without the protecting polish. I wanted to start wearing them around inside while I was studying to break them in and tamp down the leather sole. I could only wear them upstairs because they were new; otherwise, all boots were removed in the hallway at the bottom of the stairs, and you changed into slippers or indoor shoes.

On Tuesday night I proudly showed my new boots to Mrs. Highstaff. I am sure she was relieved. Her students' appearance reflected on her riding school. She admired my boots and made sure I knew how the garters were buckled correctly. "The buckles go on the outside of your knee and the point of the strap points back. The excess strap should be cut off."

I waited for the anticipated words of doom. Nothing had been mentioned on Monday evening. I expected something like, "Alexa, you will be leaving HDH as soon as your mother arrives in England."

Instead, Mrs. Highstaff thought I would be pleased to know that Mrs. Chesham was buying Frosty and would keep her here at livery for the summer for Liza.

I said, "That is great! Liza rides Frosty so well."

I thought, *That is really sweet, but whatever happened to Miss Archer?* I was quaking in my new boots and hoped Mrs. Highstaff didn't notice.

"I also wanted to compliment you on the way you handled the situation with Miss Archer. Of course, I saw the accident report Mr. Hobbs left on my writing desk when I got back, and he also wrote me a note to explain the situation. Miss Archer telephoned me yesterday. She was very favorably impressed. You know, she teaches sports and is used to dealing with injuries."

There was a slight pause. "I also wanted to tell you, your riding, particularly your jumping, has gone up another level."

Wow! This is totally different. I wasn't surprised that the lady bought Frosty—after all, she told us she "just loved her"—but we were surprised Mrs. Chesham turned out to be Liza's grandmother on her mother's side. We were sworn to secrecy since Frosty was going to be a surprise fourteenth birthday present. Liza's birthday was the first day of the children's course. Liza's parents didn't object since Granny was paying Frosty's bills.

How lucky for Liza! And it's lucky for me, my training is actually paying off!

The unexpected compliment on my riding made me feel more confident about taking Wizard to the invitational spring hunter trials sponsored by the Featherstone Pony Club.

I learned that teaching riding was not all fun and games as it had been up to now teaching the kids, but it could be hazardous. No wonder HDH was absolutely meticulous about everything being done correctly.

On Wednesday afternoon for her half-day off, Gillian went to Crowsville. She said she fancied chicken and chips. Crowsville had the best chippery that we had found and the nearest Laundromat. She also needed to do a bit of laundry. Her mother kindly requested she bring home "only one load of washing, please." She borrowed my canvas duffel bag to prevent another mishap from reoccurring.

When Gillian came back in the evening, she had a small paper bag. I didn't ask what was in it. With our previous unfortunate experiences with sleuth-like nosey dogs, and now there were two of them, Gillian asked if she could put the bag in my trunk for safekeeping. She safely deposited the little bag in the dog-proof container. I thought no more of it.

Everyone was thrilled that Frosty was sold and still staying—everyone except Mr. Hobbs. Mrs. Agatha Chesham told us, "I will be coming twice a week to take private lessons from 'that charming man.'" Since a fit, well-cared for pony could certainly be ridden more than once a day, Grandmother's lessons would not interfere with Liza's riding.

I wrote home to my parents to thank them for my new boots, which were the exact same made-in-England brand that I'd brought with me. Mom's new summer plan was to visit some friends in some remote part of Norway. I was hoping more for the culture of Venice than scenic fjords. From there we were going to Germany, another place I didn't have that much interest in, to visit some other friends. I knew Sareena was really cool and knew London inside out, and at least we would have a great time staying with her.

Dear Mom, Dad, Richard, and cats,

Thank you for the check! My new boots cost £9/9s. Please remember that I got three years of hard service out of my old ones. The new ones are not as nice (they are only top-lined) as the fully lined ones that cost 17 guineas, but they should be perfectly adequate.

On my next half-day off into Leicester, I will check on ferries schedules and costs for Norway and about sending my trunk back.

Please remember my trunk will be considerably heavier going home because I have had to buy so many books. The big blue suitcase I brought over will not fit into my trunk (three inches too long) and it is too big for me to lug around Europe. Jennifer and I had a terrible time with too much luggage to carry, trying to cross London. Maybe Mrs. Highstaff would want to buy the suitcase?

I'm getting excited about Mom coming over. I hope Mrs. Highstaff will let me meet Mom at the airport. Remember Mrs. Highstaff invited Mom to stay at the school for a few days.

Mom, please bring my navy-blue trench coat with you, my black one is worn out.

While we are in London staying with Sareena, I would like to see the City, not just the museums and monuments, but some nightclubs and a performance of the Royal Shakespeare Theatre.

About this exam, I don't really know what my chances are of passing. Over the past year or so, there has been a lot of flap over this exam. A lot of people seem to think it is a fiddle. Even if I don't pass, I am sure that this year has been well worth everything. My riding has improved immensely. And like with everything, the more you learn, the more you realize you know next to nothing.

Lots of love,

Alexa

As soon as I finished writing my letter, a shocker came on the television's evening news. The London Bridge was being taken apart, stone by stone, then numbered and shipped in crates to Lake Havasu, Arizona, to be reassembled on a man-made lake in a desert.

I wondered what the odds would be for a national landmark being sold to Americans for over a million pounds. *Why did I expect to see the London Bridge in London? I'll just cross it off our sightseeing list.*

Chapter 35

Perfect Shot

As I pulled my jumper over my riding shirt, I reflected on Browning's poem. He wanted to be in England in April. Obviously, he never worked at a riding school. The weather was horrible. In Greenleaf, we would be wearing summer cotton frocks at azalea festivals, and here we were, wearing layers of wool.

The children's holiday courses were starting, two weeks of organized havoc. For the first week, we had our favorite kids: Julian, Liza, Mary, and Susan, and the Staplefords: Peter, Violet, and Alice.

As soon as she arrived, Liza started telling us how the course was her birthday present from her parents. She was fourteen today. We joked, "It is nice of you to remind us, Liza."

Julian came back on Monday morning with a cake he'd made his mother buy in Storkey and April hid it in the pantry.

During the children's courses, no children were allowed in the stable yard until after breakfast. It was faster without their help.

In the morning, Gillian brought Frosty in from the field. After Frosty was groomed and finished her feed, Gillian hid her in the indoor school. Mrs. Highstaff found a long, multi-colored sash, probably a curtain cord, and tied a big bow around her neck. We went to breakfast and found the kids congregated in the dining hall. Mr. Hobbs marched in, looking very grim. "Don't bother to sit down. Something urgent needs attention in the indoor school. Let's go."

Straight-faced, we trooped after him like lemmings marching to the sea.

The little boys were starting to whine a bit.

"I'm hungry."

"Couldn't this wait?"

Liza trailed behind, gossiping with Julian.

We were standing in a semicircle around Frosty when Liza came through the door of the school.

"Frosty! Oh, dear! Is something the matter with Frosty?" Liza was sometimes quite emotional.

We yelled, "Surprise!"

"Surprise? Surprise what?" Liza stammered. Her parents had already told her no several times to her pleas about purchasing the pony.

"Happy birthday from your Grandmother Chesham," Mr. Hobbs piped up. Then he gave a little grimace, remembering he had to teach the private lessons.

"Frosty is your pony, Liza," said a quiet voice from the back of the group. Mrs. Highstaff had come in, unnoticed.

She continued in a happy voice, "I'll go over the details with you this evening, but now, Liza, please lead Frosty to the carriage house to eat her hay with the other ponies. Everyone else, please go eat your breakfast. We have to stick to our schedule. We have a busy week ahead."

Mrs. Highstaff started back to the Hall with the dogs close at her heels.

With tears in her eyes, Liza gave Frosty a big hug and started back to the stable yard.

We cheerfully ate Liza's birthday cake for supper and sang "For She's a Jolly Good Fellow" and "Happy Birthday."

"Hey, kids, can anyone else arrange to have a birthday this week?" Jeremy asked. Everyone laughed.

Gillian amused the kids with the story of the ghost from the first night we slept in the pink room.

Julian stood up, gave a dramatic flourish, and began to paraphrase the Rascals' song, "People Got to Be Free" by substituting puppies and kittens for people and the kitchen as the world.

As if it had been rehearsed, the Stapleford boys chimed in for the chorus, right on cue, "*Woo-woo, woo-woo-woo.*"

They sounded just like the puppy howling, so we joined in the howling. "*Woo-woo, woo-woo-woo.*"

From the sitting room, we could hear Lord Daffy and Sir Dawdle howling, "*Woo-woo.*" "*Woo-woo-woo.*"

Mr. Hobbs rolled with laughter.

Julian surprised us again. He gave us each a copy of the "Pride of the Regiment" photo from his *Horse and Hound* article.

We were thrilled. None of us owned a camera, but I was disappointed that no one had thought to take a photograph of our elegant side-saddle ride. I would ask Mrs. Highstaff if I could borrow the blue habit to pose for a photo when Mom came.

Fiona organized and taught most of the children's course this week with Jeremy teaching the three bigger kids jumping lessons. Mr. Hobbs and Mrs. Highstaff also taught a few riding classes and lectures or demonstrations.

"When am I going to have time to practice for my competition?" Fiona moaned. "When am I going to have time to study?"

I thought about Fiona. Mrs. Highstaff was providing her with practical experience to build her confidence, which was exactly what she needed.

I also thought Fiona should stop whining. She rode Wizard every day in Mrs. Highstaff's course last week.

Wizard was everyone's favorite.

Children's course or not, we still had our lessons every day with either Mrs. Highstaff or Mr. Hobbs, and we had our project horse to school.

Fiona was getting nervous about her competitions and the exam and, to put it mildly, she was getting crabby again. There were no demerits, but she was sharp. Not even a please nor thank you if you went out of your way to help.

By comparison, Jeremy seemed to take it all in stride. He was looking forward to a schooling opportunity with Heathcliff. He had frequently competed with Falstaff.

On my Tuesday afternoon off, I merrily went into Leicester and straight to the Thomas Cook Agency. My mother could not book the ferry from the United States. The ferry went to Norway three times a week from Newcastle and returned three times a week from Bergen. If we did both trips in one week, there was a reduction in fare.

Good, I hope we aren't staying with the boring, pious Svensons for more than a week. Norwegian girls think embroidery is a fun way to pass the time.

I couldn't very well book the ferry. I didn't know Mom's plans and I certainly didn't have enough money. The ferry took two days and had passenger cabins with bunks and dining rooms.

From Norway, we could take the same ferry line, but a different ship to Amsterdam, and still have roundtrip fares. From Amsterdam, we could take trains to Cologne, Germany.

I started to wrinkle my brow. I had been to Thomas Cook several times, cashing traveler's checks and looking at interesting brochures of warm, sunny places like the Greek Islands, Tuscany, and Australia.

"Don't fret, young lady," the clerk said.

I promised to get this ferry information, and I couldn't let my parents down. If I mailed these bulky time schedules by airmail, it was going to cost me a fortune. If I sent them surface mail, my mom would be in England before the brochures arrived in Greenleaf. I explained my dilemma.

The clerk said, "I can mail the schedule to your mother, in care of your friend in London. There will be plenty of time. Your mother can book the ferry at our Thomas Cook Agency in London."

I received detailed instructions for shipping my trunk. "Pack it, and as you go, fill out detailed customs forms, in triplicate. Measure and weigh it, then Thomas Cook will provide you with the shipping cost, FOB from the school. Lastly, arrange a pickup by a scheduled lorry."

When the trunk arrived in the US, a Thomas Cook agent would mail my dad the bill of lading and Dad could pay any remaining freight and collect the trunk in Norfolk, Virginia. Once it was identified and paid for, the trunk would go through customs. After clearing customs, my dad could drive home for three hours with the trunk taking up the entire back seat of the car.

This shipping process could take six to eight weeks, depending on the transatlantic ship. Hopefully, my things would be home before I started university in September.

The clerk handed me a manila envelope with a list of addresses and phone numbers and pages and pages of customs forms.

Wednesday afternoon, Gillian walked into Brickton. She bought apples and sweets and came back to study. She wanted to save her pocket money for her spring holiday break starting this Saturday.

Even though her course ended in October, Gillian was catching the cram-for-the-exam fever from the rest of us.

It was easy to work with the kids; they were regulars. They knew when to help and when to stay out of the way, so on Wednesday, we finished at a reasonable hour.

I skipped supper, something on toast, and joined Gillian lounging around in our room. While eating the apples and the sweets, we were pretending to study. We were having a fantastic time recounting travel experiences and comparing boyfriends.

We both planned to dump our boyfriends. I was leaving England in a couple of months, and Gillian just thought Arthur, as kind as he was, was a bit dull. Ian and Arthur were not horsey.

Gillian jumped off her bed so suddenly it startled me. "I just remembered my package in your trunk. May I have it?"

"Of course, it's yours." I couldn't wait to see what was hidden there.

We pulled the trunk from under my bed, and Gillian removed the little brown paper bag. She pulled out an exquisite, shiny little black box. Embossed in gold on the front of the box in Russian and English was the word SOBRANI, a brand of Russian cigarettes. They were beautiful, as cigarettes go, with black paper, tiny gold writing, and shiny gold paper-covered filters. They had a strong but pleasing aroma. You would expect the Czarina to be smoking a Sobrani from a long, enameled-gold cigarette holder. It seemed like everyone smoked—movie stars, pop singers, Mods and Rockers—everyone except the Bensons, my family, and everyone at HDH who was not Mrs. Highstaff.

Gillian told me one of the reasons she needed to go into Brickton was to buy matches.

Jeremy was in the stable yard looking for the ducks; it was his turn to take care of them. Because it was still light, even though it was after eight o'clock, the ducks did not like to go back to their pen. Huey, Dewey, Louie, and Donald (I still called them that) were in the newly mown paddock under our bedroom window greedily gobbling up the bugs that were churned up.

Sitting on our beds, we could see out into the fields, but we could not see directly into the paddock unless we were standing at the window.

No one else was upstairs. Gillian offered me one of the cigarettes, but I declined. I had never smoked before, but I asked if I could have one puff. I inhaled heartily and immediately started to cough.

Gillian laughed. "This is how you do it." She started blowing perfect smoke rings, just like Absalom the caterpillar in *Alice in Wonderland.*

Even though it was cold, I said, "I think we better open the window." Everything reeked of horse, but this different odor was quite strong.

The Russian cigarettes led us into a discussion of Commies, which were a hot topic in the US. BETTER DEAD THAN RED was a popular bumper sticker on cars at home.

Gillian finished the Sobrani. She put out her cigarette out in a little mint tin, like Mrs. Highstaff, but instead of putting the stub inside the tin, Gillian put it on her thumb and, by pinging it with her forefinger, she flicked it out the window.

It was a perfect shot.

A sweet-smelling, fancy black-and-gold bug fluttered down from above and landed in the grass in front of the curious Donald. Donald eyed it suspiciously. "What's this?"

The other ducks waddled over to see what the mysterious new creature could be. When it looked like Dewy might have a stab at it, Donald gave them a warning squawk. "It's mine," he quacked.

Donald devoured the gold tidbit in one gulp. It lodged in his beak. Donald started squawking and gagging. "*Agg ahk ahk*!"

Donald flopped about wildly, completely panicked. The other ducks started to flap around and quacked noisily.

Two black Labs came bounding around the corner from the tack room and spied the frantic ducks. Dawdle went on point. Barking excitedly, Daffy ran back to Mrs. Highstaff, who had come out to inspect the mowing.

"Here they are, Jeremy! What's this? Come quickly."

She scooped up Donald and held him under her arm like the *Little Goose Girl* and Jeremy grabbed the duck's neck with one hand and pried out the cigarette butt with his other hand.

The ungrateful duck snapped his beak shut and bit Jeremy. "*Ow-w-w!*"

Mrs. Highstaff abruptly dropped Donald. Honking noisily the whole way back, the disgruntled ducks waddled back to their pen.

Mrs. Highstaff looked up at the open window. We could not be seen because we were lying flat in our beds and being still and quiet.

The next morning at breakfast, Mrs. Highstaff presented the incriminating evidence. "Has anyone seen this before?"

"Not me."

"Not me."

"Not me."

"I can't imagine what careless person would leave litter lying around. Some inconsiderate litterbug nearly killed one of our precious ducks." She looked at Gillian and then around the room of faces.

"I remind everyone that Heels Down Hall is a no smoking facility."

"Yes, Mrs. Highstaff," we all nodded in agreement.

When Mrs. Highstaff left the dining room, Fiona looked at Gillian and put one finger alongside her nose. The "I know" sign.

Chapter 36

Dangerous Riding

The kids were having fun, because *they* were fun and because they loved HDH and the ponies, but when Fiona would put her hands on her hips and start a scolding with "Don't you know . . . ," a few tongues were being stuck out at her behind her back.

Most of the kids were enrolled in the second week of the course, and some of them were staying for the weekend, but Mrs. Stapleford said, "The Staplefords are going home to clean up and they will come back Monday morning."

Saturday lessons were busier than usual, and Fiona and Jeremy were competing in the Smith on Worthy cross-country on Sunday.

Fiona was frantic. "Somebody's going to have to clean my tack for me tonight! I still have to plait Wizard!"

This was new. You always had to clean your *own* tack. No one offered.

"I still have to write my plans for next week's course," she continued pitifully. The plans had to be submitted to Mrs. Highstaff by Sunday morning. Fiona started to whine. "No one wants to help me."

Well, you had all week to work on the plans. I was quite unsympathetic.

"We will make sure your tack is clean," piped up Gillian, who didn't really offer to clean it.

When Fiona came back into the tack room, the bridle, done up in the traditional figure eight, and her saddle positively gleamed. "Oh, thank you," she gushed. "I'm going upstairs to finish my lesson plans."

No one responded.

What's this? There are still the rest of the saddles to clean. Fiona is supposed to be supervising the kids.

Gillian's dad arrived right on time, and she gratefully grabbed her case out of our room. After her dad had a pit stop and a word with Mrs. Highstaff, they were off. I went up to the room and looked in my trunk, and just as I suspected, the Sobranis were gone.

Since the cross-country competition was close by, Mr. Hobbs would drive to it after breakfast. Fiona prevailed upon the older kids to load the trailer and the Land Rover.

"It's good practice for when you will be competing." She was right, but it wasn't their job. If she hadn't been so bossy all week, they would have volunteered to help.

First at the carriage house and then at the tack room, Fiona stood with her clipboard in hand, ticking off items on a list as they were packed: spare bridle, brush box, hoof oil. I hoped she would let me copy her list before I went to my competition.

Fiona never noticed that her tack looked a little too shiny.

They came back around tea time, with two clear rounds and no prizes. Fiona's tack was slippery, so she gingerly cantered around the course, instead of hand galloping, and incurred multiple time faults. Of course, Wizard cleared every jump like it was made of matchsticks.

Jeremy's clear round on the Irish fox hunting Heathcliff was somewhat miraculous. He could easily have had run-outs, galloping past jumps by going too fast. He would have never had a refusal; Heathcliff was a bold jumper. Nonetheless he was eliminated.

Over tea, Jeremy was very animated as he related his story. "Heathcliff was going so well I was sure we were going to get bonus points for finishing under the time allowed. There was a sharp elbow bend one fence away from the finish close to the barns and horseboxes. Spectators were milling around. The approach to the final jump was cordoned off to keep people off the course. Heathcliff zeroed in on the rope barrier like an atomic missile and I couldn't turn him. I yelled, 'Heads up!' and the spectators ran off in all directions."

I thought I saw Mr. Hobbs chuckling.

"Heathcliff sailed over the ropes like a deer. I turned his head in mid-air. We turned around, almost a half pirouette. Now we were pointing back at the barrier. *Whish*—over he went. Everyone clapped when we went through the finish, well under the time limit."

I had never heard Jeremy speak this long at one time before.

Jeremy drank some tea and continued, "Heathcliff passed the vet check and I had already weighed in when a small group, including the Steward and the competition manager, stomped over."

The manager said, "That was a fine bit of riding, Mr. Howard."

Elderly Lady Applebottom, who owns the farm, complimented me. She said, "Quite spectacular, in fact, dear." She was the only one smiling.

Then the head of the Ground Jury took over. "The committee has concluded it was *dangerous riding* and you are *disqualified.* The judges' decision is final."

"They couldn't eliminate Heathcliff for being off-course because we went through all the flags." Jeremy smiled. "I'm still very proud of Heathcliff; he has great heart."

"Quick thinking," said Mr. Hobbs.

Mrs. Highstaff spotted Fiona when she ran upstairs to change into jeans for the evening stables.

"Fiona, you do look a sight. That is quite an untidy appearance for our Head Girl to present at a competition. Your breeches are filthy. I hope you plan to have a better outfit for the Featherstone Foxhounds One Day Event next week."

Fiona's breeches were spotless when she left in the morning, but now there was a dark, wide stripe on the inner legs and across the seat.

"Yes, Mrs. Highstaff. It won't happen again." Fiona dashed up the stairs to prevent further discussion. It would not happen again, because next time Fiona would clean and check her own tack.

The second holiday course had fourteen resident children and seven extra ponies. It could have been complete chaos, but it went like clockwork.

We were all giving stable management demonstrations and teaching lessons in addition to our own riding.

Colonel Jameison came the last three days to teach the older children on our show team. Again, he asked me to ride Rob Roy as the leading file, and I was especially grateful. I loved my rising four-year-old giraffe. He was starting to develop a neck and top line muscle, and go long and round and light to the aids. Mrs. Highstaff was delighted. She told me I could take Rob Roy to the Featherstone Foxhounds cross-country course the next time they had a schooling day, to give Rob Roy some experience off the property. This was brilliant and I was pleased to be going home—that is, to the Bensons—this Saturday.

Christopher, Gillian's brother, a geology student at the University of London, and her gran picked me up at ten past seven. We arrived in Braefield about half past eight. Mrs. Benson gave us tea—pork pies and a fresh garden salad. It was a simple supper but something we never had at the Hall.

After we ate, Ian came over and we went on a walking village pub crawl. We came back a few minutes after eleven o'clock, the pub's closing time. Then we listened to mournful and funny (to me) Irish folk songs by the Dubliners. One was about a woman who kills her baby and then herself. Another song about German-made razor blades and sheets of Belfast linen was about a wife murdering her husband and a reference to the war. And poor "Roddy McCormick" getting hanged wasn't very cheery. Ian went home around one. Christopher and I debated the relative merits of the English versus American educational systems, and I didn't go to bed until half past two.

Without the bells ringing, I slept until half past nine. It would have been three hours extra sleep if I didn't stay up until half past two. It was a treat anyway. We had a light breakfast and read the Sunday papers in the sitting room. After Sunday dinner, which was a roast with all the side dishes, Christopher's friend Gavin arrived. They were going on a two-week geological field trip to Scotland. Christopher told me privately, "We intend to taste the local whiskey wherever possible."

After the two geologists left, Ian came over. We walked all over the village. I reminded him I was leaving England soon and with my mom coming over, my competition, and the exam, I probably wouldn't see him again before I left. I said we could write to each other. We both knew this was the end of our relationship. Ian wasn't much of a correspondent.

Ian said, "I might try my luck in Africa, maybe Rhodesia." He was a journeyman electrical engineer, and electricity was a valued commodity on the Dark Continent.

Ian joined us for a tea of scones topped with fruit and cream at the Bensons. He came along when Mr. and Mrs. Benson drove me back to Heels Down Hall. Mr. Benson decided to take the scenic rural route rather than the M1. The scenery was a patchwork quilt of farmland and woods dotted with villages. We passed Rockingham Castle. The leaves and blossoms were starting to come out on the trees and the fields were turning bright green. The sky was dramatic with big black and silver clouds scudding past. I held hands with Ian for the last time.

It dawned on me on the ride back that, as much as I loved horses, it was nice to get a total break from them, even if it was only for twenty-four hours.

As we turned in the drive to the Hall, I changed gears mentally and wondered how Jeremy and Fiona fared at the competition.

❧

The weather had been quite blustery at the Featherstone Foxhounds Hunter Trials.

Fiona was concentrating while she warmed up for her dressage test, and she didn't notice who was riding nearby.

"Fancy seeing you here, Fiona," Denis cheerfully called out as he cantered off toward the start of the cross-country. He was riding Minstrel and wearing a new Parkhurst Sportswear men's fashion, a jersey knit long-sleeve roll-neck sweater with large bright red and black diamonds on it.

"Denis reminds me of a harlequin clown," chuckled Jeremy.

Fiona hissed through gritted teeth. "Fancy seeing me here, indeed!"

Wizard laid his ears back.

Something in Fiona changed at that moment. "Not you, Wizard. Denis! Let's show that smart aleck."

Wizard put in a good dressage test, but with two more phases to go, it was premature to get excited.

Jeremy's dressage test was a disaster, and he finished in last place. He cantered, a very collected canter, through most of it. He scored several ones (very bad) and twos (bad). The highest mark was four (insufficient) when Heathcliff was supposed to be cantering. The general Comments read "a difficult horse, barely controlled."

Heathcliff's antics from the week before were widely gossiped about in the horsey circles. Many of the same competitors were here.

Denis came back from the cross-country, tight-lipped and with a few twigs adorning his new roll-neck sweater. He did not acknowledge Fiona or Jeremy when he trotted back to his big horsebox with PARKHURST SPORTSWEAR emblazoned on the side.

When Jeremy looked at the scoreboard, he did not tell Fiona she was ahead of Denis and if she had two clear rounds she could win the whole thing. Jeremy realized Fiona got extremely nervous if pushed too hard. If any horse could have two clear rounds, it was Wizard.

Fiona was careful on the cross-country course but went clear within the time allowed. Jeremy went too fast, not the way he'd planned. Heathcliff had one run-out, a log pile in the middle of an open field, but Jeremy circled him, and they cleared the log pile easily. They finished without any other faults. Even with the run-out, which did not happen in the penalty zone, and an extra circle, they were still within the time.

The final results would be determined by the show jumping. There were a lot of good cross-country horses in Leicestershire.

Jeremy decided he would control Heathcliff by trotting parts of the course. Jeremy was not going to embarrass himself in front of the stands with a runaway, and Heathcliff was a little geed up after the cross-country. With a couple of time faults in show jumping and the disastrous dressage test, they were not in contention for a prize. Jeremy decided Heathcliff had a good schooling and the next time they competed Heathcliff would be wearing a running martingale.

To make the show jumping more exciting for the few spectators who had braved the weather, the competitors were jumping in reverse order, those with the most penalties jumping first and the best horses going last.

Denis trotted smartly into the arena and saluted the judge with great aplomb. He looked like a winner. He looked very smart with his hunt collar and buttons on his lightly used Pink hunt coat.

Halfway around the course, it looked like Denis and Minstrel might go clear.

Damn. He ruins everything, Fiona thought. *He's going to get the better of me again.* Fiona was third from last to jump and she was getting nervous. "Dear God, for once in my life, may I be better at something than Denis," she prayed silently.

If Denis went clear, Wizard would have to jump clean and go fast. Fiona wasn't fond of fast.

Minstrel headed around the corner to jump the triple combination in front of the stands. At the end of the arena an elderly lady standing along the fence popped open her large red umbrella. "Looks like rain," she said to the old gentleman standing next to her. A violent gust of wind snapped the umbrella inside out. *Whoosh.* Jerking her arm into the air, the inside out red umbrella nearly flew out of the lady's hand.

Minstrel's eyes nearly popped out of his head, and he slammed to a halt. Denis sailed over Minstrel's neck in a perfect pike position. In the process, he managed to pull the bridle right off his horse's head. Without Denis and his bridle, Minstrel galloped around and flew out of the arena by jumping over the closed-out gate. "Loose horse, heads up!" the announcer warned.

With his red face matching his coat, Denis waved at the stands as he walked out of the arena, carrying his bridle.

Jeremy came over to stand beside Fiona. He left Heathcliff, cooled down and untacked, tied to the horsebox. Heathcliff was happy, eating from his hay-net. Jeremy watched Denis' round and laughed, "That was well worth the price of admission."

The two riders before Fiona both had choppy but clear rounds. When Fiona's turn came, instead of praying, "Let me beat Denis," she prayed, "Dear God, please let me do my best!"

Fiona had perfect form as she expertly navigated Wizard around the course. Over a large oxer in the middle of the course, they left the ground a little early and Wizard rattled a rail with his hoof as they descended. The heavy pole rolled in the cup, and after Wizard was nearly a stride away, it fell. Fortunately, Fiona didn't notice; she was concentrating on the remaining jumps.

They left the arena to a polite round of applause. "Five faults for Wizard, owned by Heels Down Hall, ridden by Miss Fiona Boyle," the announcer informed the spectators.

"That's it, it's over," Fiona said dejectedly, and she started to dismount.

"Stay put," Jeremy told her. "I'm good at maths, from being a waiter. You might still be in it."

It depended on the two remaining riders' performance to see who would be taking home rosettes; the trophy was out of the question. The last two riders were experienced show jumpers and they made it look easy. They secured first and second place, respectively.

"Will the following numbers please return to the arena for the awards ceremony and a victory gallop?" the announcer called out. He started reading off the numbers. "Number 72, please." The announcer had called out Fiona's number! She was sixth! To top it off, she was competing on a school horse.

Never was a rosette more cherished than that one. According to Fiona, this was her first major accomplishment. Whether she meant winning the rosette or finally seeing Denis get humiliated, I was not certain.

When I found out the satisfying results of their day, I was pleased as punch. If Fiona could get sixth on Wizard, I had a really good chance of winning my competition in a few weeks.

I won a dressage *and* a show jumping competition on Wizard at HDH during the winter.

Very satisfying results, indeed.

Chapter 37
I Think I Know

As a reward for all our extra work with the holiday courses, Colonel Jameison was going to teach us a three-day course, not originally on the master schedule. We had to give up our half-days off this week, but we didn't mind. Fiona, Gillian, and I secretly had crushes on the very handsome, very married, but flirty and ferocious Colonel. We were also quite determined we would not be shown up in front of him. When he gave a riding command, he challenged you, and you had to do it.

This course had a recurring theme. Whether it was a flatwork or jumping session, we were required to change horses at least three times. There was a proper way to change horses. You had to: quickly and efficiently dismount, run up your stirrups, and keep hold of your horse until the next rider had the offside rein. Then you took the reins for your next horse, adjusted your stirrups, and checked to see if they were even. After that you checked the girth and the bridle, and mounted from the ground unassisted. You had to adjust your riding style immediately to accommodate the new steed. Changing horses was a common drill in the BHSAI examination. We were glad to learn how to do this correctly before the exam came along.

We were also concentrating on "How to Teach." The Colonel wanted to make sure we understood *why* we were teaching something, not just picking an exercise out of a book and parroting the lesson.

Dr. Amsley returned Harry because it was foaling and show season and he wouldn't have much time to ride. I was glad Harry was back. I loved riding Harry; he was like a big sofa.

We were riding in the indoor school and the theme of the lesson was "the progression of exercises using cavalletti." We were standing, mounted, side by side, and the Colonel moved the cavalletti into a new configuration for the fourth time this lesson.

I was comfortably lounging, in an upright position, on the dapple-gray oversized marshmallow and hoping we would be able to do some real jumping. This stuff was so easy; we had done it all with Mr. Hobbs many times.

"Why should you *never* have just two cavalletti for an in-and-out, without any placement poles in front of it?" The Colonel looked at us hopefully. He had given us a progressive set of jumping lessons before in a lecture.

We sat there silently as if our heads were melons.

Two sets of cavalletti stacked two high were placed in front of us a distance of eighteen feet apart for cantering through.

"Or to put it another way, why should you use another cavalletti and have at least three cavalletti in a row?" The Colonel was getting impatient. He started to tap his boot with his riding crop. The indoor school was as silent as a church. There was a little adjusting of reins.

Suddenly the Colonel bellowed, "Ride! Change horses, taking the horse on your offside!"

Of all the luck, I was at the end of the row. If he would have said take the horse on your near side, I would have Wizard! As it turned out, the horse on my offside was Sword of Justice.

We hopped off in unison. Gillian, Jeremy, and Fiona held the four horses, arms apart like a chain of cutout paper angels on a Christmas tree, while I had to scuttle in front of the pack and grab Justice so the others could start the mounting procedure.

"Move along!" The Colonel tapped his whip on his boot. "We haven't got all day." There was no real need to rush. This was the last ride.

I was last to get mounted. I hated the stirrup leathers on Justice's saddle. They were latigo and did not slip over the stirrup bar as easily as the smooth leather ones. I wasn't sure if they weren't a hole too long.

"Alexa, will you please demonstrate how to take this combination at a canter?"

I hesitated. I still had my spurs on from riding Harry. *Should I take them off and cause further delay, or ride with my heels facing out the rest of the lesson?*

"Alexa?" The Colonel repeated my name. He didn't like to repeat himself. I forgot about the spurs and came out from the line, made a circle at a trot, and cantered around the school. As we turned on the line of the in-and-out, I heard the Colonel tell the others, "Nice turn."

Sword of Justice aimed at the tiny in-and-out. His ears locked forward and he switched to autopilot. Leaving long, he cleared both sets of cavalletti, set eighteen feet apart, in a single effortless bound like it was the water jump at Hickstead.

However, I was prepared for a bouncy little in-and-out, not a very, very wide jump, and I got left. I slipped my reins as we were trained to do, but on landing, my spurs inadvertently hit Justice in the sides. With great fury, he bounded forward at a gallop, and narrowly missing the wall of the school, he turned sharply right.

I became unglued but hung on for dear life. My arms were wrapped around Justice's neck, my left elbow crooked over his crest, and my left knee hooked over the top of the saddle. Somehow my feet did not come out of the stirrups. I had just enough grip on the rein to pull him wide of the jump.

Fortunately, when I was nine, I played Indians with Apache, my pony. Indians could hang off one side of their horse and use the horse as a shield while shooting arrows out from under its neck. I was determined not to fall off. Last week I was the Colonel's shining star.

Slowly I forced my left leg down and I started righting myself. The thick latigo stirrup leathers did not slide off the back of the stirrup bars like the smooth leather ones were prone to do. On the second lap around the arena, I managed, by sheer willpower, to get myself lying on top of the galloping horse's neck.

On the third wild loop, I was sitting upright and gathering up my reins. On the fourth round, I had Sword of Justice back in hand and cantering. As we approached the in-and-out, I gave Justice several half-halts to remind him I was still on board. I took care to keep my heels deliberately forced out so I wouldn't accidentally spur him. He went through the in-and-out as quietly as a school pony. I trotted the rest of the line and came back to my place in the queue.

"I think I know why, Colonel, sir," I said breathlessly. I was out of practice of being an Indian. The Colonel smiled. I knew I would never make that mistake again when training a horse or teaching a lesson. I don't think the others would ever forget it either.

After the Colonel left, the place seemed deserted, and I had an opportunity to write home. This would be my last letter to Greenleaf. Even if you replied immediately upon receiving a letter, a complete communication was still a two-week minimum turn-around by airmail. My mother would be in England in a few weeks.

I assured my family that I had not forgotten about the birthdays, two in May and one in June, but the presents were in my trunk, and I was shipping them home. The birthday cards, all placed in one envelope to save postage, were mailed previously. I hoped they received them.

I explained the ferry situation, keeping a glimmer of hope alive that we might skip Norway and go to sunny Greece where the Bensons went for holidays.

I didn't mention my upcoming competition. I had told them about it before, but I wanted to surprise Mom with a rosette, preferably royal red, first place.

I gave my parents another warning that the exam might not have the outcome we expected when I started on this adventure almost a year ago.

Writing the letter gave me a twinge of sadness; partly homesickness and partly the realization that I would be leaving Heels Down Hall soon. As much as I complained about it, and as nutty as the place was, I loved it.

Fiona's attitude improved after the One Day Event and the Colonel's course. Occasionally I would hear her make a quiet affirmation, "I'm going to pass my exam with flying colors."

She voluntarily loaned me her detailed list of "what to take to a one-day event" to copy. I was happy; it was slightly different from the lengthy horse show list I had already compiled.

On Sunday morning, not yet bright and very early, Mr. Hobbs, Wizard, and I set off to the Featherstone Pony Club hunter trials schooling rally. Gillian gave me a hand plaiting Wizard's tail. My tails tended to have a long, lazy S down the center of the braids instead of a column of "v-v-v-v" in a straight line. I really needed to practice plaiting tails in my spare time, if I had any, between now and the exam.

On the few occasions I had to show in Greenleaf, I would get so wound up and nervous that I would make myself sick. After I threw up, I felt better, and I would compete. At HDH there wasn't much time to get nervous; horse shows, or events, just meant more work than usual.

I was fine until we got to Nettles' Farm, which was not exactly what I'd expected.

Technically speaking, I was not a member, but HDH students were invited to this annual schooling rally because Mrs. Highstaff did so much with the Pony Club.

As soon as I registered and received my competitor's information packet and pinny, Mr. Hobbs helped me unload Wizard. The ramp was very heavy.

Mr. Hobbs explained to me, "Three Day Eventing started as trials for Cavalry officers' mounts and was formerly called 'The Military.'" I liked that idea.

Then Mr. Hobbs informed me, "Alexa, I cannot coach you here because of Pony Club rules. Adults are not to interfere unless there is a safety issue. I'll keep an eye on the horsebox if you have to tie Wizard up, like if you have to use the loo."

For a few seconds, I got truly angry with Ruth, my old friend who was not here. I was angry *exactly* because she was not here. If she had stayed at HDH, she would have brought Meteor to this competition. They were third here last year in their division. We should have been here together. Ruth was nearly a Pony Club B; she had been to these rallies before and she knew the rules and the ropes.

Chapter 38
Nettles' Farm

Because of Princess Anne's involvement with Pony Club, hunter trials were popular. I knew from reading *Horse and Hound* that the Princess was in serious training for eventing with Alison Oliver. I realized Nettles' Farm would hardly be Tidworth, England's premier one-day event, but winning this was important to me.

I had only been to very organized horse shows in England and seen the cross-country course at Heels Down Hall. At Nettles' Farm, three dressage arenas were running simultaneously. For the Ds, there was a mini mock cross-country course, with little logs, brush jumps, and chicken coops, and in a different paddock, a small show jumping course consisting of crossrails and cavalletti. On the other side of the long, tree-lined driveway, two large arenas were set up with respectably sized jumps, and a large holding area for both arenas was in between the two.

Even with my map of the property and my time schedule, I found the place a bit confusing. The parents were the gatekeepers, timers, starters, scribes, scorekeepers, selling the refreshments, and everything else. There was one main announcer, but at each arena, dads with handheld megaphones called for competitors. Sometimes they would press the wrong button and a loud squawk or screech would scare a pony. Bells rang and whistles shrieked. It was hard to tell what the whistles and bells meant. The dressage judges used bells, but show jumping judges blew whistles. Pony Club messengers, mounted on Thelwell ponies or lanky Thoroughbreds, dashed around with satchels filled with results for the scorers or the announcer.

Several Pony Clubs and a few riding schools had been invited. Nettles' Farm was a teeming anthill of ponies, horses, and kids. I recognized several Featherstone Foxhounds Pony Clubbers who had been to Heels Down Hall. We called out to each other, "Good Luck," but secretly we all hoped *we* would win.

I had early rides. I liked that; get it over with. My butterflies disappeared the moment I entered the arena. Wizard knew the test; it was the same one Fiona had done a few weeks before. Wizard anticipated the movements, but if he did something a step earlier than I asked, I went along with him, and the judge never seemed to notice. She said, "Lovely horse," as we left the arena. I gave Wizard a big pat on the neck, and we walked out on a long rein.

"I'll watch Wizard while you walk the cross-country course," Mr. Hobbs offered. "You will have to hurry." I accepted. Armed with my map, I set out on foot, alone, around the nearly mile-long course. The course was open for inspection yesterday afternoon, but I had no way of getting here even if I had known about it. With fourteen jumps, the track was pretty straightforward, but I wished I had time to walk it again. My section was first.

There were different show jumping arenas for the Cs and Bs but only one cross-country course. I had questions: Some jumps had options like at the big V made of railroad sleepers; do you jump the point and risk a run-out, or do you jump the wide end as an in-and-out? The C and B courses shared some jumps, and they were numbered with different colors. In some places the two tracks separated. Walking on foot, this was easy to see, but at a hand gallop the obstacles and flags would come up quickly. I noticed what appeared to be a crooked footpath, more of a trail crossing the landing side of jump number ten.

I got back in time to go to the loo and put my pinny on over my turtleneck. "Put your spurs on," Mr. Hobbs whispered. I smiled gratefully; he wasn't supposed to help me.

I was second to go. I was on the way to the start box when I heard an older male voice. "By Jove, is that you, Hobbs? Haven't seen you for years! Come on, old man, I'll buy you lunch in the tea tent." It looked like he was waving, but I thought I saw him hold up a little silver flask.

It was Mr. Hobbs's old Army buddy, here with his second wife's three boys, all competing. "They've stuck Penelope somewhere out on the cross-country course. She was supposed to sell raffle tickets, but they made her a jump judge, I think she said. Pity you can't meet her—she won't be back until the last horse goes round. I say, Hobbs, the landscape's a bit parched around here, wouldn't you say?"

"Good luck, Alexa," Mr. Hobbs said. "Keep thinking and you'll be fine." He scampered off to the tea tent like a squirrel that had found a mountain of peanuts.

On the other side of Nettles' Farm, away from the hubbub, nonhorsey Fredrick Nettle, who shared the large working farm with his sporting brother Samuel, finished milking and turned his cows out. He decided the grass was better in the millpond field. The problem was the millpond field was beyond jump number ten. The cows had to travel the path, which crossed the landing side of the jump to reach the gate into the lush field.

"Plenty of time," the nonriding farmer said to himself as he checked his watch, which was ten minutes slow. "Horsey things never go off on schedule. Any self-respecting hunter shouldn't mind a cow or two in the next field."

He gave the lead cow a whack with his stick. "Move along, Clarabelle!"

She responded, "*Moo ooo*," and set off on a leisurely stroll with the rest of the herd straggling along behind her.

When I got to the start box, the first rider had scratched. "Stung by a bee," I think the lady told me while she waved one hand around her hat.

Now I had a choice. I could either wait until my scheduled time, and possibly be stung by a bee, or go early. I hated waiting. "I will go now, please."

Wizard and I were going like clappers. I loved this! The jumps were straight forward and solid. Wizard thundered along. I was glad we had a tiger trap at HDH; he flew over it. "Good boy!"

Next was a long gallop around the edge of a planted field and on to the drop jump, number ten. I was looking forward to the drop jump. It was about five feet almost straight down onto a perfectly flat field below. Jumping the drop was truly riding Pegasus; you flew off the top and landed far into the field.

Even though the gate to the grassy field was only fifty yards beyond the drop jump, Clarabelle decided the flat field was a good place to rest.

Cows are curious by nature. The remainder of the herd wandered up behind Clarabelle and looked mystified while they listened to the announcements and inspected the penalty box flags.

Clarabelle decided the sandy landing directly under the jump was the perfect spot to lie down and start chewing her cud. Not renowned as original thinkers, most of Clarabelle's followers copied her. None of them thought to go through the open gate into the grassy pasture with lovely shade trees and a nice pond.

The inappropriately but well-dressed new Pony Club mom, wearing a tweed skirt with stockings and not-so-sensible shoes and a cashmere V-neck jumper with a string of pearls, was the substitute jump judge for fence number ten.

Penelope Peabody had volunteered to sell the raffle tickets and was dressed to impress, not for a countryside ramble.

This is as close as she had ever been to a live cow, let alone a herd of them. She didn't know what to do. "*Shoo*," she said unconvincingly from the top of the bank. She flapped her red silk scarf, dotted with tiny gold horses. The cows just blinked their long eyelashes. She waved her clipboard at them menacingly. "Go away! You're not supposed to be here!" Clarabelle nonchalantly flapped her large ears.

"Oh dear! They didn't cover this situation in the briefing," she said to herself.

The jump judge at Fence 9 blew his whistle to warn the next judge, who was out of the line of sight, that I was on the way. We thundered toward the drop with great abandon.

At the take-off spot, instead of leaving the ground, Wizard perched on the edge of the bank like his shoes were glued to it. I looked down. Several cows were lounging around directly under the jump. When I walked this course twenty minutes prior there was not a cow or even a cow patty on the place.

Damn! Loss of forward motion, refusal, penalties. One of the requirements in the Pony Club A fox hunting section was knowing how to turn back cattle, but surely not at a competition.

I couldn't jump down onto the languid cows, who had taken over the penalty zone as effectively as a college sit-in.

"Try again, dear," the helpful lady said. "You are allowed two refusals at each jump."

I couldn't believe what this woman was implying. I had already cleared nine out of the fourteen jumps and had every intention of having a clear round.

We were not supposed to speak back to the judges, but this situation was beyond the pale. Uncharacteristically I said, "This isn't fair. My horse can easily jump this, but *cows* are not cross-country obstacles."

"I agree," the disconcerted woman said, "but you have to jump it. Those are the rules."

I was completely in disbelief, but because I was told I had to jump it, I turned Wizard back several strides. Maybe the cows would magically vanish, the same way they'd arrived. This time I used my spurs. Again, Wizard wisely rooted himself safely on the top of the bank. *Two refusals! One more and I would be eliminated.*

I was just about to plead not fair to the jump judge when Fred Nettle appeared. He had been following the cows, but he stopped to pick some mushrooms along the way.

"So that's where you are, Clarabelle." He laughed. His dog started nipping at the heels of the few cows still standing. "Move along, you dozy cows, the Pony Club will be coming through here soon."

I was determined not to budge. One more failed attempt at this, my favorite jump, would mean elimination. If necessary, Wizard and I would stand on the edge of the bank until Doomsday. I would wait until a few cows wandered off, grab the pommel, lean back, lock my legs on, and jump *down* from a standstill, instead of the way I planned, of flying far out into the field.

"The Pony Club is already here!" the lady in the stockings, which already had a run in them, cried out in despair. "Look up! *Up here*!"

Fred Nettle didn't know a thing about Pony Club rules, but he had a lot of common sense, and he took charge of the situation when he saw Wizard and me tottering on the edge of the bank. "Let the rider go around!" he shouted. "Let them *pass* by. It's going to take me a few minutes to push the girls across to the millpond field."

The lady had no idea what girls he was talking about, and although she could see an open gate, she had no idea where the millpond field was because there hadn't been a mill there for over a hundred years. Furthermore, she did not know how a single man was going to budge a herd of sleeping cows.

She could not think of anything else to do. She checked the clipboard. The next rider would be coming along in six minutes. "Oh dear, oh dear, oh dear," the woman cried. "Go around. I'll make some notes."

I cantered a little way down the top of the bank and popped over an easy post and rail fence, not on the course, and continued on my way. Except for the cows, I had a clear round.

I couldn't find Mr. Hobbs to let him know what had happened.

Chapter 39
Until the Cows Come Home

The notes from Jump Judge Ten read, "Number 27, gray horse. Man pushing girls across a millpond. Sleeping cows. Gave the rider a 'Go Around Pass.'" The scorer didn't know what to make of it, so he asked the show jumping judge, who was on a tea break. "Never heard of a 'Go Around Pass.'" So, they went to get the competition manager.

"There will have to be an inquiry," Mr. Worthy huffed. "Where do these volunteers come from?"

By the time the next rider arrived at Fence 10, the cows were safely standing under the shade trees or wading in the pond like a Constable painting.

When questioned, the small messengers on the shaggy Shetlands reported they had not seen cows anywhere on the course.

Penelope Peabody was indignant. "I know I don't live on a farm, but are you questioning my ability to identify a cow?" She had just about enough of being a cross-country judge for one day. Next year she would volunteer for the tea tent.

"We don't question if you can recognize a cow, dear, but if you saw *any cows on the course.*" Mrs. Foxhaull, the head judge, was snooty at the best of times. She was a bastion of the Faraway Hunt Pony Club competing here today.

Mrs. Peabody was almost in tears. By now, both of her stockings had ladders in them and her previously perfectly coiffed hair was windblown. Her shoes were muddy. She started to suggest they page me.

Luckily, Fred Nettle came over to the show grounds to scrounge a few homemade sausage rolls and a piece of cake. He could always charm the tea tent ladies. Fred overhead the word "cows" coming from the OFFICIALS ONLY tent next door.

Fred wandered through the tent flap.

"What's this commotion about? I'm the one who told the girl on the big white horse to go around," Fred said. "The cows took their own sweet time getting to the millpond field this morning."

Sam Nettle's question had a little sting in it. "I thought you agreed to keep them in the field behind the barn?"

"Changed my mind. My, these sausage rolls sure are tasty." Old Fred was unconcerned.

"Go Around Pass granted! Let's all go out and watch the show jumping," Mr. Worthy said while he gently pushed everyone out through the flap to get them to disperse. He knew Colonel Jamieson would be highly displeased if an argument over cows lost the future use of Nettles' Farm.

He looked wistfully at the disheveled jump judge exiting the tent. "That Penelope Peabody is quite a good looker. If only she was tidier in her appearance, I might ask her to do the raffle stall next year."

By executive decision, I had a clear round cross-country. Jump Judge Number 10 had not thought to mark down any times, as she merely thought I was refusing to jump, so my time simply read "within the time allowed."

After the cross-country, I walked Wizard around to cool him down and I ate a cheese sandwich. I noticed Mr. Hobbs had not eaten anything from the picnic lunch we brought with us. I only ate a few bites. I really couldn't eat; I still had my show jumping to do. I gave Wizard the bread and tossed the cheese to old Fred's little dog.

More ponies and kids had arrived when I came back from the cross-country. Silver Spurs Riding School shipped in just for show jumping. The time schedule changed. I tied Wizard to the horsebox. He had a drink of water and munched his hay, unconcerned about the chaos.

I walked around and watched the different arenas. I loved show jumping, but this made me nervous. Wherever I looked, someone was having a knock-down, a refusal, or a run-out, or they were falling off, or going off course. It was complete pandemonium. To make it worse, all the levels and sections had different courses. I had enough trouble remembering my own. I went back to the horsebox and sat beside Wizard.

After an eternity, my group was given a ten-minute warning. I saddled Wizard and trotted smartly up to the holding area. I couldn't find a posted order of go. Two practice jumps were set up in the field. Each time I started Wizard over one, a pony would dart in front of us and knock the poles down.

I heard the paddock steward paging me. I was supposed to report to the steward, then he would add you on the order of go. I was not too late, but now I was last.

Now there was more waiting. I memorized the course every way possible: inside line, outside line; red jump, green jump, wall, oxer; and by drawing the course in the air with my jumping bat: one, turn right, and two, straight ahead.

"Number 27, you are two away."

I snapped out of my memorizing trance and dashed off to jump the bigger of the two warm-up jumps. In spite of my nerves, Wizard jumped the practice fence well. *Do I go after the boy on the chestnut or the girl on the bay?*

I trotted back to the ingate.

"Number 27, you are next," the man said. No one else was there.

"Right, let's do this, Wizard," I said, just loud enough for him to hear. He cocked an ear. The ingate was open. A whistle sounded in the arena. I was sure that whistle signified the call to start my round.

We trotted in and I saluted. I picked up a good canter from a walk, a bit of a show-off, and we sailed over the single jump on the diagonal, an easy upright made of red and white striped poles. More whistles! People started to shout, "Stop! Stop! Stop!"

I didn't know who they were yelling at, but we cleared the green and white jump number two with ease. When we rounded the potted plants, I saw the boy on the chestnut. His horse refused the triple bar and knocked the jump down in the process. *What on earth are they doing here?* The jump was being rebuilt and the boy and horse were milling around.

Completely stunned, I stopped Wizard with a pulley rein.

The main announcer blared out, "Number 27, please leave the arena." I hoped Mr. Hobbs, wherever he was, did not remember my number. I left the arena completely dejected. I patted Wizard on the neck. None of this was his fault. I was eliminated for going onto the course before the other competitor finished.

The paddock steward apologized to me. "I turned my back, and the gate must have blown open. Look, since you are the last rider, I'll have a word with the judge, and after the boy finishes, I'll have him let you do the course *HC*."

"HC? What does that mean?"

"French. *Hors Concours*. You can jump the course without being judged."

"Thank you," I said and I waited for the chestnut to exit the arena. On his way out, the boy gave me a very dirty look. The paddock steward had a quick word with the judge. I was given the nod. I rode the course as if we were in the Olympics. Wizard was brilliant; everything was perfect.

"Wizard, you really are a true champion," I said as I gave him a pat on the neck.

"Well done," said the judge who was at an extended walk on the way to the loo after a long afternoon and one too many cups of tea. "Learn the rules and you'll be fine next time."

"Thank you for letting me ride," I called out after him, wondering if he heard me.

Like an elf, Mr. Hobbs appeared out of nowhere. "Alexa, that was a beautiful round. You could have won the whole thing."

I suppose he thought that would make me feel better.

I thought of a new saying to write in my riding journal. Mrs. Malapropos would be proud of this one. "Don't throw your heart over the jump until the cows go home."

Since I was the only one at the competition, I had to ride to and from the rally in the horse box with Wizard. As we pulled out of the drive at Nettles' Farm, I looked out over the top of the ramp.

Four boys of assorted sizes had a puppy with a bow around his neck in the basket saddle on Sally's shaggy pony. Sally's brother commandeered the pony and stuck Sally in an empty pushchair outside the loo. "Don't worry, Sally, we'll only be gone a few minutes."

"Pony, pony," Sally wistfully cried.

The boys paraded their prize puppy around the grounds, until they found the Peabody's.

A very tattered Jump Judge Number 10 and her slightly totted dapper husband were surrounded by the boys, Sally's pony, and the prize puppy.

The kids excitedly cried out, "Mummy! Mummy! Look what we won in the raffle!"

Chapter 40

Off to the Races

As disastrous as I thought my competition on Wizard had been, Mrs. Highstaff thought otherwise. "You had a very respectable dressage test. It was hardly your fault they let cows wander onto the cross-country course. Mr. Hobbs said your show jumping round was commendable."

"You must remember this one thing. You are not competing against the others. You and your horse are competing against the course. Each time you compete, you will learn what you need to improve."

Although I had no tangible award to show for my efforts, amazingly I still received a "well done."

It was quiet at the Hall with the kids back at school. We were busy riding or working, having and giving lectures or demonstrations, and studying.

It didn't stay quiet for long.

Fortunately, Tuesday afternoon was my half-day off. I saw written in the Ledger: "2 p.m.–4:30 p.m., 12 boys, Richlands Boys Preparatory School, beginners, six ponies, Fiona to teach, Gillian to assist, Jeremy to run the yard." After the boys learned how to groom and observed how to saddle and bridle, the next thing the boys would learn would be how to lead the ponies at a walk and trot and how to turn. The boys would take turns leading each other and riding, so in addition to riding lessons, the boys would be jogging for miles.

Mrs. Highstaff had been courting the custom of Richlands School for a while. The school would pay for the lessons in advance for the whole term, whether all of the boys came or not.

Mr. Quincy Manners, headmaster of Richlands, was excited about adding riding to his school's sports curriculum. "Quite a splendid touch."

After his family attended our Riding Display in March, his daughter Cecily started taking lessons. But when Mr. Manners presented the idea to the boys, they didn't share his enthusiasm.

"We don't want to learn to ride ponies."

"Riding is a sissy sport."

"Too many girls."

Most of the Richlands boys had sisters who rode or were taking lessons.

It was true. A lot of girls and women were involved with horses, especially among amateurs, but many men hunted, and in the highest levels of professional equestrian sport, men dominated the field in racing, show jumping, and polo.

After the spring holiday, Miss Archer, their sports teacher, arrived at Richlands with her arm in a plaster cast and a sling. When the boys found out how she broke her arm, riding became the cool thing. They started daring each other to learn to ride. Now the school had a waiting list for the six-week session.

Mr. Manners told Fiona, "If this pilot program for Physical Training goes well, Richlands will be coming to HDH on a regular basis starting in the fall."

After lunch I watched the television news. Left-wing student riots were going full blast in Paris, shutting down most of France. I knew my dad would never let Mom and me go there now. *Just another example of the revolting French*, I thought. The French, especially Parisians, seemed to be up in arms about something for as long as written history.

When my family visited Paris in 1960, the so-called City of Lights was black from the soot of centuries of coal fires. When I found out the gold horse heads hanging over quaint shop doors were not signs for tack or equestrian apparel shops but were *horse butcher shops*, I disliked the French. *The revolting French ate horsemeat! Barbarians, cannibals! Sacre bleu! Sacrilege!*

As much as I disagreed with the socialist French and their Yankee-go-home attitude, the student riots made me consider the power of students.

Leaving the unrest of Paris and the chaos of Richlands' first day behind me, I was on a new quest on my half-day off. I didn't mention my intention to anyone before I set off. I read about Thoroughbred racing in Leicester in *Horse and Hound*, and I thought watching some live horse racing would top off my horse experiences in England.

Luckily, Mr. Dingby drove the bus into town today. He kindly gave me directions. It was easy. "From the Clock Tower go to the London Road, follow it until you turn right onto Leicester Road. Walking it should take you about an hour. Don't know why you want to go there."

Without answering, I thanked Mr. Dingby. *Dingby doesn't get it. It's obvious, I want to see the racing.* With Mr. Hobbs winning on his flutter on the Grand National, I wondered what the minimum amount for a bet would be. Winning a little extra cash for the trip to Europe would be nice.

After a hamburger at the Wimpy Bar, I set off in great spirits. *I watched the Queen ride side-saddle, I have groomed at horse shows, I have competed in a horse trial, but I have only seen racing on the television.*

What old Dingby failed to mention was the walk to the racecourse was uphill the whole way. *Well, make the best of it. It will be all downhill on the way back.* I chuckled at my joke on myself, "all downhill." I'd only get to see about two hours of racing because I had to walk back to the bus station. I would definitely be riding the bus back to the Hall after this hike.

I was hoping to see some of the colorful characters that Gillian had told me about. Her mother was quite a horse racing fan and sometimes Gillian accompanied her on a bus to the Towcester races.

I briefly wondered why Leicester didn't have a bus out to the races.

Gillian told me about Towcester. "The National Hunt Races are held in the late winter and spring. Sometimes Mom and I sat upstairs on the bus, particularly if it was raining, and we would have a good view of the start of the three-mile course. The Starter would drive down the grass-covered course in a black and yellow trap pulled by a snow-white pony. The jockeys would look like drowned rats in their wool silks. You had to hike past the start of the two-mile course to reach the stands where the colorful button-covered Pearlie people collecting funds for charity and the bookies were, but the

Prince Monolulu was in a class by himself. He was a black man who wore an ostrich plume headdress and a bright waistcoat over flowing robes. The self-proclaimed Prince sold punters a list of potential winners, singing out, "I've got a 'orse, I've got a 'orse for you that can beat the favorite."

I knew Monolulu wouldn't be there. He had died two years earlier, in 1965, by choking on a piece of Black Magic chocolate, which somehow seemed fitting. He claimed to be a Falasha, an Ethiopian Jew. I thought this was highly unlikely. The pious Ethiopian Jews were an ancient society dating back to King Solomon. The Falasha lived on a remote mountaintop and were a quiet, self-contained community known for weaving beautiful cloth and cotton blankets.

Monolulu was from the West Indies and was probably a Rastafarian. Marijuana-smoking, dreadlocked musicians and Rastafarians claimed to honor Haile Selassie as a god and used the Ethiopian flag as a symbol.

An hour later and only three-quarters of the way to the races, I started to flag. I could use a cup of tea when I got to the racetrack for sure. I had learned long ago that cold drinks were unavailable.

It was an unusually warm day. I stopped in the shade under a tree on the edge of a large green lawn. People were sprawled on blankets, chatting or playing games. Nearby me, a young man was lying down on the grass, reading. He had a stack of books with him. He looked a little bit like Gillian's brother, Christopher.

"Sorry to bother you," I tentatively ventured, "but can you please tell me how much farther it is to the racetrack?"

"Yes," he replied in a soft voice. "It's not much farther, about two miles. Why do you want to go there?"

Two more miles, I thought wearily.

"To see some racing?" I replied with some disdain for the non-horsey people of the world.

He sat up. "You won't see any today," he said matter-of-factly. "May I ask if you are American?"

Well, if this guy was going to ask questions, so was I. "Are you a student?"

This was a master-of-the-obvious Sherlock Holmes deduction. The stack of books, his beard, and wire-rim glasses were a dead giveaway. "I'll just go look at the horses if there are no races." I didn't have a clue about racetrack security. "How did you know I was American?"

I was disappointed on all counts.

"Yes, I am a student. Most of the people in the park today are students. That is the University of Leicester." He pointed toward some very modern buildings about a block or so away. "I thought you might be American by the way you are dressed." I was wearing wheat-colored stretchy American jeans. "I couldn't quite place your accent, but you said racetrack, not racecourse. There aren't any horses at the racecourse now. They only come in for short meets, sometimes for only a day or two. My name is Peter."

"Pleased to meet you, Peter. I'm Alexandra." We thought that was funny. We both had Russian-ish names. "Most people call me Alexa." I was named after my Danish great-grandmother, nothing to do with Russians, but I didn't mention it.

If there wasn't any racing, I hoped Peter could tell me where to get some tea. I was not familiar with this area, but I knew students had to eat somewhere cheap. Peter said he was ready for a break. I walked with him a few blocks. He dropped his books off at a small brick house where he rented a room, and we walked back toward the town center. Before we reached the Market Square, we turned onto a narrow cobblestone back street and went through a door and upstairs into a very curious place. I would have never found it by myself.

The room was an attic with skylights, and crammed full of racks of matted old prints, lithographs, and maps. Framed prints with discreet price tags covered the walls and stairwell. Part of the room contained little round tables surrounded by three or four mismatched chairs. One table offered a chessboard set up ready to play.

Tucked in the back corner of the room, a short, polished wooden counter topped with a silver tray offered baklava and tea cakes on ornate plates. An exotic aroma of citrus, lemon, orange, cinnamon, cloves, and sugar wafted from a giant silver samovar surrounded by trays of sparkling glass cups.

It was the type of place where I would expect to find a beatnik reading poetry or see Dr. Zhivago clomping up the stairs in his frozen coat and hat. It could have been a meeting place for spies.

It was early for the traditional tea break, so only a few student types occupied the tables, reading or whispering together. Cautiously, I wandered around and looked at some of the prints. There were a good many horses by various artists.

"*Dobros pozhalovat*, welcome," said a wizen old man when we sat down at a table. He served us tea in the glass cups. There was no menu and only one beverage. We talked about "university," what we wanted to study, and what we would do after graduation. I was getting hungry looking at the delicacies on the counter and I wanted a sweet, but Peter offered to pay for the tea, so I didn't ask for one. I didn't know Peter, and I did not want to feel indebted in any way.

I decided to try this psychological trick I read about in a ladies' magazine. The theory was something like this: When you are talking to someone, look directly into their eyes and try to keep as much eye contact as possible, without staring, and the other person will start to like you.

Every time I spoke to Peter, I would look deeply into his eyes. Every time he talked to me, I would look at the prints on the walls. It seemed to work. Still speaking in his soft voice, he suddenly said, "Alexandra, you have beautiful eyes."

I was a little spooked. I quickly remembered I had something else to do in town before I went back to the Hall, which really was nothing more than eating supper at the Swiss Chalet. We exchanged addresses and arranged to meet next Tuesday afternoon.

Chapter 41
Needmoor

The crew back at HDH was in a right tizzy when I got back that evening. Gillian had to run beside almost every boy until they got the hang of leading the ponies. She was exhausted. Jeremy picked up bushes, girths, lead ropes, and hats, and answered questions nonstop. Fiona could barely talk. She had never shouted so much in one afternoon. The boys wanted to go fast and jump. Finally, Fiona put a rail on the ground and taught the boys jumping or galloping position, by holding on to the neckstrap. Then she allowed them to walk over the pole on the ground. "This is your first jumping and galloping lesson," she told them. Brilliant. The boys loved it; they were coming back. Mrs. Highstaff was delighted.

I did not mention racing, Russians, or Peter, and I went upstairs to watch TV before I went to bed.

The rest of the week went without incident. We were riding at least three times a day. In addition to our regular lessons, we were getting a lunge line lesson without stirrups twice a week. In the exam, you had to be able to ride every school figure and jump with and without stirrups.

The days were getting longer, and more kids were coming for riding lessons after school. As a result, we were finishing later. Julie and Caroline came a few extra times for lessons or to school Mango and Marigold. They were going to a show in Derby on Sunday, with Gillian going along as a groom.

On Saturday afternoon I was going to be the ring steward for Mr. Hobbs, who was judging the prestigious Needmoor School of Equitation Annual Show. Mr. Hobbs told me he would give me more details on the way to the show.

Needmoor was a two-day show and gymkhana starting on Saturday afternoon. The games were so popular they required two judges. Show classes were held on Saturday. Mr. Hobbs would judge: Best Leading Rein Pony, Best Working Pony, Best Riding Horse, and a fun class: Best Mounted Leading Rein Combination, Adult and Child.

Sunday's show schedule required two show jumping judges. Needmoor held the Junior Foxhunter Jumping Competition, the Daily Express National Foxhunter Class, plus Grade B and C Show Jumping, and more gymkhana classes.

Post entries were double the price.

Relishing being away from HDH for the afternoon, Mr. Hobbs and I were in a jolly frame of mind.

On Saturday morning the riding lessons were busy as usual. As soon as I finished teaching my morning class, Mr. Hobbs told me to tidy up and we left before lunch. Mr. Hobbs's tall boots were polished like a mirror. I was in my cleanest attire.

Riding in the sought-after front seat of the Land Rover, I found out I was responsible for the safety of the competitors in the arena. "If you spot anyone in trouble, you are to inform me at once. When I ask you, you will line up the contestants in the proper order, in the proper place, and ensure all entries are in the arena." On the QT, Mr. Hobbs told me, "Keep track of any obvious mistakes a horse might make while I am looking at another entry. It's easy to miss something," he said, although I had never known him to miss a mistake by anyone the entire time I was at Heels Down Hall.

At the show, Mrs. Chuffley, head of hospitality, greeted us and gave us our badges and escorted us to seats in the official's tent. "Just show your badges at the food tent. Refreshments are courtesy of the show committee."

The showing classes were interspersed with the games to make it more interesting for the spectators and to give the judges built-in breaks.

After a quick trip to the loo followed by a cup of tea and a nice but tiny sandwich of something green, Mr. Hobbs was handed the first judge's card. We entered the ring.

The ponies started coming in and they didn't stop. The line of ponies in the holding area went past the secretary's stand. I looked at the sheet with dismay. Best Leading Rein Pony, 12-2 hands and Under, had twenty-nine entries including toddlers to kids a day under eight. Some kids appeared to be expert pony jockeys and others resembled stuffed dolls.

White armbands tied on a rider's jacket sleeve indicated they were competing for a Special Award for the Most Promising Pony of Five Years or Under. The ponies ranged from Thelwell types to exquisite china horse fine, from four years old to ancient. The handlers were fathers, mothers, instructors, or older siblings. If the siblings wore riding attire, they made it clear that this was *their* pony.

Only three places plus one prize for Most Promising Pony were to be awarded. The points from the Leadline MPP would be added to the points of the Working Pony MPP. Often a ride-off was required for determining the winner of the Special Award.

Three prizes—okay, stretch it to four with a different winner for the "Five-and-Under"—out of twenty-nine entries leaves *twenty-five* disgruntled handlers.

The Most Promising Five-and-Under winner was easy to pick, a Welsh pony that had won several national breed shows. The diminutive rider was accomplished, and the handler was a local instructor.

As for the others . . . Mr. Hobbs asked for an announcement to be made. "Because all our entries here today are so good, the judge will make the final decision by asking the riders questions." I doubt whether the questions had much to do with the results, but they were taken seriously. The children gave their answers with thoughtful or confident faces. Some of the answers were correct, and some were reasonable guesses.

"What color is your pony?" asked Mr. Hobbs.

The toddler scrunched up her face and replied, "Purple."

I tried not to laugh aloud.

"Purple is her favorite color," explained the exasperated child leading the piebald pony.

Mr. Hobbs picked three numbers and gave me the card to run to the announcer. "Grab some cakes and come directly back to the official's tent," he said.

Miss Farley, one of the gymkhana judges, presented the awards. There were quite a few sour faces when the winners were announced. The Welsh Most Promising Pony did not place. The pony was as hot as a pistol, and it required an expert pony jock to keep it calm. None of the show committee's children placed.

"Suitability of mount to the rider," Mr. Hobbs confided to me, "not who has the most money. Ask yourself, would you trust this pony with your own child?"

At the Flatlanders horse shows, someone figured out if they gave the Leadline kids a large lollipop *before* the winning numbers were announced, the kids didn't care who won. I suggested the idea to Mrs. Chuffley. "Brilliant idea," she said. "I will ask the local candy maker to sponsor the class. I've been after them for years."

After a rousing Open Trotting Race, we were back on duty with Best Working Pony. All of the Most Promising Five-and-Under ponies that competed in Leadline were entered in the Working Pony, as I had speculated.

I was glad I had been to the shows with Mango and Marigold. This class had twenty-five entries. Flatwork on the rail as a group was followed by individual tests for all twenty-five entries. The top five were chosen to perform the judge's test. The others were dismissed.

The class took forever. Eventually, three places were awarded. Actually, with accurate scoring, the class requirements easily sorted out the winners.

The Most Promising Pony was won by an exquisite Exmoor pony that was too large to be in the Leadline class, and not won by the little Welsh. There was some titter around the grounds about the result.

The ride-off for the Special Award was held immediately after Working Pony. Both ponies were excellent examples of their breed but quite different. When the Welsh pony started to dance around while the other pony finished its test, the Exmoor pony won. "Manners are very important in a child's pony," Mr. Hobbs confided.

The Special Award turned out to be one of those new synthetic headcollars that Mrs. Highstaff did not allow us to use. The presentation headcollar was tiny, sized to perfectly fit the minute Welsh pony. Miss Farley saved the show from an embarrassing moment. "Exchange the headcollar at the tack stand that sponsored the class," she whispered to the little girl with pigtails and a broad smile. It was the first time her beautiful Exmoor had ever beaten the Welsh pony.

The Leading Rein Musical Poles was run in heats. It went on and on, so I took advantage of a few more free sandwiches, looking for chicken or other more substantial fillings. Mr. Hobbs refrained from eating. He said he would ride the top horses in the next class, Best Riding Horse, Mare or Gelding, Hack or Hunter Type. A Special Award for the Most Promising Five-and-Under was offered, which meant there would likely be a number of young horses in the class.

Hacks and Hunters were very different types of horses, and they wore different tack. The Hunter went low, long, and covered a lot of ground. The Hacks were fancy, high-stepping dandies. I was glad I wasn't the judge; I had never ridden a show hack.

The format of Best Riding Horse was exactly the same as Best Riding Pony. This time there were seventeen entries: ten Hunters and seven Hacks, eight of which were entered in Most Promising Horse.

Unlike the children, the adult riders tended to look down their nose a bit when you asked them to move here or stand there, especially if it was lower in the line.

A little to my surprise, some of the Hacks had beautiful individual tests. Mr. Hobbs made the final cut, three of each type. Instead of the riders performing his test, he was going to ride the top six and the other horses were dismissed.

I was to head each horse. After checking the girth, I would either hold down the opposite stirrup or give Mr. Hobbs a leg up. While he was riding, I supervised the lineup and had the next horse ready.

On the horses placed third through sixth, Mr. Hobbs walked, trotted, and cantered one lap on both reins, and did a halt and rein back. After Mr. Hobbs mounted his new horse, I helped the last competitor remount.

Mr. Hobbs was clearly having fun and the horses went well for him.

The horses that placed first and second were magnificent animals. One was a Hunter and the other was a Hack.

Mr. Hobbs performed his Best Working Pony test on the Hunter, and the horse went beautifully. The spectators clapped. The smiling owner-rider thanked Mr. Hobbs.

I gave Mr. Hobbs a leg up on the big Hack and, *whoops*! The stirrup leathers wouldn't go short enough. Mr. Hobbs just crossed the stirrup leathers over the horse's neck and proceeded through the test as if by magic. The maneuvers were so smooth it appeared the test was the horse's own idea. The horse's carriage improved; it became as light as a feather.

I was standing by the rider, also the prospective buyer, when she gasped. "I didn't know Harvey could move so well."

I recognized Harvey's trainer, Archibald Smithwick, Esq., standing outside the arena. Smithwick was probably thinking, "Thanks, Hobbs, the price just went up on that one."

The crowd clapped a bit more enthusiastically than they normally would for a Hack at this show. Even so, the Hack was second to the Hunter. "It needs to go at least almost as well for the rider," Mr. Hobbs explained. The Hack won, without question, the Most Promising Horse award.

Immediately after the class, Mr. Hobbs and I nipped into the bar tent and had a small sherry. Mrs. Chuffley popped in and joined us for a drink. "A fortifier," she explained. She told us "the general consensus is that you are doing a wonderful job. It is so refreshing to get a different perspective. You ride beautifully, Mr. Hobbs, and young lady, you are doing a lovely job."

Personally, I was impressed that the horse show had a bar. I thought it was very civilized. None of the Bible-belt Flatlander shows had bar tents, although I sometimes saw a few cowboys tip out some cola from a bottle and top it up with bourbon.

Mrs. Chuffley downed her sherry and hurried off to ensure the awards were ready for the hilarious Obstacle Race, already in the arena.

Mr. Hobbs promised me that we would have a rather substantial nosh before we left the show.

"I hope evening stables are finished when we get back," I said hopefully.

Mr. Hobbs wistfully agreed. "That would be nice."

Class Seven was "The Best Mounted Leading Rein Combination, Adult and Child." This class, which we thought would be a lark when we read the prize list, was hotly contested. Even at double the entry fee, there were several post entries. Riders came from miles around just to enter this class.

First place would be awarded the Needmoor Perpetual Challenge Shield, an enormous real shield, a genuine antiquity. Winners' names were engraved on it, starting from 1920, when it was donated by Lord Wilberforce Flyghtee, a local WWI hero.

After the Great War, the local horse show was reorganizing and there was a shortage of prizes. When the horse show committee knocked on his door, Lord Flyghtee was embarrassed to be a little short on cash, but, displaying the quick thinking that made him a hero, he detached a shield from a suit of armor in the hall of Needmoor Castle and donated it with the proviso that it would be a perpetual trophy. Flyghtee realized he would not have to donate again. He could present the shield at the show every year.

Chapter 42

View Holloa

This year, the current Lady Flyghtee was presenting the family's Shield. Mr. Connor Robbins, a local banker, the second gymkhana judge, was presenting the silver silent butler. The Vicar was awarding a china horse statue. Photographers and reporters from the parish magazine and local and county newspapers were on hand to record the presentations. Lady Flyghtee was an attractive older widow and always made the society pages.

There were thirty-seven pairs entered. Mr. Hobbs suggested to the show manager that the class should be split into two. "There are enough entries to cover the prize money," he reasoned.

The show manager insisted, "It is out of the question and simply impossible because of the trophy. There are less than the required forty entries to split. The arena is enormous and can hold all the entries."

The class remained huge, and to top it off there was no judging criteria written on the judge's card.

After a brief conference, Mr. Hobbs decided how to handle it. "Alexa, have them enter the arena in single file, at a walk, and proceed around the perimeter. Give everyone time to enter. After the leader circles back to the ingate, have them go across the diagonal in single file and change the rein. On the diagonal line they will individually trot a short distance and walk before they get back to the rail." This routine enabled Mr. Hobbs to clearly judge both sides of the pairs and keep control of the class.

The Mounted Leading Rein class would have been a beautiful sight on Rotten Row in Hyde Park on a Sunday afternoon in a bygone era. Elegant foxhunting parents led Pony Club children riding plaited ponies. There were fathers with daughters and fathers with sons. There were mothers with sons and mothers with daughters. There were a few grandparents with grandchildren. Fizzy hacks led tizzy ponies.

Thirty-five in, thirty-six, and then, the thirty-seventh entry, a voluptuous blonde in the style of Jane Mansfield, tallish, wasp-waisted, and long-legged. She was wearing a pink form-fitting sweater, over a white shirt with a big ascot tie, sand-colored tight jodhpurs, without the usual flare, and a bright lipstick smile on her face. Her waist-long, wavy blonde hair was blowing in the breeze from under her bowler hat. As she entered the arena, there were distinct sounds of gasping, throat clearing, and coughing.

Major Everett just arrived and was standing in the bar tent. He was waiting for Marion and his horse van to get to the show for overnight stabling. His sons were competing in the Junior Foxhunter competition tomorrow.

He whistled into his large whiskey. "View Holloa."

Ms. Melody Mellyn, star of stage and screen, albeit mostly in fairly risqué productions, was riding a snow-white Connemara pony, led by her teenage son, the spitting image of Sir Galahad, mounted on a fiery black pony-sized Thoroughbred. They were the last ones in the arena and, therefore, the last ones to trot.

When they trotted across the diagonal, the lady's enormous bosom heaved and bounced in rhythm to the trot.

Mr. Hobbs was already marking his judge's card. "Have them halt where they are on the rail. Leave all the entries in the arena. Tell the announcer to give out the awards in reverse order to create some suspense. I'll have the presenters come stand in the middle to save the show some time."

I arranged the class around the perimeter of the arena, and Mr. Hobbs gave me the card to run to the announcer. Mr. Hobbs had decided to have the announcer read his overall comment for each winning duo.

As I handed the card to the announcer, I saw Mr. Hobbs, backing quietly but steadily toward the out gate.

The fourth place was given to the grandmother, who looked a bit like Queen Victoria in her later years, mounted on an ancient bomb-proof polo pony, towing a shaggy Shetland with little Sally in the basket saddle. "Safest

Combination," the announcer proclaimed. Sally waved her rosette and the crowd sighed, "*Awww.*"

Third place was awarded to a father and son on a beautiful pair of bright bays. They were matched in every way except size. The man and the boy wore identical outfits. All the tack matched. The horse and pony worked well together. It was obvious they had planned and practiced. They accepted their prize money and rosettes graciously to a round of polite applause and stopped for a photo for the local paper. "Most Polished," read the announcer.

Mr. Hobbs was halfway to the gate.

The second place went to the MHF of the Faraway Hunt and his lovely daughter riding side-saddle. They won the Shield last year and they hoped for a repeat victory. "Most Traditional." There was some applause of a tentative nature.

Mr. Hobbs had his hand on the out gate.

Who would be First? The mayor's chubby wife mounted on a fat cob and his tubby son on an even fatter pony, or the charming Mrs. Honeycutt, who owned the grounds where the show was held, and her weedy daughter, Ivy. Unbeknownst to us, the coveted award was often based on local politics, not necessarily on merit.

Mr. Hobbs motioned for me to go to the Officials Tent.

The announcer took a sip of water. "The moment we have all been waiting for . . . . The Needmoor Challenge Shield and First place this year will be awarded to—" There was quite a bit of fidgeting among the thirty-four remaining entries.

"—Melody Mellyn and her son Lance, who were judged to be 'Most Pleasing.' The Village of Needmoor welcomes the Mellyns to our small community. They have just moved here from London."

Photographers charged into the arena and there was an explosion of flashbulbs. Horses spooked. There were a lot of huffy "well, that's who it is," and "well, I never," and quite a few "imagine that," and several "I really can't believe it" grumbles from the non-winners leaving the arena in a disorganized mass exodus. Spectators crowded into the arena, trying to get a closer look at the celebrity.

Outside the arena, wives checked to see where their husbands were, and mothers searched for their teenage daughters. Mr. Hobbs caught up with me. He had already stuffed his JUDGE badge into his jacket pocket. Major Everett popped out, grabbed us both, and tucked us into the bar tent. "Have a quick one, Hobbs. You earned it." The Major handed me a drink. He was very generous when he didn't have to pay. "You better get that down and get out of here. I'll have the manager post you the judge's fee. Lady Godiva rides again, eh, Hobbs?" The Major laughed.

We caught sight of Mrs. Chuffley heading toward the bar tent at a good pace. From the expression on her face, we didn't think it was to compliment us.

"Here comes the hospitality," warned the Major while he lifted the back of the flap of the tent and pushed us through.

Although we never got the hearty nosh we were planning on, we laughed and laughed on the way back. Mr. Hobbs gave me a ten-shilling note. "You earned it," he said.

We arrived back at the Hall in good spirits, a little after eight o'clock.

Chapter 43

A Place for Everything

Fiona, Jeremy, and Gillian were just coming out of the tack room when Mr. Hobbs and I walked around the corner from the car park. *Perfect! They're finished and we're not too late for supper.* The tiny sandwiches I ate at the horseshow wore off long ago.

Gillian reported that the horsebox was packed for the morning. Everything seemed in good order. Caroline and Julie stayed all day and groomed the ponies to the *nth* degree. Mango and Marigold were plaited and bandaged, ready to go. Mrs. Highstaff suggested the girls stay at the Hall, but the mothers insisted the kids go home and have a bath. They planned to leave at sunrise. It was going to be an early Sunday morning for all of us.

With their tails waving and tongues lolling, the two black Labs came bounding up the walkway to greet us. Mrs. Highstaff intercepted us at the hallway door.

She addressed Mr. Hobbs pleasantly. "How was the Needmoor Show, Mr. Hobbs?"

He touched his hat. "A good day out, ma'am. Very interesting indeed."

"Good. You can tell me more about it later."

I looked at Mr. Hobbs. He looked very tired, and I could be certain he was hungry. I was starving.

Mrs. Highstaff turned to the rest of us. "I have just come back from my evening rounds," she began conversationally.

We knew this already because she always did an evening check, often more than once.

She continued with more emphasis on each word than usual. "We, here at Heels Down Hall, believe that there is a place for everything, and everything should be in its place." We had heard this platitude many times before but never with such dramatic delivery. There was complete silence. "One hoof pick is unaccounted for. Does anyone have it?"

We looked at each other. I thought I might be exempt from whatever was coming next because I had not even been here this afternoon, but *au contraire*. I had studied French in school. French was a useful language in East Africa, the French Foreign Legion, and all that. The hoof pick could have been lost at any point during the day.

"The hoof pick must be found. To make it easier for you, it is one with a red handle."

The handles were painted red, blue, or green. We hoped that "must be found" might mean tomorrow. I was even thinking I might offer to buy Mrs. Highstaff a replacement. I was feeling rather flush with my ten shillings. A hoof pick only cost a couple of bob.

She continued, "We will all go back up to the stables *right now* and conduct a systematic search until the hoof pick is found. Mr. Hobbs will search the tack room and horsebox. If it is not found on any ledges, or in the courtyard, or passageways, we will start removing all the bedding stall by stall, straw by straw until the hoof pick is found."

She was absolutely serious. I could not fathom why all this fuss was being made over one hoof pick, but I soon found out the reason. Mrs. Highstaff continued with real feeling in her voice, "I will not allow one of my beautiful animals to be accidentally lamed by stepping on a sharp object that someone was too lazy to pick up. Just think, all this trouble was caused by a careless groom who dropped a hoof pick."

Wow! The possibility of a lame horse never occurred to me. We went back to the stable, hopeful the hoof pick would appear quickly.

It did not.

It was already dark. We split into two teams to search fourteen box stalls. All the straw was removed from each stall and laid on the muck sacks in the yard. The empty stall was examined under bright torchlight by

Mrs. Highstaff. When no hoof pick was found, the straw was replaced, and we went on to the next stall. I had a horrible thought that if we didn't find the hoof pick, we would have to dissect the muck heap. I couldn't even tell Gillian about the hilarious horse show. This search was no laughing matter.

We were clearing the straw out of the third set of stalls when lights appeared under the carriage house arch. A car's headlamps stared into the gloomy scene. Without turning off the engine, Julie's mother, Mrs. Wainwright, jumped out of her car and dashed into the courtyard holding the missing hoof pick up in the air. "It's here! I have it! I have it!" she cried. Mrs. Wainwright was visibly shaking. She almost couldn't believe what she was seeing, but there we were, just as her ten-year-old daughter had predicted, out in the dark, looking for a four-inch hoof pick.

"What's here? What is all the commotion?" Mrs. Highstaff was in Topaz's stall in the carriage house. "Julie took the hoof pick home by mistake. I found it in the back pocket of her jeans when I was putting her clothes in the washing machine. Julie insisted we telephone at once. We tried telephoning several times but there was no answer. In fact, my husband is probably still trying to ring through now. It was so late. Julie said you would be looking for it, so I thought I better bring it back."

"Thank you so much for driving here from Storkey tonight. You best get back home. I'll inform Mr. Wainwright you are on your way. Do drive carefully. We will see Julie in the morning." Mrs. Highstaff was genuinely thankful.

She walked Mrs. Wainwright back to her car. Mrs. Wainwright carefully backed the car out from under the archway, turned around in the car park, and left.

Mrs. Highstaff spoke to us unapologetically. "Please finish putting the beds back together and sweep the courtyard, and you may go in. We have an early start tomorrow." After a slight pause, she said, "Now you see the importance of everything in its place."

As she headed down the brick path back to the Hall, in the complete quiet of the country night, I thought I could hear the telephone faintly ringing.

Without talking, we mechanically put everything back in order and swept up. We skipped supper. Beans on toast had lost its appeal by now and we went straight up to bed.

In spite of the lost hoof pick incident, Julie and Caroline brought home some rosettes. Mango racked up another win in Most Promising Pony under Five in the Large Pony division. Julie placed above Caroline in Best Rider. Although it was not the stunning victory we were hoping for, we were back on track.

April was in an unusually good mood on Monday. She giggled to herself all morning, but we didn't find out why until lunchtime. The Sunday edition of the *Leicester Times*, folded open to the Entertainment Page, was laying on Mr. Hobbs's dinner plate.

A photo dominated the page. Melody Mellyn, in glorious full profile, was kissing the Needmoor Perpetual Challenge Shield held by Mr. Connor Robbins, kneeling on one knee.

Before the photo was taken, Robbins had seized the Shield from Lady Flyghtee, brushed her off, and handed her the silent butler to present to Lance. In the background, the disgruntled Vicar was holding both ponies.

The caption under the photo read, "Another challenging conquest for film star Melody Mellyn. Ms. Mellyn was the big winner yesterday at the Needmoor School of Equitation Annual Show held at the picturesque Village of Needmoor."

"I don't suppose Needmoor will invite me back to judge again next year," sighed Mr. Hobbs. Secretly he was relieved. There had to be an easier way to make a bit of extra money than judging local horse shows.

I was looking forward to meeting the mysterious, soft-spoken Peter on Tuesday afternoon. By now, I had visited all the major attractions in Leicester. With the exam coming up, I might need to go to the tack shop for new gloves or something, but I was pretty much finished shopping. I needed to save my money for food and bus fares. With the nicer weather and the daylight in the evening, the cinema had lost its allure.

I arranged to meet Peter at three o'clock. That gave me time to get to the bus to Leicester and walk about a mile to Peter's lodging house. He was going to give me a tour of the University and take me to tea in a neighborhood of Leicester that I never had explored.

When I arrived at the brick house in the unremarkable residential neighborhood, I rang the bell. I thought Peter would greet me, but an older lady wearing an apron over her dress answered the door. She pointed to a small Rooms to Let sign and then to a No Vacancy sign under it. "I'm afraid we don't have any rooms to let now, dearie. Everything is taken until the end of the term."

"I'm not looking for a room to rent. I am supposed to meet Peter."

The previously composed lady's head snapped back a little and she got a little flustered. "Here to meet Peter? What is your name? I'll see if he is in. I'll have to go upstairs and knock. Please wait here." She made a little frown and shut the door.

I stood on the doorstep, not invited into the house. I waited and I waited. I hated waiting. Finally, Peter appeared at the door, not happy to see me at all. "Oh, Alexa, I didn't expect to see you today!"

He came out and closed the door. He took my arm and was walking me out to the garden gate, back toward the pavement.

What! Not expecting me! It was his idea for us to meet. He arranged it. My tone was indignant and incredulous. "You told me to meet you here at three o'clock. You gave me the address."

"I am *so* sorry. Something has come up. I wrote telling you we had to postpone until next week."

"I never received a letter." You can believe me, there was no letter this morning. I checked the post counter twice a day.

"I am so sorry, but I must cancel. You must leave here now. I can't see you today."

I had never before been told I must leave somewhere. I was steamed. I looked back at the cozy brick house. On the first floor, I noticed the bottom corner of a window curtain being lifted. A pretty blonde girl's head peeked out. When the girl realized I was looking directly at her, she dropped the curtain.

Now I understand why Peter isn't able to see me today.

I stomped back toward the town center in a terrible huff. I hoped his girlfriend grilled him like the Gestapo.

I heard his voice trailing off as I marched away, "I will write and explain everything."

Write? Right! You could have written in the first place and told me not to come and embarrass myself and waste my half-day off.

I managed to find the Russian tea shop. There were students engaged with their friends at some tables, but they were not in the least interested in a stranger. I had a cup of tea and splurged on a piece of baklava and browsed through a bin of matted prints near my table. Much to my amazement, I found a reproduction of the *Doomsday Book* map of the area. A castle, probably more of a watchtower, once stood where the Hall was standing now. I loved the old map, but it was quite expensive, so I had to leave it at the shop.

The tea was reasonably priced, but the baklava was more than I planned on spending, and I still wanted an omelet at the Swiss Chalet.

I was very pissed off at Peter. It was still early in the afternoon, so I decided I would hitchhike to the Hall to amuse myself and save some money. This time I would ride the bus to the Black Horse, cross over the roundabout, and start hitching from there.

At the Swiss Chalet, I was devouring my mushroom and sprouts omelet, the cheapest combination on the menu, and I started thinking about Mom coming next week. I was not going to be able to meet her at the airport, or even at the London City Terminal. I wasn't happy about that, but we were too short-handed.

Probably because I was thinking about America, I started laying down my knife between bites and eating with my fork in my right hand.

A few tables away from me, an attractive couple, dressed in business suits, were enjoying coffee and biscuits. The lady had a notebook and was jotting down notes. I couldn't help overhearing them because there weren't many people in the place. "We've done the Aqua Center, the Tennis Club, the Golf Club, and this afternoon we're going to the Cricket Club."

My, these people are really quite the sports enthusiasts, but they don't look particularly athletic.

The lady offered a suggestion. "Rugby?"

Rugby? I couldn't picture these polished people playing rugby. I almost laughed.

"Possibly," the man countered, "but I was thinking of something with more of a universal appeal."

He turned slightly toward me. "Excuse me, young lady," the man said in a pleasant voice with perfect diction. He had been slyly watching me eat my omelet. "You don't seem to be from around here. Are you alone?"

Of course, he knows I'm alone; I'm sitting by myself. He guessed I was American by the way I ate. I was wearing a leather miniskirt, shirt, and sweater I'd borrowed from Gillian. I looked English and I wasn't talking. I remembered a war movie that I had seen where an American, who spoke fluent German with a perfect accent, got caught when he sat down to eat.

Crickey, am I ever going to get this right? I really wanted to be able to pass as English. "I'm in town on an errand. I live in Leicestershire." I never liked to give out too much personal information.

"Oh dear, excuse my manners," the man said. He smiled reassuringly when he saw my apprehension. "I am Basil Cameron, and this is my associate, Miss Sophie Laurels. We are with BBC Radio Leicester."

These people look safe enough to talk to in a café. "That *is* amazing," I said without introducing myself. "I know Timothy Dashet and Sareena, who work for the BBC in London."

The two people looked as stunned as if I had smacked them with a mackerel. The names I gave them were big-shot news commentators at the holy grail of radio broadcasting, BBC International.

"How do you know them?" the lady queried.

I explained briefly about my father's work in East Africa.

The man glanced at his watch. "We're covering a cricket match in Storkey in an hour. We have to get there early to set up our equipment."

I couldn't believe my ears—Storkey was only three miles from Heels Down Hall. I decided to be slightly more forthcoming. "My name is Alexandra. I'm an American student at Heels Down Hall in Brickton. I'm taking the bus back there shortly." That was as big of a hint as I could give without directly asking for a ride.

"Heels Down Hall? That sounds intriguing." Ms. Laurels continued, "I have an excellent idea. I think there is enough room in the car. Why don't you ride with us to Storkey? We have to get going now, but I would love to find out more. We can talk on the way."

They stacked the sound equipment, and I squeezed into the back seat of the newish Hillman Hunter. Instead of hitchhiking, I had landed a ride with the radio announcers who were producing a series of programs on sports called "Let's Get Leicester Moving." The conversation I overheard earlier in the Swiss Chalet was a list of program topics.

I gave them the same "Benefits of Horseback Riding as Physical Exercise" speech that I gave to Ms. Archer when she broke her arm. Ms. Laurels was taking notes. She jotted down the school's address and Mrs. Highstaff's phone number. I told them about our Riding Display in March and how we were studying for our BHS exams. Before we knew it, we were at Storkey.

Strawberries and champagne were not forthcoming at the cricket match, so I decided to head back to the Hall. Strawberries and champagne were about as much interest as I had in cricket. I thought it was an inferior game to baseball because I had actually played on a baseball team.

I missed the bus connection at Storkey, so I started to walk back to Brickton. It was only three miles; I could be there within the hour. I had just reached the outskirts of the village when a car pulled up behind me. *Not more curb crawlers*, I thought with dismay.

This was turning out to be a crazy day.

Chapter 44
Newmarket

"Hello there! Alexa!" a deep male voice called out.

Good grief, they know me. I hope it isn't one of our students' parents!

A battered Mini pulled up on the verge behind me. The driver was Tommy, April's boyfriend. "I'm just off to the Hall to see April." Cheerily he asked, "Need a lift?"

On the way to the Hall, Tommy gave me a short but very stern ticking off. "You should not be wandering around on the roads in the countryside by yourself."

Another perfect example of how to be annoying while being helpful, I thought, but I was pleased to get the ride and grateful it was Tommy who had stopped.

When I got back to the Hall, I found a small brown envelope waiting for me on the counter. "That came this afternoon." Fiona rushed past me, up the stairs, to grab my favorite chair, the captain's chair at the table by the window.

The return address was from Mr. P. Nutshall. *Nutshall? More like a P Nutshell.* By now, I thought Peter was another empty-headed student.

He wrote on a ragged piece of lined notebook paper a note scrawled in pencil:

> *Dear Alexa,*
>
> *I cannot meet you as planned on Tuesday.*
> *Are you available the following week?*
> *I would really like to see you again.*
>
> *Sincerely,*
>
> *Your new friend,*
> *Peter*

Well, he sent a note after all, but I don't call that scribble a letter.

It was postmarked yesterday morning, but the twit put a second-class stamp on it. For another few pennies, with a first class stamp, the letter would have arrived in this morning's mail and would have saved me all the trouble.

Mrs. Highstaff came into breakfast on Wednesday morning, smiling. "Because of the money we raised for the Animal Health Trust, we have been invited to have a tour of the new equine operating theater and veterinary research center in Newmarket tomorrow. Jeremy, I hope you don't mind switching your half-day to Friday afternoon."

Jeremy readily agreed. His half-day off always consisted of visiting Falstaff.

Newmarket was quite exciting news. The ancient town of Newmarket was the largest center of Thoroughbred horse racing in England. The town had a royal heritage. The kings James I, Charles I, and Charles II all built palaces there.

"We will start the morning stables half an hour earlier tomorrow and leave after breakfast."

Newmarket in Suffolk was over one hundred miles and more than two hours away by car. I wondered who would drive.

Today was Gillian's half-day off. Gillian, who had an A level in Art, thought she would try to find the tea room and print shop this afternoon. I drew a little map for her. I didn't know all the names of the streets. "I hope you can find the curious place."

On Thursday Mr. Hobbs stayed behind to run the yard and to school a few of the horses. Mrs. Highstaff had rescheduled the outside lessons.

The trip to Newmarket was a real safari. Mr. Highstaff drove the Land Rover. He had a keen interest in all branches of science, and he truly loved animals. He was an integral part of the display. After all, he set up and operated the sound system. Mrs. Highstaff sat in the passenger seat armed with a large road atlas. We occupied the four fold-down, hard bench seats in the back. A picnic hamper took up most of the floor space between us.

Mr. Highstaff, like Mr. Benson, preferred driving on the rural routes. This suited me perfectly. I loved the English countryside. I was obsessed with the brightly painted pub signs and their romantic or historically significant names and emblems. The masses of illiterates in "ye olde Merrie Englande" could easily recognize the landmarks. I started wondering if I could go with Mom to Portobello Road and buy an antique sign to ship home, or if Mom would be willing to paint a pub sign on the wall of my room in Greenleaf? *Hmm, which one of the thousands of designs do I like the best? Definitely something with "Free House" in the name.*

Mrs. Highstaff explained where we were going. Along the way, she would point out things of interest. The ride to Newmarket was pretty quiet. We kept our thoughts to ourselves. One never really knew quite what to say to Mr. Highstaff, and Mrs. Highstaff might not find our conversations amusing.

We arrived in Newmarket midmorning. On the way to town, Mrs. Highstaff surprised us again. "We are stopping at Lord Derby's Woodland Stud to see a life-size bronze statue of the famous horse, Hyperion. The statue was created by John Skeaping, a renowned contemporary sculptor and equine painter. Hyperion was an example of 'good things come in small packages.' He only stood at 15-1 hands, but he was one of Britain's most famous racehorses." Hyperion, we found out, was one of the most successful British-based stallions of the twentieth century.

We admired the statue on the beautiful estate, and then after driving past some training grounds, we went to the National Stud. We had a tour and admired the stallions, mares, and foals. Our guide told us a brief history. "The National Stud was founded in 1915 because of a shortage of Thoroughbred stallions needed to breed cavalry mounts. Colonel Hall Walker donated a generous gift of land in Ireland and his personal string of Thoroughbred horses to start the operation. The location of the stud farm moved several times, and HM The Queen just opened this facility in Newmarket last April."

We visited the National Stud for about an hour and went off to have our picnic lunch. We could look out and see the famous gallops where the racehorses would work out in sets in the morning. We were too late in the day to watch them, but after the visit to the stud farm, I could imagine the beautiful horses thundering past us.

I missed galloping across the unfenced plains like I used to do in East Africa.

The Animal Health Trust headquarters were on the other side of Newmarket. On the way through the town, we drove past Tattersalls where the Thoroughbred auctions are held in the fall and winter.

At one o'clock we arrived at the gate of the Animal Health Trust compound. Mr. Chugwig, who spoke at our Display, greeted us like foreign dignitaries. He told us "the purpose of the Animal Health Trust is to fight disease and injury in animals. It has been helping dogs, cats, and horses in the UK, and around the world, to lead healthier lives since 1942." We had a tour and met veterinarians, researchers, vet techs, and some of the animal patients.

Of particular pride was the new equine operating theater and special operating table, the first of its kind in the world. One of the veterinarians explained the system. "The horse is led up to the well-padded upright tabletop. Next, the sedated horse is attached quite securely to the operating table and then anaesthetized. The tabletop with the attached horse can be rotated ninety degrees to be parallel to the floor and positioned at any desired height. After the operation, the tabletop is lowered level with the floor and the animal is released before it wakes up."

It was amazing, a real masterpiece of medical equipment.

He concluded by saying, "I am convinced we will be able to operate more successfully with this new operating table." Mr. Chugwig nodded in agreement.

Our minds were boggled by the advances in equine veterinary medicine, but Mrs. Highstaff sternly reminded us, "On your Minor Ailments exam questions, you are not to offer any veterinary solutions for major injury or illness. Only list the symptoms for the ailment and write the correct first aid treatment until the summoned veterinarian arrives. You are Horsemasters, not junior veterinarians."

"We still have a little time left before we need to start back," Mrs. Highstaff joyfully announced. "I think we would all enjoy a visit to the Racing Museum." Another few minutes in the Land Rover and we were in the center of the town.

Along the Newmarket High Street, we passed by the Jockey Club and came to the wrought-iron, black and gold archways, which led to the courtyard of the Racing Museum. "Don't try to look at everything in detail," Mrs. Highstaff said for our benefit but particularly for her husband. Mr. Highstaff stopped at the very first exhibit and was reading every word of explanation. "You will get a better overall impression if you go through the whole place and only look at a few things in detail."

She was right; the place was impressive. Gillian and I liked the sporting paintings. Jeremy favored the more technical exhibits. Fiona followed Mrs. Highstaff around, absorbing every word like a sponge.

At the top of the High Street was a large village green where horses could work out or gallop. A permanent blacksmith shop stood on the corner of the green near the road. When we were leaving the horsey mecca of Newmarket, an equine customer was getting shod.

The blacksmith shop reminded Mrs. Highstaff of the upcoming events at Heels Down Hall. She thought aloud, "I must call Rodney when we get back. While we are checking all the horses' feet, we might as well check their teeth."

Mrs. Highstaff checked all the horses' teeth regularly. If a horse chewed its food in an irregular manner, or suddenly started tossing its head, or playing with its bit, the horse's teeth would be checked. We had many young horses that were constantly teething and several old horses that sometimes needed help with chewing.

After a careful examination of their mouth, Mrs. Highstaff could grab the horse's tongue with one hand and rasp off the offending sharp point with the other. She had the most calming effect on horses I had ever seen. The horses would stand there quietly, grateful their mouth no longer hurt. If the problem was more than a rasp could fix, Mrs. Highstaff would call Rodney or Dr. Amsley.

Mrs. Highstaff shifted gears mentally. "Let's not spoil our lovely day out by thinking of all that just now. Let's sing some songs to pass the time." We thought it was corny, but soon we were all joining in with gusto, even Mr. Highstaff.

We sang long songs like "Waltzing Matilda" and "Ninety-Nine Bottles of Drench on the Wall." We then played I Spy with My Little Eye and the Alphabet Game. Mr. Highstaff told us, "Your task is to find objects outside the car whose name starts with each letter of the alphabet in turn." I hoped Z, a zebra crossing sign, would be on my side of the car so I could win. I saw a sign, LARGE PLANT CROSSING. I laughed, "Giant rutabagas?"

When we got back to the Hall, we thanked Mr. Highstaff for driving and Mrs. Highstaff for arranging such a great day, and we went up to change back into our work clothes. A day out or not, we had to do the bedding down, feed and water, and sweep the yard. I was in a good mood. *I might offer to clean Mr. Hobbs's tack for him as a thank you for taking me as ring steward to the horse show.*

At the top of the stairs, as I rounded the turn to go through the lounge and into our bedroom, I thought I saw Dawdle disappearing down the hallway toward the Highstaffs' quarters carrying something white. *I wonder what that dog has now.* The door to our room was cracked open. I was sure we had shut it before we left for Newmarket.

"*Aggkk!*" Our tiny room was covered in bits of white fluff. The window was open and white particles whirled around the room. It wasn't snow this time; it was bits of fur. The arms were torn off my fashionable Afghan coat; one arm was missing. The rest of the coat was chewed, mangled, and ripped into the jigsaw pieces of hide that had once been sewn together. Artemis and Apollo were curled up in cozy piles of fluff. The cats apparently had won the battle over the shaggy Afghan field, and the puppy sloped off with his spoils of war.

There was no time to clear this mess up now. I kicked the cats out, shook my work clothes out the window, and would deal with everything after supper.

Chapter 45
Nuts in May

Later Gillian laughed when she saw me trying to sweep up bits of flying fur. "Never throw out clout, till May is out."

"What on earth does that mean?" I was bewildered by English sayings.

Gillian explained the meaning. I laughed again, "May is out enough for me. The remains of this coat are going in the boiler tomorrow."

The animals inadvertently did me a favor. Fashionable or not, and even if the coat was in perfect condition, Mom would not want to travel around Europe with me wearing this shaggy, smelly heap or want me to pack it in my trunk.

Mr. Hobbs was in a jolly mood. His flutter on the Epsom Derby paid off handsomely. Lester Piggott and Sir Ivor, an American-bred horse, came through for him.

Liza and Julian were taking their ponies, Frosty and Caesar, to a low-key gymkhana on Sunday. I thought gymkhanas were great. They taught the kids to be fearless, athletic riders and to control their ponies. The thing I loved best about the gymkhanas was that the kids and the ponies had fun.

I noticed a lot more boys riding at the gymkhanas than in the shows in Greenleaf. Back home, the English riders seemed to think it was foolish to play games. It was beneath their southern-fried dignity, or something, for young girls and ladies to be jumping on and off horses like wild Indians. Only the cowboys played games on horseback.

Mr. Hobbs told us, "*Gymkhana* is from India and simply means games on horseback. Cavalry troops throughout the ages used gymkhana games as part of their training."

I liked the Jumper classes. You knew exactly why you got a prize or not. Children's riding instructors in the States seemed more interested in producing cardboard cutout equitation riders than letting little kids fly around jumper courses. The speed element appealed to the boys.

There were many real, thriving Pony Clubs in the USA, but they hadn't reached Flatlanders.

This was the first time either of the young people had competed at an away show. With two novice competitors, Mrs. Highstaff thought Mr. Hobbs might need extra help, so both Gillian and I were going along as grooms. When we went to the shows as grooms, we always wore our riding attire, jodhpurs and boots, green shirt, tie, and hacking jacket. We had our helmets in case we had to ride the ponies for any reason.

The show was going full tilt when we arrived. Games in one arena and classes of show jumping of every height in a larger area. The place was teaming with Pony Clubbers, pint-sized kids zooming around, jumping on and off ponies like trampolines.

The show jumping was not as frantic but was teeming with entries.

Liza was a beautiful rider, but not very brave, which is why she and Frosty got along so well. Frosty was pretty placid and generally lacked impulsion.

They entered in the lowest jumping height for which they were eligible. Liza was confident: "I know the course." They set off with great gusto. As the pony approached each fence, she got slower and slower. Jump one was at a reasonable canter, jump two was at a lackluster trot, and then Frosty started to walk. Mr. Hobbs grimaced. Liza glanced over to the side of the arena. Mr. Hobbs made a sign, a downward flick of his wrist, meaning "give her a whack with the stick." Liza gave the lazy Frosty a good whack. The pony jumped the little upright fence from practically a standstill. On the landing side of the jump, Frosty stopped. Liza tumbled off. Frosty licked the top of her hard hat.

"Disqualified," said the ring steward.

Uninjured except for pride, Liza waffled, "I don't think I am cut out for show jumping."

"Your pony can easily jump this height, even at a walk." Mr. Hobbs smiled a little at the last part. "There is another jumping class you could enter if you want to try again. You just have to light a fire under Frosty's tail," he said figuratively.

"Oh dear! That sounds rather drastic." Liza looked at the games arena enviously. "Maybe I will try some games."

When we played games in the lessons, Liza loved it. I accompanied Liza to the secretary stand. There weren't a lot of choices, since we wanted to leave the show early in the early afternoon. Musical Sacks, Pole Bending, and Balloon Sticking were later in the day. "I guess I have to enter the Boot Race and the Bun Eating Contest."

For the Boot Race, all the competitors were told, "Take off your boots." This was easy because all the kids wore Jodhpur boots. The ring steward collected the boots and threw them into a pile at the far end of the arena. He mixed them up, so they were not in pairs.

The idea was easy. Ride down to the far end of the arena, find your boots, put them on, remount, and ride back.

With the other ponies running, Frosty got into the spirit of the race and was one of the first ones to the boot pile. They were third across the finish line. The trouble was Liza returned wearing one brown boot and one black one. When she tried to snatch her own boot out of the pile, a bigger boy pushed her out of the way.

"Disqualified," ruled the judge.

It took a few minutes to find the other child with one black and one brown boot, but we got it sorted out.

Julian had been uncharacteristically quiet ever since we set off this morning. I wondered if it was because he had a crush on Liza or if he was nervous about competing. Julian loved jumping. Caesar personified the point-and-go type. Like a kangaroo, the pony could jump anything.

In Julian's first jumping class, Caesar jumped well, but they went off course, which was another disqualification. "I don't know what happened," Julian said, "but I just can't concentrate." He put his hand on his stomach. "I don't feel so well."

I sympathized. Back in Greenleaf, I used to get sick before my shows because I put so much pressure on myself to win. As working students at

HDH, horse shows and competitions just meant extra work for us. There wasn't any time to have the luxury of feeling sick.

There was a break before his next class.

Julian definitely looked a little green. "Sit in the shade and sip some water," I suggested. I went with Liza, and left Gillian, who loved Caesar, to stay with the ailing Julian.

The Bun Eating Contest was next. A long clothesline stretched across the bottom of the arena. Large, undoubtedly stale buns were tied by pieces of string to the clothesline at intervals. The plan was to run down, eat the bun without using your hands, and return to the start/finish line. It was a simple concept. Encouraged by the other ponies, Frosty enthusiastically cantered down toward the buns tied to strings.

With a well-executed pulley rein, Liza stopped Frosty squarely, within easy reach of the dangling bun.

Frosty eyed the bun hungrily and decided it was a good time for a snack. The greedy pony reached around and grabbed the bun. *Munch, munch, munch.* The pony devoured the rock-hard biscuit. The other riders were struggled to eat even a few bites of the dry scones of stone.

Liza didn't know what to do. The bun was gone, and so she turned around and cantered back. They were first over the finish line! There were tears in her eyes when the judge said, "Disqualified."

I decided to speak up. After all, I had been a real show steward. "How can they be disqualified? The whole bun has been eaten, and Liza didn't touch it with her hands." Some other riders started to straggle over the finish line and to look for their moms and cups of tea to wash down the dry crumbs.

"Please stand off to the side and wait here," said the gymkhana judge. After all the prizes were handed out, he gave Liza a flat, pale pink rosette. "We will have to add some words into the rules next year," said the smiling judge. "The bun must be eaten by the rider, not the pony, but since it wasn't in the rules this year, we are giving you a special rosette."

Left over from a flower show held on the grounds the week before, the flat, pale pink length of ribbon was stamped with a Tudor rose on the top and the words Original Composition.

Liza beamed. "Thanks for helping me, Alexa. I'll give the rosette to Granny Chesham. She is an original composition, if ever there was one."

Julian's second jumping class, for 14-2 hands and under ponies, riders aged sixteen and under, was rapidly approaching. The showgrounds were close to his home and his mother turned up. She was a gorgeous woman, fortyish, a former ballerina, with a handsome polo player attached to her arm. Now I realized why Julian spent so many Saturday nights at the Hall. Fortunately for Julian, he truly loved horses.

We got Julian mounted and everyone wished him good luck. He was our last hope of winning. Since he was pretty far down in the jumping order, he started to warm up Caesar after all the lolling around. Suddenly he jumped off. "I have to go to the loo!" He threw the reins to Gillian. Mr. Hobbs had to make a choice: either we execute a daring plan or go home empty-handed, which would be a terrible blow.

"Alexa, plait Gillian's hair in two pigtails. Liza, give Gillian your hair bows. Gillian, do you know the course?" She had been watching the kids ride the same course at different heights for quite a while.

"Alexa, go tell the gatekeeper there is a change of rider." I quickly plaited Gillian's hair and ran off on my errand. "Entry Number 134," I told the gatekeeper. "Change of rider, please, sir. It will not be Julian. It is now Gillian."

The gatekeeper radioed the change to the announcer.

"That's fine, dear, it's all set now."

I rushed back and gave Gillian's boots a final wipe-off. Liza had already painted the hoof oil on Caesar's feet.

"You look smashing, Gillian!" Liza gushed. Gillian was short, and without makeup, and with her hair in pigtails and bows, she looked about fourteen.

Gillian confidently entered the ring. She clicked with Caesar. The pair sailed flawlessly around the course.

"Clear round but unfortunately a tad slow. Right now, Caesar is in second place." The announcer read the time.

After five more rounds, they miraculously stayed in second place.

Julian emerged from the loo just in time to pick up his pony's blue rosette. The nice lady handing out the prizes said sweetly, "Your sister rode beautifully. It was nice of you to allow her to ride your pony." She handed him the blue ribbon and envelope of prize money.

While Julian was busy collecting his pony's prize, the polo player, with his South American panache, whispered to Mr. Hobbs, "My good man, I am sorry to say that I may have contributed to Julian's collywobbles. I took the Lockharts to the new Indian restaurant in Leicester yesterday evening and the food, although it was delicious, it was very spicy."

As we were leaving the show grounds, we passed Marion driving Major Everett's horse van into the show grounds. Ruth was riding shotgun. We waved vigorously to our old friends. We yelled out of the Land Rover's rolled-down windows, "Good Luck!" Secretly we were recounting our good luck that the Major's crew didn't arrive an hour earlier.

When we got back to HDH, it was still early afternoon. Julian left with his mother directly from the show grounds, so Liza and Gillian were taking care of both ponies. I volunteered to clean the tack.

Cricket had come down to the Hall with her mother today as she usually did on the weekends. We were too busy to pay much attention to her.

From the open door of the tack room, I could watch little Cricket skipping around the grassy lawn. Cricket was singing what sounded like "Here We Go Round the Mulberry Bush," which would have been almost appropriate. The blasted gooseberry bushes grew along the courtyard wall.

Cricket's lyrics didn't make sense:

Here we come gathering nuts in May,
Nuts in May, nuts in May,
Here we come gathering nuts in May,
On a cold and frosty morning.

Lord Daffy and Sir Dawdle were sitting on the lawn, curiously watching Cricket skip back and forth. The next verse was the same as the first, except for the first and third lines:

Who will you have for nuts in May?

This song went on and on. The cats wandered out of the kitchen and lay on the grass with tails twitching.

We'll send Daffy to fetch him away,
Fetch him away, fetch him away,
We'll send Daffy to fetch him away,
On a cold and frosty morning.

All of a sudden, the cats pounced toward Daffy, and he sprinted back to the door into the Hall with Dawdle close on his heels.

Cricket cried out in dismay, "Alexa, they are not playing the game properly!"

I had no idea what they were supposed to be doing, and the only nuts in May I could think of were two-legged ones, and one person I named Nutshell.

"Don't worry, Cricket. Your song is pretty." The little girl smiled and started the whole thing over again.

Later, I asked Gillian about nuts in May. "Surely nuts are collected in the fall?" I ventured.

She laughed. "Oh, that old song, it's been around for centuries. It's a game. We used to sing it when we danced around the May Pole. Anyway, it's not 'nuts in May;' it is '*knots* of May.'"

I told her about Cricket's song. "Oh yes," she said. "I always thought that was silly. A lady, Enid somebody, finally wrote down the words in the late 1800s and she may have changed the word from Knots of May to Nuts. I don't know why they teach it to kids. It's pagan and medieval. Knots of May are sprigs of Hawthorne, the first flowering tree of the spring. You collect it and give it to your lover."

I would not be making Knots of May this year.

Chapter 46
The One Question

Mrs. Highstaff was in a matter-of-fact mood on Monday morning. "I shouldn't need to remind you; we are only one month and a few days away from the Assistant Instructor's Exam to be held here. I am sure that we want Heels Down Hall to look its best. Our appearance is a reflection of all of us. Unfortunately, there can be no more Sundays off until after the exam. To compensate you, after the exam each of you will get a two-day holiday before we start our summer programs."

We could have guessed as much. Last year there were six students at this time, five WPs: Rachael, Ruth, Marion, Denis, and Fiona, and one very helpful resident student, Janet.

Mrs. Ainsworth was coming to teach her combined training course next week for all of us. Last year my American friend, Jennifer, and I were not advanced enough to ride in it. Mrs. Ainsworth, who the girls previously described to me as "pretty good," turned out to be a world-renowned horsewoman, trainer, and instructor. She was the only woman pupil of a famous French Saumur *Maître de manège.* Her list of accomplishments included training several Grade A show jumpers and high-level dressage and event horses, including a Badminton winner.

To get the place shipshape for the exam, we had an odious, extra cleaning task added to our daily routine after supper to fill the longer daylight evening hours. Tonight, the stable windows had to be washed. Many of the windows were above your head, and dirty water would run down your sleeve. Tomorrow the cobwebs had to be knocked down and gritty dust would land in your eyes, face, and hair. On Wednesday evening the smelly drains had to be cleared; the overpowering ammonia would sting your eyes and nose. Even without an exam, these tasks were necessary spring-cleaning activities. Mom would be amazed at my stable cleaning skills.

Across Britain, women in industries were striking for equal pay for equal work. Striking never entered our minds. It wouldn't have done any good. We didn't get paid. We, or our parents, paid for our food and lodging. We worked in exchange for our training.

Despite our petty grievances, we made a crackerjack team. Four of us were running the yard as well as six did the summer before. All the young horses continued their schooling and progressed. I could now properly and thoroughly strap a horse in half an hour. It took me an hour per horse when I first came. I was as physically fit as I had ever been in my life.

I was excited that Mom was arriving in London tomorrow and coming up to us by train on Thursday afternoon. I was going to be allowed to take Friday as my half-day off. Mom would stay in one of the guestrooms and eat with us. She was bringing a camera. Mrs. Highstaff gave me permission to ride Wizard side-saddle for photographs. We were going to take pictures of all the horses and people. Jennifer's promised photographs never materialized. April and everyone else looked forward to meeting Mom.

After lunch Mr. Hobbs took the Land Rover and disappeared. He came back with a slim Italian boy, Luca. Fifteen-year-old Luca was here for a week of riding instruction and English lessons with Mrs. Highstaff. His father and oldest brother, Pietro, were in London finalizing a deal with an upscale supermarket chain for olive oil from their family villa. Luca's mother thought a trip to England would be good for him. He could combine his love of riding with an opportunity to improve his English.

Luca looked a little shocked when he saw the place. He commented, "Beautiful horses," and went upstairs. He left his suitcase sitting on the cobblestone path.

Unlike the English kids who came to stay, Luca had no interest in helping out in the stables. He spent his free time upstairs writing or on the lawn reading. He wanted to be a famous novelist. I wondered if we would be characters in one of his books. When I found out he was supposed to be learning English, I made him engage in conversation.

Luca's family was interesting. "My oldest brother will inherit the villa and business, and my younger next brother, Francesco, is a bishop in the Church, and my next brother, Mario, is a captain in the Army. Because of Mario's connections, I have met the famous show jumping brothers, Colonel Piero, and Cavalry Officer Raimondo D'Inzeo."

I had seen their photos in *Horse and Hound* in the international show jumping section. I admired them. The handsome brothers rode with perfect positions while maintaining light contact with their horse's mouth, and they never used gizmos.

Luca told me, "It is amusing. I came to England to ride horses and to converse in English, which I am. The funny part is that while I am in England, I end up talking to an American."

Luca was a good rider and he loved jumping. When Julian came after school to ride, he allowed Luca to ride Caesar, who had recently won second place in show jumping at the gymkhana. Instantly the two boys became friends and Luca joined in Julian's lessons.

Luca rode three times a day. He had private lessons or semi-private riding lessons with Julian, taught by Mr. Hobbs. Every day, he had two English lessons in the classroom taught by Mrs. Highstaff. He dressed smartly. In street clothes, he tied a silk scarf around his neck. Luca was what the Mods aspired to be. His riding attire was tailor-made. He loved Meteor and wanted to buy him, and he hated Atlanta. He was passionate about everything.

Other than when he was in the yard preparing to ride, we mostly saw Luca at mealtimes. He was used to coffee, sparkling water, and wine with dinner, not tea and tap water. He didn't like the food and he hardly ate anything. He would say things like "I am fed up" after the meal. When he walked into the student lounge he might say something like, "This place has an air about it." Then he would wave his hand in the air. I was not sure if his phrasing was because of his lack of knowledge of English idioms or because of it. He was right about the sun rarely shining and damp weather. He always complained of the cold. I think he was homesick for sunny Tuscany.

A small brown envelope arrived for me in the post. It contained a paperback book, a previously read copy of *The Cherry Orchard* by Anton Chekhov. A short note written on notebook paper was tucked inside the front cover:

Dear Alexa,

I enjoyed meeting you and wish you well in your exams.

This book should explain more.

I hope we can stay in touch.

Your friend,
Peter

I was delighted to get a present. I would have happily read a book about anything, except horses, at this point. My brain was saturated with horse this and pony that. I was happy I could cite this book on the reading list for my upcoming University scholarship interview.

After I read the play, I decided I would *not* mention it in my college interview and that Peter was undoubtedly a Commie sympathizer.

Mr. Hobbs collected Mom from the train station on Thursday afternoon. Her arrival cheered all of us. The place sparkled, cleaner even than its usual immaculate and orderly appearance.

April promised to make the meals as nice as possible for my mom's visit. She served peas and carrots along with our cabbage and potatoes.

On Thursday evening, we did something rare. We all, even Luca, sat around the dining table and talked together. Mom was interested in young people, and she listened with great interest when they spoke about their families or plans.

On Friday morning Mom watched us ride and gave us a hand sweeping up the stable yard before lunch. In the afternoon we photographed all the horses. I asked Mrs. Highstaff to be in the side-saddle photos with me and Wizard.

On Friday night we discussed our trip to Europe. We were going to Norway and then to Germany. Ferries, trains, and buses were involved. I would have to carry my passport at all times because we would cross multiple borders on the train from Denmark to Germany.

We reminded each other to pack lightly. We had to carry our own luggage.

In the meantime, Mom would stay with Sareena in her flat in fashionable Chelsea. She could explore London in a leisurely manner using public transportation. Mom promised we would see a play and do other cool stuff in London.

I gave Mom the delicate china teacup, the birthday present I bought for her earlier this month. She helped me pack it in a small box and I prayed it would not break in my trunk on the way home. Mom liked the presents I purchased for Richard and Daddy, which were also going home in the trunk.

She looked at my large pile of books. She told me, in no uncertain terms, I could not ship home anything that could not fit in my trunk.

On Saturday midmorning Mom walked the grounds with Mrs. Highstaff, Lord Daffy, and Sir Dawdle. Mom loved dogs. Since my earliest memory, we had always owned a dog. Mom was used to hiking. She had hiked portions of rough mountains on the Appalachian Trail. The hillsides of Heels Down Hall were easy for her.

After lunch, Mom said she was going into the village. April reminded her that shops would close by four and to come back for tea.

Mom hiked down the lane and out of sight. We continued with our normal teaching and stable duties. We gathered in the dining hall for tea, before tack cleaning, when a slightly weary and bedraggled-looking Mom appeared, laden with two huge bags that she carried back from Brickton.

One bag bulged with fruit and goodies: oranges from Spain, local strawberries, biscuits, and cake. The other bag contained a stuffed toy pony for Cricket and other surprises. April received a pretty floral print apron, and everyone else, including Mr. Hobbs, got a chocolate bar.

Cricket was excited. She was enrolled in the first children's summer course. She showed me where her name was first on the roster. Mrs. Highstaff promised Cricket that if she did well in the summer courses, she would sponsor her in the Featherstone Pony Club. Cricket loved ponies; she watched them every day from her bedroom window in the gatehouse. For now, Cricket was only allowed in the stable yard if she was holding April's hand.

April was delighted. Working as a housekeeper, April would have never afforded Cricket's riding lessons, let alone afford to sponsor her in Pony Club.

Hearing the commotion, Luca casually wandered downstairs from the student lounge to the dining room for his tea. Spotting the bowl of bright oranges and the plate of red ripe strawberries on the table, he looked at my mother and cried out, "Fruit! Fruit! Fruit in this house! Signora Goodwin, you are an angel!" He kissed Mom on the cheek. "*Mille Grazie, Mille Grazie*!"

On Sunday morning, Mrs. Highstaff and Mom went together to the gothic High Church in Storkey. They were hitting it off.

On Sunday afternoon, Mr. Hobbs was taking Mom and Luca back to the Leicester train station. Luca was happy Mom was traveling with him to London. He was not quite as adventurous as he pretended to be.

Mrs. Highstaff and the dogs came out on the courtyard lawn to say goodbye. Out of the blue, Mom asked the one question I hoped would not come up during this visit. I am sure it was on her mind the whole time. "Mrs. Highstaff, what do you think of Alexa's idea of a career with horses?"

Mrs. Highstaff did not hesitate. "Alexa has certainly studied hard and increased her knowledge. Her horsemanship and riding have improved greatly. She has the makings of becoming a fine riding instructor and horse trainer."

My mother looked relieved.

I stood there silently. I was dismayed.

There was no mention that I had the guts and talent to be a brilliant international show jumper if only I had the backing of a sponsor. After talking to Luca, I had dreams of competing against the D'Inzeo brothers in Rome.

I *could* make a fine riding instructor if I could *pass* the exam. I only had one shot at it. If I failed the first time, my parents would never let me stay in England to take it again. Worse, I would have to travel around Europe with my mom as a failure. Even worse, I would have to explain to my former riding companions, Astrid and Kari, why I had spent a year at an English riding school. Worse still, those non-riding kids, who we would be visiting in Germany, were the same kids I used to chase out of the stables. I knew they would tease me about not passing an exam about horses. The worst thing of all would be facing my dad when I got home. Dad would think I wasted a year of my time and his money when I could have finished a year of college like all my high school friends.

I was passionate about horses. I wanted to prove I was really good at riding.

Now, more than ever, I was anxious about the exam.

Mom and Luca left. I wondered if Luca had ever invited us to visit him in Tuscany.

I felt sad to see Mom go, but not for long. Mrs. Ainsworth was coming tomorrow morning for our combined training course.

Mr. Hobbs was right about one thing, eventing was fun. I was hooked. Cross-country jumping was thrilling.

Horse vans started to arrive before we had even gone into breakfast. Grace Edwards brought Jasper. Tina, Marion's friend, appeared with her new competition horse. She sold Kilkenny and bought Larkspur. Both riders would ship in every day. We didn't have any empty boxes and they lived close by. Mrs. Ainsworth's van was last up the drive.

Dignified and lithe, Mrs. Ainsworth was Epona, the horse goddess, personified.

I was to be in charge of Sampson. I wondered why Fiona, as Head Girl, did not have to take care of such an important horse. Sampson would be occupying Rob Roy's stall. His stall was the largest, in the past frequently used for foaling. Rob Roy had been relegated to the paddock.

I did not know what to expect.

Chapter 47

A Mere Trifle

Sampson clomped down the ramp like a lumberjack. He looked like anything *except* graceful. He was a gentle giant, and somewhat comical in appearance. His markings made him look like a clown, long ragged stockings on three legs, one sock on the other leg, a large head with a bald face, and large, kind eyes. We had been studying conformation. This horse was a textbook case of over at the knee. Yet this clownish-looking horse, who started his long career as a show jumper, had won countless dressage championships. Sampson retired from competing long ago, but he still earned his keep. Mrs. Ainsworth brought him to her clinics for demonstrations and to keep him fit and interested in life.

The theme of the course was "Dressage is the foundation of jumping," whether it was show jumping or cross-country. Dressage meant "to train" (in French, *Dresser*). Of course, Mrs. Ainsworth spoke fluent French.

"Riding should be like dancing with your partner, your horse, not like ordering around a reluctant servant. In order to dance, you need soft and invisible aids. Your supple position and balance must be in concert with your horse. You must anticipate what the horse will do, not just react after something happens. You must feel what the horse is doing. The correct timing and correct placement of the aids are more important than the strength of an ill-timed or ill-placed aid.

"If the horses are not lame or terribly unfit, most horses that are going poorly are moving poorly because they are doing exactly what the rider *is* telling or allowing them to do. The more trained and sensitive the horse, the more obvious this becomes. Many horses must learn to put up with and even ignore their riders' conflicting aids out of self-preservation."

Another theme of the course was "there are no shortcuts." "There are no shortcuts in training the horse, no shortcuts in training the rider, and no shortcuts in conditioning the horse. Horsemanship is as important as riding in the training of a competition horse."

Whenever we finally understood and implemented whatever it was that Mrs. Ainsworth had told us to do, our horses performed effortlessly. We were constantly amazed at the improvements all week.

At the start of one of our wonderful but mind-boggling sessions, Mrs. Ainsworth gave us a mounted demonstration before we left the stable yard. We had just mounted and assembled to ride out in the big field for our flatwork lesson. This lesson was preparation for our cross-country jumping lesson this afternoon.

Mrs. Ainsworth had a commanding but not loud voice. "Ride, may I have your attention, please. *Halt* does not just mean *Stop*. And *halt* does not mean what the foxhunters do at a check, stop and stand, although all horses should be able to do that."

Halt? From the dressage tests we knew that the horse had to halt squarely, remain on contact, and move off smoothly.

"*Halt* means 'immobile at attention.' That is, from the halt, a horse should instantly be able to go forwards, backwards, or sideways. I will demonstrate this when we are out in the field, and we have sufficiently ridden-in our horses. Right now, I want you to observe this."

Sampson had started to doze, so she moved him a few steps forward and halted. Samson transformed from a sleepy old horse into a study for a da Vinci equestrian monument. His neck was round, his poll was flexed, his feet were square, and he was completely attentive.

Then Mrs. Ainsworth did something, but we couldn't really see what she did. Mrs. Ainsworth did apparently nothing and the giant Samson leaned forward as far as he could, but his feet never moved. At first, I thought I had imagined it. The big horse came back to the center and stood perfectly square. Next, he leaned right until if he went any more right he might topple over. Magically, the gentle giant returned to upright. And then, he leaned so far back that I thought his forelegs were going to come off the ground. Once again Sampson centered himself. A few seconds later, Samson perilously leaned to the left, but again his feet never moved, and slowly he regained an upright position. His clownish face seemed to be grinning at us. Sampson loved showing off; he could also bow and shake hands.

Sampson marched off at an extended walk on a loose rein.

Mrs. Ainsworth called out, "The whole ride, in single file, follow me."

We rode out to the field, past the indoor school. On that short hack, I realized that as much as I had learned in the past year, I knew nothing at all about riding. I already knew there was more to equitation than a good position and a daring attitude. I wasn't sure that realizing how little I knew was the lesson I needed to learn a few weeks before the exam.

Gillian had a letter from her parents. Her good fortune was also my own. Sunday was Whitsun, a church holiday. "Because there are no more Sundays off until after the exam, my parents arranged with Mrs. Highstaff that they would drive up and take us out to dinner provided we are back at HDH by half past two."

At quarter to three, we had to be in work clothes with a shovel or a rake in hand and be in the indoor arena. We were going to be filling in the ruts in the track of the indoor riding school. After it was leveled, flattened, and raked smooth, the indoor school would be off-limits between now and the exam, unless it was pouring with rain.

During her course, Mrs. Ainsworth always made us ride outside for every lesson, flatwork or jumping.

During our evening lecture, Mrs. Ainsworth insisted, "If you seriously want to compete, you must read and study the book by my friend, Hungarian cavalry officer Lieutenant Colonel A. L. D'Endrody, a former Royal Hungarian Olympic Equestrian team member. He has done race riding, three-day eventing, and show jumping with international success." The book, *Give Your Horse a Chance,* was quite technical and over five hundred pages long.

"The Duke of Beaufort has given D'Endrody, who is in exile from the Communists, refuge on his estate at Badminton, where this gifted equestrian is still living." I discovered the Three-Day Event competition at Badminton had started the year I was born.

We crowded around the book to see the photographs. There were pages of photographs of the author riding several magnificent horses in all paces, the extended walk on a loose rein, and the ordinary, collected, and extended paces in walk, trot, and canter. What impressed me was that every horse photographed was out in the countryside, going up or going down a hill in perfect balance at every pace, not just the usual photographs of dressage horses parading around a flat arena.

We were amazed by the marvelous photographs of examples of flawless jumping over difficult cross-country obstacles. There was never a photo where the rider interfered with the horse's back or mouth.

I was glad I paid attention to geometry and algebra. There was a lot of math involved with jumping: parabolas over jumps, speeds, and distances, strides between the jumps or the jumping elements.

The real bonus of the book was the last chapter, "Distribution of Time and Work: for the preparation of the three-day event (one-day event) horse and show jumping." Subtitled: "From the time of taking them under instruction until reaching the stage of their complete education."

This book made *Training the Young Horse and Pony* that we were required to know look like a primary school reader.

After our evening lecture, Fiona confided in me that Mrs. Ainsworth gave Sampson the aids to make him lean by using her back, buttocks, and thighs. Fiona had taken the combined training course last spring. This year Fiona was riding Jazzy in most of the sessions, and he was going brilliantly. I hoped to ride Rob Roy in the clinic, but he was not far enough along in his training. The rest of us rode different horses every day, with a flat work lesson in the morning that specifically related to the jumping exercises we would be doing in the afternoon. All the horses in the clinic would be in the exam and they benefited from the lessons.

After our last session, I was the first one back into the yard and I quickly untacked Atlanta. I did not enjoy spending extra time with the crabby chestnut mare. Mrs. Ainsworth was the last one into the yard. By the time she dismounted from Samson, Mrs. Highstaff and dogs appeared in the courtyard with an important message. "Mrs. Ainsworth, your Head Girl telephoned. She asks that you ring her back as soon as possible."

Usually, Mrs. Ainsworth unsaddled Samson herself and gave him a quick brush over to make sure the old horse was still in perfect condition, and I would give him a thorough grooming later.

I noticed what was going on, and since I was in charge of Samson, I cheerfully volunteered. "I'll untack him for you, Mrs. Ainsworth."

She paused, with a quizzical look on her face. "Untack? What a curious phrase. Surely you mean to say unsaddle. It used to be saddles off, in the old days—"

She paused and then asked, "Alexa, I hope you don't mind me asking this, but are you from the South?"

The South? Was Mrs. Ainsworth clairvoyant as well as being a superb horsewoman? I had never considered myself to be *from* the South. I was born a Yankee and I had lived abroad. I had lived in North Carolina for less than two years. I was really floored. I thought I had a pretty good English accent by now. Other than the brief visit from Mom, I hadn't spoken to another American since Jennifer left. This dead giveaway was disastrous.

I didn't know what to say, so I stammered, "I have lived in a lot of places, but I only lived in North Carolina for two years. I didn't realize I had a southern drawl."

Mrs. Ainsworth laughed. "So that's it. Oh no, dear, all week your accent has been puzzling me. I thought you were from Surrey; I have some friends who live there."

Wow! This is exceedingly good news. My accent can pass as English if I just don't flub up and use American jargon instead of the correct BHS terminology. I made a mental note to review the glossaries of the *Manual of Horsemanship* and the other Pony Club publications one more time.

I had heard enough about the unsuccessful fate of many Americans and the BHSAI Exam and did not want to advertise my nationality.

The lessons on Saturday were as busy as ever with little time to contemplate the finer points of Mrs. Ainsworth's combined training course. The day passed quickly. Both Gillian and I looked forward to a decent meal—anything, even fish and chips—and getting away from the school for a while. Fiona and Jeremy were looking forward to a couple of hours of silence. Mr. Hobbs said he was planning on a kip.

The only restaurant nearby open on Sunday was Luigi's in Crowsville. It was not fancy, but very cheery. A menu was posted by the door. We didn't do this in America, but I thought it was brilliant. The prospective diner knew how much the dinner cost before he sat down and was handed a menu.

Red and white checked tablecloths were draped over the tables. Candles in wax-drizzled Chianti bottles covered by straw baskets and white crockery canisters containing delicate breadsticks welcomed the diners. Plaster casts of famous statues stood in the corners watching over the feasting patrons. A garland of green grape leaves with bunches of purple grapes decorated the shelves behind the bar. Ropes of real garlic and onions hung by the kitchen door. Light twinkled off the bottles of red and white wine. We enjoyed a fresh green salad, crusty Italian bread, and pasta with tomato marinara sauce, washed down with a glass of Chianti. For dessert, we savored delicate cannolis and sipped rich coffee. We felt very Continental.

The parents, as we called Mr. and Mrs. Benson, always made us laugh. When Gran discovered my mom was in London, she said, "I will write to her and invite your mother to visit us in Braefield."

Mr. Benson looked at his watch. "We better get back. We don't want to upset Mrs. Highstaff."

Back at HDH, as we were getting out of the car and saying thank you and goodbye, Granny produced a dish out of a basket. The glass bowl contained a lovely trifle. She handed the yummy cake, with layers of fruit covered in clotted cream, to Gillian, who started to say something. The car window closed; there was no time to explain. The Bensons drove away.

We only had a few minutes to get this trifle upstairs without being seen. We had to get ready for the afternoon's fun-filled festivities of shoveling dirt.

We were not allowed to keep food in our rooms, but this was the best plan. We were going to eat it in a couple of hours. We couldn't very well walk through the main doorway carrying a bowl of trifle in our hands. If we put the bowl in the pantry or kitchen or dining hall, it would be for everyone.

Gillian said, "I'll wait in the tack room with the trifle. You scout out the situation, go upstairs via the main steps, and come down into the kitchen from our room, and let me in. This way we can sneak the trifle up to our room without being detected."

I never got past the kitchen window. April came back to the Hall earlier than usual to wash the dinner dishes. She was standing at the sink in front of the window. Cricket was playing with the toy pony Mom had given her, making it jump up and down the steps to our room.

Across the lawn, opposite the tack room and kitchen, some spooky old wooden sheds with arched wooden doors leaned against a section of the courtyard wall. Usually, the sheds were kept padlocked shut, but today one of the doors was ajar. We hastily devised a new plan. "Alexa, you go into the kitchen and engage April in conversation, and get her and Cricket to turn away from the window and I'll pop the trifle into the open shed."

"I hope Mr. Highstaff doesn't come along and lock the shed later." Mr. Highstaff was so absent-minded that he might not notice a trifle sitting on the shelf. Minutes were ticking away, and we still had to change clothes.

We made it down to the indoor arena with about ten seconds to spare. As a result of being last out in the yard, I had the rake with one tine missing and Gillian had the shovel with the short handle, but our plan worked. The trifle was secure and neatly covered with a paper bag.

We didn't know it, but we were not the only ones who noticed that the shed door was cracked open.

There was no way to eat the trifle at tea time, as Gran thought we would, but fortunately, the door to the shed was still unlocked. We could have eaten it at tea time if we wanted to share it, which we did not. It would not go far for five people.

After supper we had to wait to retrieve the trifle, our perfect treat to end the day. As luck would have it, on the one evening you wanted everyone to disappear off to their respective corners, Fiona and Jeremy decided to have a long chat in the kitchen. My mouth was watering. I skipped the beans on toast, my least favorite supper. I didn't want to spoil the large Italian dinner earlier and the trifle yet to come.

Finally, Fiona and Jeremy went upstairs to the lounge to watch their new favorite TV show. I turned off the kitchen light so the lawn would not be illuminated by light coming through the big window. Under the cover of darkness and with her torch in her pocket, Gillian snuck out of the kitchen, and crossed the lawn to the shed. "If Fiona goes back to her room instead of watching TV in the lounge, I might be spotted."

"It's more likely that Mrs. Highstaff will come out for a random evening round."

If the busybody dogs didn't give us away, Mrs. Highstaff with her excellent powers of observation might notice the shed door was open. She might shut the door and lock Gillian in there. This would have dire consequences, especially as we had extra privileges by eating out earlier in the day.

Gillian didn't want to risk knocking the trifle off the shelf by bumping around in the dark. In the gloom, she switched on her torch. The light flashed on four gleaming eyes that appeared quite close to her.

From the kitchen doorway across the lawn, I heard a gasp, followed by a crash.

On further inspection, the paper bag was laying on the shed floor and the eyes belonged to Artemis and Apollo, who were busy washing their faces. When startled by Gillian, they jumped off the shelf and knocked over an empty flowerpot on their dash out of the door.

Luckily, the dogs, who were still inside the Hall, did not hear the crockery pot break and start barking.

The top layer of fruit on the trifle was completely exposed, not one drop of thick cream to be seen. I was glad the next layer of the trifle hadn't been cake, or the cats would have probably eaten the cake too.

"I remember reading that a dog's mouth is cleaner than a human's mouth and so I think the same thing would be true for cats."

We were thankful the cats discovered the trifle before the mice. We wiped off the fruit with a handkerchief and ate the remains of the trifle with no ill after-effect, proving to ourselves that the dubious animal hygiene theory was correct.

Now all we had to do was hide the empty bowl and smuggle the spoons back into the dining hall.

Chapter 48
Ladders

Kris Kringle, Dr. Amsley's heavyweight hunter, came back to spend the summer at Heels Down Hall. This was great—I loved him. Riding Harry was like jumping on a sofa and, undoubtedly, he would be used in the cross-country section of the exam.

I recently started riding the two Irish mares Mrs. Highstaff had imported last fall, Tara and Cashel. Cashel was a year older and the larger of the two, and she would be ridden in the equitation on the flat portion of the exam. Tara was easygoing but too green. She and the ancient St. Christopher would be used in practical stable management skills. They were patient. Exam candidates would be putting on and taking off the same equipment over and over again on them for hours.

Mrs. Highstaff recruited guinea pigs for the Powers of Instruction portion of the exam. The riders had to be old enough and skilled enough to groom, tack up, and put away the ponies. Julie and Caroline, although very competent, were too young. Liza was too emotional, and Julian was too chatty. The big horses would be in our riding portions of the exam so the guinea pigs would ride the large ponies, like Ghost and Biscuit. Therefore, the guinea pigs had to be of a suitable size. Other qualities for guinea pigs included being sensible enough to not purposely, or accidentally, do anything outlandish that would jeopardize a candidate's chance of passing the exam; and yet, they must be capable of executing some mistake that a simple instruction could correct.

It was an advantage for us to know the guinea pigs in advance. We would know the rider's tendencies. Do they lean too far forward? Do they hold the reins too long or too short? Do they have hands like puppy paws? Are their legs too far forward or too far back? Do they have a tendency to look down?

Gillian would, of course, be a guinea pig. It would give her a chance to see how the teaching portion of the exam was conducted in preparation for her exam in October. Miss Archer was a natural choice. Because the term was nearly over, she could get away from Richlands for the day. Granny Chesham volunteered to ride Frosty.

The final two riders were a newly married, short, and cheery couple, Henry and Beth Lovell. They ran a real estate agency in Storkey. Beth specialized in selling country residential properties, so horse knowledge was a plus. Henry managed business properties, shops, and factories, and he liked to get out in the country air. On the day of the exam, their secretary could answer any calls.

They planned to take the Riding Club Stages at a later date. The Riding Club, with achievement levels similar to Pony Club, was designed for amateur adults and it was active in our area. Granny Chesham told us after her lesson, "I am considering joining a Riding Club. Mr. Hobbs' thinks it would be good for me."

The examiners had not yet given Mrs. Highstaff the schedule for the actual exam day. We were hoping it would be similar to last year.

A postcard arrived for me from exotic Madagascar: a view of the magnificent Indian Ocean, palm trees, and with some woven baskets filled with spices placed on a white sand beach. It was postmarked in April. Trevor traveled through Africa in eight months. The card took two months to reach me in England. "While I was in Sudan, the only transportation available was a camel caravan. I am heading back to Australia, as a crew member on a tramp steamer. Good luck with the horses."

Good luck to you, Trevor. I wonder what my life would have been like if I traveled with you? I hope you get back home safely. There are a lot of pirates around Madagascar and the Indian Ocean is treacherous. If you write your stories down, they will make Hemingway's adventures look like Tales of Captain Milk Toast. I couldn't write to him; no Australian address to reply to.

We found out that Martin Luther King's assassin, James Earl Ray, was arrested in London. I prayed that there would not be another anti-American march in the City. My mom was there wandering around on her own. It seemed there was no escape from the insanity of humanity.

Mrs. Highstaff had been getting inquiries wondering if she was going to hold a BHSAI Examination preparation course. There was not one listed on the master schedule, posted on the tack room wall since winter.

Only one full week remained open between Mrs. Ainsworth's course and the exam. Mrs. Highstaff intended to let us all take the horses on hacks that week to refresh everyone's attitudes, but the other five other exam candidates practically begged to come for a course. Rather than walking in cold, knowing the facilities, horses, and stable setup was a huge advantage.

The ladies agreed they would each care for one horse during the week, theoretically lightening our load, but in reality, it would make us teach them the routine at Heels Down Hall.

Mrs. Highstaff previously planned to review the written and oral syllabus with us in any case.

The exam was in ten days.

This Saturday there would be regular riding lessons. Sunday would be the horses' day off and we would complete another unsavory chore. The final exam prep course was set for next week, Monday through Friday. The three days before the exam—Monday, Tuesday, and Wednesday—we would just exercise the horses and do the final physical exam prep, like having all the equipment, and props gathered together for easy access.

The extra task this Sunday was filling the carriage house loft with enough straw for the next fortnight or more. With Mrs. Highstaff's course and then the exam followed by a short-staffed weekend, having the loft full would save valuable time. The hay had been delivered and stacked over St. Christopher's box last week. We were going to fill the loft, above the ponies' tie stalls, with the straw bales from one of the big ricks we had made last September.

The straw rick we were about to start dismantling was covered with the tarps that protected it through the winter. It happened to be located outside the paddock underneath our bedroom window. After we removed some of the tarps, I volunteered to climb up the heavy wooden ladder to throw down the straw bales. I liked being up high and looking at the view of the fields, the rolling hills, and the edge of the village.

The choice of which bales to start throwing down required some thought. Throwing the wrong ones down could cause the corner of the rick to tumble down in a landslide and break the bales. While I was up there figuring out which bales to start throwing down, I noticed I could see into our bedroom.

I started throwing down the prescribed number of bales. Gillian transported them to the barn on a barrow, Jeremy threw the bales up to the loft, and Fiona was in the loft stacking.

It was a pleasant late spring day. I fantasized, *Maybe a handsome prince will ride by, climb into our room, and rescue us like in Rapunzel.*

A plan began to hatch in my mind. *The ladder is the right height to climb into our window. There are no windows below our room on this side of the house. Jeremy and Mr. Hobbs live on the second floor in the attic and the windows in their rooms overlook the lawn and into the stables. Fiona's room overlooks the courtyard.*

After her evening round, Mrs. Highstaff usually spends the evenings in her study with her mollycoddled dogs curled up on their favorite armchairs. The study was located far away in the front of the house, diagonally opposite from our room.

Exam jitters were starting to take over; everyone was getting edgy.

With the confidence of Tom Sawyer, I decided that we needed an adventure. In one of my favorite TV shows, *The Prisoner*, the main character, Number Six, tried to escape every week. I had watched countless TV sitcoms and movies where people made undetected or timely escapes by climbing out a window and down a ladder. It seemed to me that windows and ladders were an acceptable exit route.

As the day went on, my plan started to enlarge. *All we have to do is move the ladder from the rick and put it against the wall of the Hall under our window before we come in for supper. When the coast is clear, we can leave the window open and climb down the ladder. Once we are down, we will lean the ladder back against the rick.* It helped that the sun wouldn't set until about half past nine and it wouldn't be dark until almost ten.

I loved challenges. As a kid, when we used to play hide and seek outdoors, the other kids never found me. I hid so well I had to turn myself in, in time to eat.

After supper the kitchen door is locked, so to get back in, one person will have to use the ladder to climb through the open window. We will replace the ladder on the rick while the person inside comes down our back steps into the kitchen and unlocks the door and guards it until we all are in. From the kitchen, we can go upstairs into our bedroom.

Using the same "you can't get me in trouble if you're doing it too" psychology that I used on my brother when he discovered I was sneaking candy from the pantry when our parents went out, I decided we should take Fiona with us. Fiona couldn't see us out her window, but her room shared a wall with ours and both of our rooms opened up into the lounge. Fiona would be the busybody to discover we were missing.

In the tackroom, I whispered to Gillian, "I won't get Fiona involved until supper. If she doesn't cooperate, the plan is off."

Later in the kitchen I whispered to Fiona while she waited as I sliced the hard cheese for my toast, "Fiona, Gillian and I would like you to join us on an adventure this evening."

Her face lit up. "Ohh, this is exciting."

"*Shhh.* Jeremy is coming over. Come up to our room in a half-hour."

She nodded. Jeremy popped his toast into the oven.

Fiona appeared in our room right on time.

"Right! Musketeers, follow me!" Gillian gave the order as she disappeared out the window and down the ladder.

I didn't like the idea of being the last one out, but I said, "Fiona, you go next." *This way she can't back out.* Fiona climbed down like an itsy-bitsy spider. I was last and was glad I was not the one who would be climbing back in. The ladder seemed a lot more secure buried into the straw rick than leaning on a smooth stone wall.

Once I was on the ground, Fiona asked curiously, "Where are we going?"

"Escape to nowhere!" I proclaimed.

Military style, we crept along the fence to cross the front pasture out to the road. We couldn't go into Brickton. The shops were closed on Sunday evening, and we could easily be spotted, recognized, and reported. We turned left and went past the Hall Farm. In about twenty minutes we reached the semi-deserted village.

Of course, nothing was open here. I doubt if there was a shop in the place. Only a few of the tumbledown cottages even had lights on. A dog started barking. *Rats, I forgot about the dog that attacked Rob Roy last fall.*

We stood at the corner of the tiny hamlet, wondering which way we should go.

"Hear! What's that? Who is out there?" A loud male voice challenged us. The voice came out of the cottage a few doors down the lane. A bearded head popped out of a window. "Identify yourselves or we'll let the dogs out!"

Gillian called out, "Just some girls taking a walk."

"Funny time to be taking a walk," said the gruff man. Then he softened a bit. "It is a lovely evening for a change. You best be getting home. Where are you from anyway? I haven't seen you around here before."

"We are from the riding school," Fiona piped up. We were all pretty confident that these rustics would not have a telephone.

"Well, you best be getting back there," said the man.

Another twenty minutes later, we were back at the school. It was just getting dark. We looked around to see if Mrs. Highstaff, Daffy, or Dawdle were about, then we moved the ladder from the straw rick back to the window. Gillian volunteered to climb up. She scrambled up like a squirrel. I was glad. My enchantment with ladders was somewhat diminished by now.

Fiona and I leaned the heavy ladder against the rick, and we crept around the tack room to the kitchen door. Gillian was waiting with her torch. We couldn't turn the lights on; it was after lights out.

Mrs. Highstaff's course was starting in the morning, and we had to get to sleep.

It was a miracle that we pulled off the whole escapade. There were so many times when we could have been detected and gotten into trouble. Forget about the fact that someone could have been injured by falling off the ladder.

The silliest thing was that if we had asked Mrs. Highstaff if we could take a walk after supper, she would have more than likely allowed us to go.

Including Fiona in our madcap evening adventure turned out to be a good idea. It was a bonding we needed before the exam.

Chapter 49

You Will Ruin My Horse

The course participants started arriving on Monday morning while we were still upstairs changing from our morning work clothes into riding kit.

As previously instructed, they assembled in the tack room. Mr. Hobbs and Mrs. Highstaff greeted everyone, and we were introduced to each other. I had been very curious to see who else would be taking the exam with us. Of course, it took us a while to discover the details about our fellow exam candidates.

Mark Smith was married, attractive, clean-cut, forty-ish, pleasant, and no-nonsense. He could ride before he could walk, and he saw the business advantages of being an approved facility and certificated as an instructor. He owned and operated a nearby family-run livery yard, which he had recently taken over from his father, who had taken it over from his grandfather before that. Fox Hollow specialized in the care and upkeep of hunters. His family had a solid working relationship with HDH through several generations.

Gwendolyn Jones was an Amazon. She was about twenty-five with a close-cropped pixie haircut. She already looked a little weathered like a female rugby player, wiry and tough. "I work in a dealer's yard. My boss wants me to get the Horsemaster's certificate." Gwen, as she wanted us to call her, arrived in a little ancient Ford. "I purchased my car with my own money. I am staying at HDH because I calculate it is cheaper than driving back and forth from home." She seemed a little cocky to me.

Amanda Thompson was our age. She had been a WP for one year at a highly respected riding school in the Faraway Hunt country, called

Woodlands. "I did quite a bit of Pony Club when I was younger. I hope to stay on at Woodlands as part of the teaching staff after I pass my exam."

Jane Porter, also from Woodlands, was just old enough to take the exam. Like Ruth, Jane started as a WP at fifteen and a half after she left school. She had been at Woodlands for two years. Unlike Ruth, Jane was noticeably quiet. "I think I will apply to work as a Girl Friday for a private family with ponies and kids." It didn't seem like a very ambitious goal to me.

Amanda and Jane were amazed when they found that Mrs. Highstaff arranged winter schooling shows at HDH for us, and more amazed that we competed with our horses in outside competitions.

They remarked, "We saw your photo in *Horse and Hound* after the Musical Ride."

Jane, Amanda, and Gwen were staying in the big front bedroom. While it was fun to have some other girls to talk with, it was simultaneously distracting. It also was annoying, for example, if they were staying in the bathroom too long. We had gotten used to only three girls using the loo.

Woodlands was not a residential riding school. "We live in the village with local families and walk to work every day." They weren't used to living dormitory-style.

Gwen lived at home. "I pay my mother for lodging and I drive to work."

She annoyed us with her disparaging remarks about every one of our horses. "Wouldn't get much for that one."

"Conformation like a giraffe."

"Couldn't jump over a set of matchsticks."

Gwen was careful not to let Mr. Hobbs or Mrs. Highstaff hear her judgments, but she knew it needled us.

The final participant in the course was pretty Penny Stafford, thirty-something, wife of a Leicester banker. She dressed in the latest equestrian fashion from Savile Row, not Lewes Equestrian Emporium. She had riding instruction from a young age and had competed as a teenager. She had probably read every horse book printed in English and subscribed to every equine magazine. She had no interest in working anywhere, let alone working in a stable. You could tell this by the way she mucked out a stall.

She was not at all snobbish; she was very pleasant, almost ingratiating, which made people go out of their way to help her with difficult or unpleasant tasks. "I want to prove to my husband that I can pass the exam." She drove a stylish late model Swedish car, a Volvo.

Mark and Penny were day students. Penny took lunch with us, but Mark went home. I say Penny ate with us, but after the first day, she brought a picnic hamper. "I think I will eat my lunch in the car park."

Mark probably got a home-cooked meal when he went back to Fox Hollow. His excuse was, "I'm going home to check with the lads in my yard." He added, "I only hire boys and men."

Mrs. Highstaff made it clear before we started. "This exam is not a competition between you. Each person equally stands a chance to show their knowledge and competency is at, or above, the prescribed standard."

Mark had a million questions. "What's the format of the exam?"

Mrs. Highstaff went over the setup, procedures, protocols, and expected behavior for the candidates in the exam. "There should be no unnecessary talking, no conferences, and no frivolity. Ask questions only if absolutely necessary to clarify an instruction by an examiner. Follow the instructions given carefully."

Our morning ride was equitation on the flat, for an hour and a half, and consisted of the movements that would be on the exam. "You will have to know the definitions, the aids, the movement of a horse's legs, and how to execute all the school figures correctly, down to the minutest detail," Mrs. Highstaff reminded us.

After the lesson, Mark went home.

Then Fiona, Jeremy, Gillian, and I schooled our young horses every day before lunch. Mrs. Highstaff would exercise Topaz out in the field with us. She would ride around to each rider and horse combination and make corrections or give us different exercises to do, always accompanied by encouraging remarks. Rob Roy was being used in the course. I was riding Tara this week; she was a sweetie.

While we schooled the young horses, the other candidates groomed horses and bedded down the stalls. Mr. Hobbs supervised the correct way to muck out, bed down, and other horsemanship skills required for the exam. Gwen would often interrupt him with, "My boss likes it done like this—"

Mr. Hobbs would not reply and would just continue with his demonstration.

After lunch we had our jumping lesson, either in the jumping paddock or in the cross-country fields. Mark commented to Mrs. Highstaff, "I'm impressed with your array of solid jumps. I plan to add a few more at Fox Hollow." The riding sessions were going well and included lots of changing of horses, which is one of the reasons why they all came here. Penny turned out to be an elegant and accomplished rider.

After jumping we had a coffee break.

We had plenty of teaching practice. Mrs. Highstaff told us, "It is harder to teach a short, effective lesson than a longer one. In the exam, you will have to limit your topic, selected randomly by the examiners, to fifteen or twenty minutes in duration *and* show a marked improvement in the riders in that limited time frame."

Because we had two commuters in this course, we had our lectures after bedding down the horses in the late afternoon, before tack cleaning, instead of in the evening after supper.

Mark was excused from tack cleaning. He had probably cleaned more tack in his one lifetime than all of us put together. Tack cleaning seemed to be a fascinating experience for Penny. "I like everything sparkling."

We needed guinea pigs for the teaching practice. As an incentive, whoever could get to HDH early enough to volunteer got a free ride. We could see now why Mrs. Highstaff did not use the kids in the actual exam. They either tried too hard or got silly, but we got through the entire curriculum in spite of them.

The adult guinea pigs joined us at least once during the week, to give them an idea of what to expect. Beth Lovell came on Thursday afternoon. She joined us in the tack room after the ride.

"Alexa, what jacket are you planning to wear during the exam?"

When I left the USA last summer, my mother told me to pack my beautiful tailor-made black linen show coat, but I had only used it a few times since I got here. I always wore my heather-green and forest-brown houndstooth hacking jacket. I noticed the Brits mostly wore tweed hacking jackets, even at the competitions. Wool was better suited to the climate.

"Why this one, of course," I said. After a year of wearing the jacket almost every day, my tweed hacking jacket reeked. It could almost ride a horse by itself.

"You never get a second chance to make a first impression," Beth suggested innocently. I could see why she was a top sales lady—she got you to think her idea was your idea.

"I was wondering how I could get this jacket clean," I said. "I am afraid to wash it. It's wool."

Mrs. Highstaff's words drifted through my mind. "Our appearance is a reflection on all of us."

"Oh no," she said. "You mustn't do that. I'll tell you what. Henry and I are coming for our lesson on Saturday. You don't need your coat on Sunday. I'll tell Mrs. Highstaff what we are planning. I'll take your coat to the dry cleaners in Crowsville, and I'll bring it back the morning of the exam. You are only hacking the horses on the three days before the exam, so maybe she will let you wear a sweater instead of your jacket."

I crinkled up my face; the timing was close. "Don't worry," she said reassuringly. "Henry and I are driving here separately on Thursday. I'll be here before you go into breakfast."

My appearance was important, and my options were limited, so I readily agreed. Beth spoke to Mrs. Highstaff. She would pick up my jacket on Saturday. I felt good about having a clean coat for the exam. I was relieved.

Before I left North Carolina, my beautiful tweed hacking jacket was tailor-made for me, but now it was too big. When it was cold, we rode with a few extra layers under our coats, so the roominess was helpful. If it was hot, which was rare, we were allowed to take our jackets off when we rode.

On Friday afternoon Mrs. Highstaff told us, "Today we will ride down to the farthest field where it is flat at the bottom of the hill. You will work on some of the jumps on the hillside, jumping up and downhill."

Before we left the yard, Fiona discovered Jazzy's right front shoe was loose. Mr. Hobbs pulled the shoe off to prevent possible injury. "Rodney is scheduled for Monday, so Jazzy can just sit this session out." Sword of Justice was substituted at the last minute. Mr. Hobbs reassured us, "Mrs. Highstaff is not going to use Justice in the cross-country portion of the exam, so don't worry about it." Justice was only allowed to jump single fences, or maybe a combination, but never a whole course out in the big fields.

I started off on Atlanta. I actually looked forward to riding old Attila. *One thing about her, she is trustworthy over the jumps. Mark has Rob Roy. That's okay; he does great with him. Mark gives all the horses confidence.*

The exercise at hand was to canter individually from the front of the ride to the back of the ride and to complete a large circle at the empty end of the arena. There wasn't really an arena, just a fairly flat, grassy rectangular field. Heathcliff had finally stopped tearing off with people thanks to Jeremy. Wizard, Cashel, Harry, and Marigold had already gone.

While one horse cantered, the rest of the ride remained trotting, rising, or sitting, and changed the rein at Mrs. Highstaff's discretion. "To save time, as soon as the previous rider completes their circle, the next rider should start."

We would complete the canter exercise in both directions before starting to jump. Gillian just started her turn on Caesar. Somehow, Atlanta and I were placed behind Gwen on Justice. Her insult for him was "broken down, useless old nag." Gwen was sitting heavily at the trot, and Justice started to elevate his steps, almost a *passage*. Gwen was literally winding him up. He was lathered; his tail started to thrash from side to side. Mrs. Highstaff admonished her in no uncertain terms. It was the first time in a year that I heard her shout. "Gwen! Lighten your aids—you are far too strong! Lengthen your reins!"

Gwen did not change anything she was doing.

Mrs. Highstaff was livid. She yelled, "You will ruin my horse!"

It was the only time I heard her shout at anyone or tell anyone they were ruining a horse, no matter how pathetic they were.

Instead of lengthening the reins and being softer, Gwen shortened her reins and pulled Justice into a tight frame. Mrs. Highstaff had enough of Gwen pulling her horses around all week. I thought I saw steam coming out of her head.

Gwen did not wait. As soon as Gillian finished her circle, Gwen set off. She managed her canter circle, but the old horse was frothing with lather.

I was mentally preparing to start my turn.

Before I could start, Mrs. Highstaff gave the command, "The whole Ride, Walk please, Turn in and Halt." We did as we were instructed. I thought we were going to get a lecture on the necessity for soft aids. Then the unthinkable happened.

"Dismount and take the horse to your left." I really couldn't believe that I got Justice. I had been riding him from time to time and been getting on with him fairly well. Sword of Justice and I had called a truce.

"Alexa, will you please demonstrate how to do the exercise *softly*?"

Yikes! Okay. Breathe deeply, say a nursery rhyme. On Justice and Heathcliff, you did not actually give any aids. You just pictured in your mind what you wanted to do, and they would respond.

I trotted around once, and Justice stepped into a canter. I started silently singing, "Row, row, row . . ." I never got to "your boat." On the fourth stride of the canter, Justice exploded. He launched me like a rocket. I sailed through the air like a guided missile. I could see the blades of grass beneath me; it felt like a slow-motion movie. *Thud.* I landed a good twenty feet away. Justice did not gallop back to the stable as I suspected he would. He stood there, a bit stunned. He looked almost apologetic. He wasn't mad at me; he was angry with Gwen.

After a quick assessment of myself, I said, "I'm okay."

I remounted and Justice behaved perfectly for me. I completed the exercise and I jumped over the park bench, my favorite illegal jump I used to practice over with Harry.

The exam was less than one week away and now I had a big bruise and a goose egg on my hip in the same spot that was bruised when I flew off Cherokee last summer.

I was glad these girls were going home today. I was going to ask Mrs. Highstaff if I could soak in the tub with some Epsom salts tonight.

I hope Gwen's rickety old car will break down on her way to the exam so she wouldn't be able to come back and piss off all our horses with her heavy-handed riding.

Chapter 50

Box 9

The Saturday lessons were packed. The children were excited the summer holiday had started. The parents enrolled the children in holiday courses and inquired about shows. The Stapleford children made us good luck cards. Everyone wished us well and told us to do our best in the exam. Brenda took my hacking jacket with her to get it cleaned.

At supper Fiona was uncharacteristically off her feed. She said, "Thinking about the exam makes me feel sick."

I was a little nervous myself. My dad's birthday was coming up; I had sent the card weeks ago. I hoped he received it. Today was the same day I had arrived in England a year ago. It occurred to me that Fiona and I were the only remaining students from last year. Then, she was an experienced veteran WP, and I was a complete greenhorn.

Suddenly I thought of something to say. I struck a pose with my hands on my hips like Fiona did when she was telling us off. In my best Fiona imitation, I started, "Hey, Fiona, do you remember this? We must all try to get along better. We need to work together as a team. With the BHSAI exam, we have a good opportunity to show the world what good riders and what great horses we have here at Heels Down Hall."

She laughed. With a tiny modification, it was the same pep talk she had given us before the Musical Ride.

Gillian piped up, "Fiona, you sorted out those little boys from Richlands School. The kids love your lessons. Just teach like you always do."

Jeremy chimed in, "Fiona, don't forget how you beat the snobby peacock Denis at the Featherstone Foxhounds Horse Trials."

We all laughed. Denis getting tossed and pulling the bridle off Minstrel in front of the grandstands was a favorite story at Heels Down Hall.

Mr. Hobbs voiced his opinion. "All three of you are well prepared. Do your best, keep thinking, and don't get flustered. I have a good feeling about this exam. If I were a betting man, I would lay odds on you all passing."

We laughed some more.

Fortunately, most of the heavy cleaning tasks were finished by Sunday. Some of the examiners were also inspectors for the BHS Approved Establishment scheme. Our distinctive blue and silver horseshoe plaque was proudly displayed on the carriage house wall.

While Mr. Highstaff was eating breakfast, Mrs. Highstaff handed him a list of tasks that we were not allowed to do, like replacing the fire extinguishers and replacing burned-out light bulbs. The lights in the stalls were suspended from rafters in the middle of the stall. The large bulbs were covered by a wire cage to prevent injury from any possible broken glass. The job required a ladder, a screwdriver, a new bulb, and knowledge of electricity.

After lunch, instead of enjoying a break, we were busy working. Jeremy and I turned out horses and we scrubbed the zinc water troughs in the fields. Fiona was in the loft filling and weighing hay-nets. Gillian scrubbed out the buckets and wooden water tubs in the main yard.

Mr. Highstaff consulted the list on his clipboard. He was holding it close to his face as he passed Gillian, who was kneeling on the cobblestones scrubbing a tub.

He didn't acknowledge her, and he was talking to himself. "Fire extinguishers: Carriage house. Tick. Kitchen. Tick. Light bulbs: Classroom. Tick. Box 9 . . . is next."

He looked up. Box 9 was straight ahead. He marched past Gillian, clomping along in his oversized Wellies, with a light bulb stuck in his pocket and the stepladder slung over his shoulder.

The resident of Box 9, Sword of Justice, was standing with his head in the back corner of the stall, snoozing and resting one hind leg. When he heard the kick latch clatter and the bolt latch clank, his ears went on full alert. He aimed his hindquarters toward the door. As the stall door swung open, Justice fired a well-aimed shot toward the open door. With agility any cutting horse would have been proud of, ears flattened, eyes blazing, and nostrils flared, Justice whirled around, stretched his neck out full length, and bared his teeth.

Mr. Highstaff made a hasty retreat.

Gillian said, "I have never seen Mr. Highstaff move so fast. Justice did not run out into the yard as he could have. With the spooky ladder and Mr. Highstaff removed, Justice went back to his corner and resumed his snooze. I closed the stall door and bolted it."

Mrs. Highstaff, followed by Dawdle and Daffy, were walking up the stable yard. She was nearly bowled over by her husband rushing toward the shed, dragging the ladder behind him. The dogs started to tag along behind the clattering ladder.

Mrs. Highstaff raised her voice, which was highly unusual. "Clive! What on earth is going on?"

He stopped in his tracks. "I'm not going in there again. That horse is possessed."

"Which horse?"

"The big red devil in Box 9."

"Oh dear, oh dear." Mrs. Highstaff looked up to the yard. "Why didn't you just ask Gillian to remove the horse from the stall?"

Mr. Highstaff pulled a handkerchief from his back pocket and wiped off his bottle cap glasses. He replied matter-of-factly, "I couldn't remember her name, Margaret, and I did not wish to be rude."

Mrs. Highstaff calmly said, "Come along, everyone."

They walked back to the stable yard.

Mrs. Highstaff looked at Gillian. "Gillian, please get a headcollar and lead Sword of Justice from the stall so Mr. Highstaff can replace the burned-out bulb."

At our tea break, Gillian's impression of Justice chasing Mr. Highstaff out of the stall was just the thing to cheer us. Mr. Hobbs wondered out loud, "How has Mr. Highstaff managed to live this long or, at the very least, how has he managed to avoid seriously injuring himself?"

I figure it is Mr. Highstaff's angels protecting him. I hope my angels will be on hand to bail me out of any sticky parts of the exam.

Rodney came on Monday. He replaced Jazzy's shoe and reset the others. All the horses to be used in the exam had their feet checked. As we took turns holding horses for Rodney, he made sure we knew the proper name and use of each tool. He was leaving a neat box of new farriers' tools on loan for the exam, and he would fetch it next week.

"Yankee Doodle, are you still here?" he called out cheerfully.

It was obvious that I was still here. "Yes, Limey, but not for much longer."

Then he surprised me. He took a new horseshoe nail out of the box, and he hammered it into a ring for me. "I know you can't wear it when you are riding, and I wouldn't want you to, but keep this to remember us by." I had tears in my eyes. I was sad to be leaving soon. I hugged Rodney goodbye. I would not be here when he came again. I was relieved when I could saddle up Rob Roy and go for a ride around the fields.

True to her word, Mrs. Highstaff did not have lessons or lectures for us the three days before the exam. We got to ride our favorite horses. Our only instructions were "enjoy the pleasure of riding such beautiful animals."

The fine weather on the morning of the exam was a real gift. The exam started at half past nine. We got up half an hour early to have extra time to make ourselves presentable. I was really worried because my coat was not here yet. The other candidates and examiners had already arrived.

I waited by the tack room completely dressed: hairnet, helmet, and brown gloves, everything except my jacket. I paced around anxiously.

At nine o'clock Beth arrived. She was breathless and her cheeks were red as she rushed along the path. She carried my jacket, concealed by a paper bag labeled SONNY'S DRY CLEANING, CROWSVILLE.

"Good morning," she began. Without pausing she continued, "Sorry I am a little late. There is no charge for the jacket."

I thought she had paid for the dry cleaning. I replied, "Oh wow, thank you."

"Don't thank me, Alexa, I am so sorry! I don't know what to say." She removed the bag from the jacket. It was ruined! There were big brown scorch marks on it. The wool was singed; I knew that smell from old St. Christopher's tail.

Beth realized I was about to panic. "You can wear my jacket." She was taking hers off while she spoke. "I have an old one at home, and I'll have Henry bring it for me." I tried her jacket on, but it was too tight. I tried Gillian's jacket on; it was better but too short. We were going to have to be present for introductions and instructions in the stable yard as a group in twenty minutes.

Gillian had a brainstorm. "Alexa, wear your beautiful black jacket—an exam is certainly a formal occasion. Even the weather today is right for wearing it."

Gillian bolted into the kitchen and up the backstairs and brought my show coat down to me. Luckily, I always kept a pair of black gloves in the pockets. I silently thanked my mother for making me bring my linen coat.

Mr. Hobbs saw me nervously getting ready and said quietly, "Do your best. Keep thinking, and don't get flustered."

Gillian reinforced his sentiment. "Keep calm and carry on."

The four of us walked up to the stable yard to face the assembled group and the formidable examiners.

General James Gordon Barnes (Retired) had been on several Army equestrian teams. He was a *Fédération Équestre Internationale* steward and on the FEI Rules Committee. He authored many articles and books, including a book titled *Games on Horseback*.

Mrs. Harriet Winthrop, FBHS, owned and ran a huge equestrian and BHS testing center in the north of England. She was also an equestrian facilities inspector. She was not smiling.

Ms. Phoebe Lamb, BHSI, worked in the office at the new BHS facility in Stoneleigh. Ms. Lamb was an experienced equestrienne in an era when men dominated the sport, and she coached many successful junior riders since then. Although she seemed pleasant enough, she had written parts of the Pony Club manuals and the exam.

At exams held in exceptionally large yards, horses for the riding portions are brought to the candidates already tacked up. We did not have this luxury.

The examiners walked around the yard and peered into this stall and then another. With a clipboard and pen in hand, they made notes as they followed us around. Even though we performed these tasks flawlessly almost every day for the past year, I started to question myself if I was doing it properly today.

For Equitation, all of us rode together in the indoor school. We changed horses three times and performed the movements with and without stirrups. General Barnes bellowed the orders, and the ladies marked their score sheets. No one fell off or got run away with, but other than that, I couldn't comment on anyone else's riding, I was too busy concentrating on my own horses. After the riding was over, the examiners watched us like hawks while we put the horses away.

Ms. Lamb proctored the written Minor Ailments test in the classroom. She handed a list of typed-out questions and a blue answer booklet to each candidate. The horse skull and cut-away hoof were on the podium. We sat in a checkerboard pattern around the room, far enough away from each other so there could be no chance of copying.

I was glad the Colonel made us figure out what to do if we were out hunting (which I could only imagine) and your horse suddenly pulled up lame. I had firsthand experience dealing with colic. I thought I was doing well, happy that my teachers in high school gave us a lot of essay tests. Penny asked for a second notebook, and she scribbled as fast as she could. Fiona was chewing the end of her pencil.

While we were in the classroom, Mr. Hobbs, Gillian, and General Barnes were busy setting up the numbered stations in the indoor school for Practical Horsemanship: 1. Preparing a Horse for a Journey, 2. Bandaging, and 3. Fitting Tack, which included a double bridle with a curb bit and bridoon. The final station was 4. Pulling and Plaiting the Mane and Tail.

Tara, St. Christopher, and the large ponies, Biscuit and Ghost, were used in the practicals. Mrs. Highstaff and Mrs. Winthrop went through the stables and feed and tack rooms to set up more exam questions.

We were divided into two groups of four, or sections, as the General called us, for the Stable Management. I was tootling right along with all the various tasks as we rotated through the stations. I was happy that the singeing lamp would not work in the indoor arena and that it was the wrong season for clipping. Those subjects would be oral questions. I was glad I practiced the spider bandage for the hock. I have to say it turned out better than I expected. I had already demonstrated how to pull a section of Biscuit's mane, although he didn't care for his mane being pulled. I managed to put in a respectable sewn-in plait that looked like a ball, instead of the narrow strips secured with rubber bands that we called braids in Greenleaf.

"Thank you, miss. Now please demonstrate how to plait the tail." Mrs. Winthrop wrote something.

Ughh, this is it. I was never happy with plaiting tails. Mine always had a gentle S curve down the center, or the strands were too fat or different sizes.

I just started the tail when General Barnes looked at his watch. "Attention, everyone. Attention. This portion of the exam is finished. Please put all your equipment away. This section is dismissed. At ease." His booming voice saved me.

Our guinea pigs were helpful, and they were invited to lunch so they would be on hand if it was necessary to alter the schedule. Under Gillian's guidance, they came into the school and led the horsemanship horses back to the carriage house.

The program after lunch was more Stable Management, in the yard and tack room, followed equitation, jumping, either the show jumps in the paddock or cross-country in the field; followed by the final portion of the exam, the Powers of Instruction.

The lunch was nice: stacks of roast beef and ham sandwiches, with tomato and lettuce salad and jelly roll cake, but only the volunteers and Gillian ate very much. In Greenleaf, on a nerve-wracking day like this, I probably would not have eaten anything and gotten sick to my stomach. One of the things I learned at HDH was food is fuel. I had a sandwich and part of a jelly roll. What I didn't do was drink a lot of tea and water. You couldn't very well jump off a horse and run into the loo in the middle of the exam.

The lunch was quiet. Like a sequestered jury, we were admonished not to discuss anything with anyone until the exam was completely over. Other than comments like "What a nice day" and "Please pass the jelly roll," the only other conversation of interest was that Mark invited us to go cubbing with him at Fox Hollow this fall. Penny said, "I may contact you about that."

Gwen asked Mark, "Do you have any horses for sale?"

Then Penny asked me, "Where did you get *your* jacket, Alexa? It is exquisitely made," which made me uneasy.

The examiners ate lunch with Mrs. Highstaff and Mr. Hobbs in the formal dining room.

With all the exam candidates and guinea pigs milling around, there was no place quiet. I wanted to gather my thoughts before we started again. We weren't allowed in the stables, tack room, or classroom unless the exam was in session. The only other place I could think of was the car park.

I was probably out there a little longer than I thought. *I better nip back in and use the loo.*

I was just rounding the corner of the tack room when I heard Mrs. Winthrop's unmistakable voice. I stopped dead in my tracks and backed up cautiously. I couldn't believe what I was hearing.

The tack room was Mrs. Winthrop's exam station after lunch. She wanted to ensure there was a sufficient variety of bits to use since all of our horses went in snaffles.

"Yes, fine, this is a good selection of bits." I could hear the clinking sound of metal bits being put into a box.

"Hobbs, just for the record, I would like to set one thing straight. I *know* it has been rumored that I am harder on foreign exam candidates. I am not."

"Ma'am?" Mr. Hobbs was off guard; he wasn't expecting that subject.

Bloody hell, I am doomed.

Mrs. Winthrop continued with a tinge of disdain in her voice. "Ever since that book *The Horsemasters* was published ten years ago,[1] followed by the fairy-tale Disney movie version,[2] young people from the corners of the globe swan over here expecting to be spoon-fed the knowledge they need to pass. When they arrive, all they want to do is tell *you* how they do things in Hong Kong, Australia, or Canada, most of which has little to do with horsemanship in Great Britain. If they manage to pass the exam, they don't stay in touch with the BHS afterwards. God knows what they are actually teaching. They go home and set themselves up as experts when the BHSAI is only the first rung on a long ladder."

After a long second, Mr. Hobbs replied, "All of our candidates are working pupils." Then he resourcefully changed the subject. "We are due to resume in quarter of an hour. Would you like another cup of tea?" He ushered her out of the tack room.

I waited until they went into the Hall. April didn't mind that I cut through the kitchen wearing my tall boots. I zipped up to our room, more determined to pass than ever. What Mrs. Winthrop failed to take into account is that most of those foreign students came to England to study horsemanship because they thought the British Horse Society would give them the best training available in the English-speaking world.

---

1 *The Horsemasters*, Don Stanford (New York: Funk & Wagnalls, Co.), 1958.

2 *The Horsemasters*, Disney film, released 1961.

Chapter 51

The Nameless Kernels

After lunch Ms. Lamb quizzed us with oral questions on Practical Horsemanship in the stable yard, while the General roamed between the tack room and the stable, making his own observations and notes.

I was nervous. Knowing two names for many things wasn't especially helpful. I knew the correct name for everything in this stable yard; we used it every day. Rodney had grilled us on the farrier's tools. I aced those questions. *I must be certain to give the English names for all of the grooming kit.* Before I answered, I remembered Mr. Hobbs saying, "Think and don't get flustered." I hoped that thinking before answering didn't make me seem hesitant.

Next Ms. Lamb took us into the feed room. The feed chart on the blackboard had been wiped clean; only the names of the horses and ponies remained. Thank goodness, Fiona got the question "How many pounds of hay should a fit, stabled 16-hand hunter, hunting twice a week be fed?" and the question to Mark was "How many pounds of corn (grain) should be fed to the same animal?"

There were pages and pages of feeding charts in the *Manual of Horsemanship*. Penny answered in a vague fashion and smiled sweetly, which had no effect on the women examiners and garnered only a glance from the General. I got an easy question. "Identify the root vegetables and explain how to feed them." Carrots and swedes. I had never heard of swedes as a vegetable before coming to Heels Down Hall; before that, a Swede was somebody from Sweden.

Then Ms. Lamb asked rapid-fire questions, pointing to the grains in the various bins. "What's this? What's this?"

She pointed to me. I started to answer, "It is *teff*, the grain we fed our horses in East Africa."

I coughed on the word *teff*. Mrs. Winthrop's tirade flashed in my mind. *What would happen if I said that? The War Department's Animal Management mentions teff, but if I tell a BHS examiner about something we did in Africa, it could be disastrous.* My mind went completely blank. I said, "We feed it boiled to the old horses and ponies."

Ms. Lamb shook a scoopful of the nameless kernels. She asked again, "Yes, yes, but what's its name?"

"I'm sorry, but I can't think of it."

Fiona smiled sympathetically. She knew what it felt like to know the answer but not be able to think of the word.

Ms. Lamb frowned while she marked her score sheet. "This section is now going to the tack room for Saddlery with Mrs. Winthrop." She was so busy writing she didn't look up.

I could feel Mrs. Winthrop scrutinizing my black show coat when I walked into the tack room.

We knew the names and parts of the bits. Mrs. Winthrop almost smiled when Fiona and I knew the parts of the side-saddle. Mark was knowledgeable about fitting saddles; he had to keep his working horses free from sore backs. Fiona and I were well versed on types of saddlery. Penny was good on theory. We didn't have much firsthand experience with girth galls, but we knew how to treat them. Our tack room was correctly organized, and it was spotless, so there wasn't anything to find fault with on that score.

At last, it was time to ride. As with the flatwork in the morning, Mrs. Highstaff assigned the horses we would start on for the jumping.

Topaz was the only equine on the property able to avoid the exam entirely. We were grateful that Caesar and Meteor substituted for Sword of Justice and Heathcliff. The two large ponies were bold honest jumpers, but riding a smaller mount amplifies every little mistake. Four candidates were short enough to look good on them. *I hope I don't have to ride one of the ponies. Thank God I'm starting with Rob Roy.*

Mounted, it was a five-minute walk from the stable yard to the jumping field. Mr. Hobbs came out of the Hall and hopped over the ha-ha to meet us.

We were instructed to ride our horses in, or warm them up, for a quarter of an hour. We spread out around the various parts of the field and did whatever we thought was best. When we were called back we had to explain our warmup to one of the examiners. Mrs. Highstaff had done that exercise with us many times.

After riding in, we trotted in single file over a small X fence a few times and then we cantered over a small vertical in both directions.

The General assembled us in a semicircle and he gave us instructions for our jumping assignment. "Mrs. Highstaff has listed the jumps we may use." He read the list. "Mr. Hobbs has confirmed that all of these horses have previously jumped all of these obstacles." The list included everything except the drop jump and/or slide, the water jump in the lower field, and the pile of logs in the farthest corner.

General Barnes inspected the ride by walking between and around the horses. Then he stood in front of us and gave us our orders. "This is what you will do: Using at least six obstacles, but not more than eight, design a course of your own choosing. You must include a warmup circle, at least one change of rein, one trot fence, and a halt somewhere on the course."

The General and Mr. Hobbs remained in the middle of the field, with a good view of five fences, and the ladies marched off to opposite ends. Then the General authoritatively added, "You may not ride another person's course."

Yikes! The exam question just got exponentially harder. I started thinking up an easy course. I wasn't great at remembering courses. I liked to learn the course by walking it on foot. I was second from the end of the line. *Okay, that's a good one, now I need another one in case Fiona uses my first course.*

The General pointed his shooting stick at Mark. "Mr. Smith, will you lead us off?"

What? Mark is at the far end of the ride. I am next to last.

Mark used the exact course that I thought of, and he had a beautiful round on Harry. Jeremy on Atlanta used my second course.

All the horses jumped clear, but some rounds had better pace or better turns and lines.

By the time it was my turn, all the good courses had been used. Fiona looked worried; she was probably thinking the same thing. No one jumped the stile. It was on a slope flanked by overgrown prickly holly. A few sections further down the fence line on flatter ground was an easier post and rail.

I used a large circle to get up some steam, and Rob Roy flew over the tiger trap. No one had started with it; some riders didn't jump it at all. Rob Roy might look like a giraffe, but he could jump like Pegasus. If you didn't think of the ditch under the tiger trap, the jump was just a hog's back.

We jumped in and out of the sheep's pen, over the big log, over the woodpile, over the stone wall, and then I turned left down over the stile. I disappeared out of sight for a moment and was turning right to come back into the top field over the post and rail when my left foot slipped out of my stirrup iron.

Thank you, Mr. Hobbs, for making us practice taking our feet out of the stirrup irons and putting them back into the irons at all paces.

Ms. Lamb could not see me at that instant and even if she could, my foot was on the side away from her. My guardian angel slipped my boot back into the heavy stirrup iron, and with four good canter strides, Rob Roy flew up and over the post and rail. Upon landing in the top field, I trotted and then did a square halt directly from the trot. Resuming a trot, we easily jumped over the big log heading home, then we walked on a loose rein back to the ride.

Fiona gave me a grateful look. She rode my course in reverse, over the log, halt, trot the post and rails, then canter, turning left and sailing uphill over the stile, and ending with a spectacular picture-perfect jump over the tiger trap. Meteor proved he could jump as well as any of the big horses.

General Barnes tapped his boot. "Right, that's everyone. The Whole Ride, Dismount. Take the horse *two* to your left and jump the same course on the new horse."

Fiona, first to my left, was the end, so that meant I got Harry. I could not believe our good fortune. *I have Harry, and Fiona has her beloved Atlanta!*

Harry and I had jumped the stile many times because I thought Mrs. Highstaff could not see it from her office. Little did I know she could see all the jumps from her bedroom window. No doubt, she was up there now watching the cross-country portion of the exam.

Gwen had a run-out on the point-and-go Caesar, who was tired of being kicked in his ribs and being jabbed in the mouth. Amanda had lackluster rounds. Milquetoast Jayne had poor Wizard chipping in or buried at the base of every fence. To her credit, Penny jumped well on both horses. Her years of lessons paid off in the riding portions of the exam.

While we were in the field jumping, Gillian organized the volunteers for the Powers of Instruction. When we returned to the yard, they were leading their saddled horses into the indoor school.

Mounting would be the first exam lesson. *I hope I don't get that one. Granny Chesham needs a leg up.* She always used the mounting block in the yard.

During the coffee break, we received the briefing for the final portion of the exam.

Gwen never planned to take the Powers of Instruction portion of the exam since they did not teach riding at the dealer's yard. Her boss promised her a raise if she passed the Horsemaster's. Looking rather confident, she left.

I did not hear what Penny asked Mrs. Winthrop, but I overheard part of the reply. "Of course, you can take the teaching section of the exam, you have paid for it, but it might be a waste of time." She suggested Penny join a Riding Club. Penny left with tears in her eyes.

For a moment, I was secretly happy. With two candidates gone, the exam would be over half an hour earlier.

To be fair, the order of go for the Powers of Instruction was picked from a hat. We would be teaching in the indoor school, and would be sent down, one at a time, in fifteen-minute intervals. When the person before you left, you would draw your lesson topic from the hat, allowing you fourteen minutes to mentally prepare your lesson. The first candidate chosen would teach mounting, position, and the aids. Amanda got the mounting lesson; she was smiling slightly. She had that lesson completely memorized; she had taught it hundreds of times at Woodlands.

While we were waiting to teach, we could help in the yard with setting fair the stables, but Gillian and the guinea pigs had already bedded down the stalls and topped up the buckets while we were jumping.

So we could not overhear their cross-examinations, we were instructed to wait outside of the gate until the candidate teaching exited the indoor school.

I was in the middle of the order to teach. *Rats, I have the lesson 'Improving the Rider's Sitting Trot.'* Improving something could be harder than teaching a new subject.

After I greeted the class, I checked all the tack, including the girths and stirrup lengths, and I gave them the lesson for the day.

"Today we are going to improve the sitting trot."

Ms. Lamb piped up. "They have been doing quite a bit of rising trot already. You may proceed directly to your topic."

"The whole ride, prepare to walk, and walk. Ride, prepare to turn in, turn in, and halt. Ride, quit, and cross your stirrups."

I knew I would have to show Granny Chesham how to do it, so I used her for the demonstration. I showed them how to hold the pommel of the saddle lightly. I demonstrated the disastrous results of allowing your legs to creep up, go forwards, go too far back, or lean off to one side. "Pull your seat bones down into the saddle and pretend you have bricks tied to your feet to keep them down." I reviewed the aids to trot, the aids to return to walk, and how to correctly hold the reins in one hand.

After each person had a turn, immediately followed by constructive criticism so they could improve on their next try, I had them change the rein and do sitting trot as a ride, followed by more constructive criticism for each rider. Then I had the whole ride hold the neck strap and reins in one hand and do body turns and arm circles to make the riders more supple and improve their posture.

I would have enjoyed teaching if it was a regular lesson and not the exam. The riders were cooperative good sports. However, this *was* the exam, and every word had to be perfect, and there could be no ad-libbing or making it up as you go.

I started to give directions for another exercise when the General interrupted me. "That is enough, Miss Goodwin. Please come over here. What would be your future program for this class?"

I suggested more mounted physical exercises, riding up and down hill at a walk to improve their balance, lunge line lessons, and games. At the mention of games, the General looked interested.

"*Humph.*" Mrs. Winthrop made a funny noise. "Games for adults?"

I thought we were going to get into a discussion of the value of games in riding, and which games would be appropriate, certainly not Bun Eating or the Boot Race, when I realized I had left the Ride walking around unsupervised after I was called over for questions.

I panicked.

Chapter 52
Hopeful Venture

For the last year, we had been taught to project our voices. "*The Whole Ride! Prepare to Halt! Ride, Halt! The Whole Ride! Turn in. On a long rein, make much of your ponies.*"

"There's no need to shout." Ms. Lamb made more notes. "We are standing right here. That will be all, thank you."

I gave Jeremy a thumbs-up sign when he went in to teach his lesson.

Another half an hour and the whole exam would be over. I felt brain dead. I had no idea if I had done well or not; I kept thinking of all my mistakes.

After the exam when the examiners and outside candidates left, Mr. Hobbs told us we wouldn't be riding tomorrow, and we could clean the tack then.

During supper Mrs. Highstaff came into the dining hall, which was very unusual. April had thoughtfully put the leftover sandwiches on a platter covered with a tea towel on the table.

Mrs. Highstaff started by complimenting Mr. Hobbs and Gillian on the unobtrusive way they kept the yard running all day. She said Gillian had organized the volunteers brilliantly. Although she was exhausted, Gillian was beaming.

Mrs. Highstaff told us, "The examiners were favorably impressed overall but not everyone has passed. We will have the results by tea time tomorrow, by telephone, and the written results will be posted a few days later to the address on your BHSAI Exam application." My written results would be sent to my home in Greenleaf.

Mrs. Highstaff had more to say. "The horses are having a well-deserved day off tomorrow, so you will follow our Sunday routine. Even though it is Friday, you will have extra time off in the afternoon. There is racing at Ascot and it is televised."

Next she reviewed the upcoming schedule. "Mr. Hobbs will be off tomorrow and Saturday. Gillian and Alexa will have Sunday and Monday off. I have contacted your parents, Gillian, and they will pick you and Alexa up late Saturday afternoon. Fiona will be off on Tuesday and Wednesday and Jeremy will take Thursday and Friday off."

The first summer residential children's courses would start on the Monday of the following week. Mrs. Highstaff left us to mull over our futures. We ate silently.

About five minutes after he finished a few sandwiches, Mr. Hobbs went up to his room and appeared downstairs with his suitcase. He already was aware of the time-off schedule, and he was heading out. "Be sure to watch the races tomorrow because the Queen will be there." He winked. "And she has a good horse in it . . . . From what I saw of your cross-country jumping, you all rode well. I sincerely wish each of you the best of luck."

I would not see him again. I gave him a hug, and a kiss on the cheek. "Thank you for everything, Mr. Hobbs." He blushed.

Mr. Hobbs left, and I went upstairs.

I started to flop onto my bed and stumbled over the pile of books stacked on the floor.

The realization hit me. *I'm leaving here on Saturday with Gillian and not coming back. I have to pack.*

I had one suitcase, my purse, and a small carry-all that I would use for the rest of the summer, and I had to pack my trunk, which would be shipped home after I left.

Fortunately Mom had helped me make a list of what I should take on our trip. "Take a week's worth of underwear, jeans, shirts, skirts, sweaters, and one pair of dress shoes." It was pretty much a mix and match wardrobe. I looked at all the rest of the clothes, jackets, books, boots, and other things I had accumulated since I arrived. I looked at the trunk. I started to despair.

"Never mind," yawned Gillian. "I'll help you tomorrow. We have lots of time. Tonight, why don't you just put your books in the trunk?"

I made a list of my books as I packed. I was surprised at how much room they took up but leaving them behind was out of the question.

Gillian fell asleep within minutes. I was tired, but worried. *The success of my whole year in England comes down to the exam I took today.* I slept fitfully and had the Sinbad the Sailor dream again, but this time the pirates stole my horse.

By the time we got to the stables on Friday morning, Mrs. Highstaff had already neatly rewritten the entire feeding chart for over twenty horses and ponies on the blackboard. She was making up the feeds while Mr. Hobbs was off.

After breakfast I zoomed upstairs, made a list, and prioritized my packing. At Gillian's suggestion, I put my suitcase on her bed and packed that as we went along. I wasn't going to take my black rubber Wellies home, and my short black leather ones needed heels and soles. I wouldn't need long underwear or my heavy wool plaid winter car coat in Greenleaf. The coat was made in Maine; I thought it looked like something a lumberjack would wear.

We started a giveaway pile in the corner. My gabardine trench coat, like the ones the TV spies wore, was threadbare, but Gillian wanted it. The little bedroom started to resemble the church Jumble Sale. Next in the trunk went all the riding essentials: boots, spurs, crops, helmet, breeches, and show coat.

I decided to leave my burned hacking jacket behind, and I hung it on a peg at the foot of the stairs. *Dad is going to hit the roof, but I don't have time to go to Sonny's in Brickton and demand my money.* We kept a detailed list of everything that went into the trunk because I had to fill out shipping and customs forms.

It was good to be busy; waiting for the exam results was nerve-wracking. We did our stable chores, and every chance I got I went back to packing. I organized the gifts for my family, my eighteenth birthday, and the Christmas presents.

I traded my purple suede leather miniskirt for Gillian's smooth royal blue one. The dress Aunt Helga sent me, my purple velvet mini shirtdress, the bell-bottom jeans with the leather inserts and brass stars I made after the Jumble Sale, my leather jerkin, and my riding Mac absolutely had to go home. No one in Greenleaf would have anything like them. "I am seriously running out of space in this trunk."

After lunch Fiona and Jeremy tried to relax while they waited for the races to start. I came into the lounge with an armload of sweaters. "Do you want these?

Even though it was warm outside, the lounge had a chill in it. Fiona asked, "May I have the one with the embroidered flowers on it?" She took it and promptly put it on.

Jeremy said, "I'll take the two plain pullover sweaters. If you don't want them, may I have your old rubber Wellies, to keep at Falstaff's stable as a spare pair?"

I gave the rest of the clothes to April.

The BBC coverage from Royal Ascot came on the tiny black and white television. This year, instead of arriving in stately horse-drawn carriages, the Queen and her family rode their elegant horses down the Long Walk from Windsor Castle to the racecourse. Obviously, the Queen changed clothes somewhere; shortly thereafter, she appeared in different clothes with a matching hat. Jeremy said, "People wager on the color of the Queen's outfit every day."

We cheered when the Queen's horse, the odds-on favorite, Hopeful Venture, a bay three-year-old colt, ridden by Sandy Barclay, a nineteen-year-old stable jockey, won the Hardwicke Stakes.

I felt like that was a good omen. *That's what I have been betting on this past year, my own hopeful venture. I pray my venture has a successful ending.*

I commented, "The Queen's jockey is wearing unusual silks."

Fiona replied, "I wish you could see the Queen's racing colours in color, because they are stunning. The jacket has a purple body with scarlet sleeves and gold braiding. The jockey's black velvet cap has a gold fringe which looks like a tassel on the top."

Jeremy added, "The Queen didn't design her racing colours; she inherited them. The gold braid looks like frogs, like the fastenings on military uniforms from long ago."

Just then the telephone rang. The office door had purposely been left open so the important call would not be missed. We heard the heavy door close. We waited.

Fiona, Jeremy, and I looked at each other. I thought Fiona might cry. This was the third time she had taken the exam, just missing it twice. Gillian crossed her fingers.

After an interminable period of time, we heard Mrs. Highstaff and the dogs pattering around downstairs, going into the pantry, dining hall, and kitchen. No one dared to ask if that was the call we were waiting for or if it was it something else.

Mrs. Highstaff walked to the foot of the stairs, rang the bell, and called up, "Will you all please come down to the dining hall."

"Please sit down," she said.

To our surprise there was a plate of fancy biscuits and a pot of coffee on the sideboard.

If this is going to be our exam results, why doesn't Mrs. Highstaff speak to us individually?

Mrs. Highstaff said with a serious tone, "As you are aware, some candidates did not pass the exam."

Then she smiled. "But I am *very pleased* to say that *all* three of you *passed*!"

We cheered. "Hurray!"

Fiona started to cry. Jeremy sparkled. If I weren't sitting down, I would have said my feet didn't touch the ground.

"And all of you achieved scores *over eighty*," she said proudly.

The magic number to pass was seventy-five points. She continued with a serious tone, "It probably will not surprise you to learn that Gwendolyn Jones, Penny Stafford, and Jayne Porter failed. Jayne made the seventy qualifying marks, but not the extra five points overall. Mark Smith and Amanda Thompson passed with scores under eighty.

"Enjoy your coffee and biscuits and in half an hour, we will go up to feed and do evening stables. After that you may each come into the office and telephone your parents to tell them the good news. We won't keep them in suspense any longer."

Even when Mrs. Highstaff was generous, she was practical. Telephone rates went down dramatically in the evening. I could call Mom in London. I would write to Dad this evening.

The sun blazed early on Saturday, and the Rascals' song "It's a Beautiful Morning" kept running through my mind. Julian brought us a box of chocolates. "My mom thought you would enjoy them no matter what happened," he said. There was a spirit of joy throughout the place. Excited congratulations were given all around. The guinea pigs were glowing. The kids knew I was leaving today. At lunch they sang "For She's a Jolly Good Fellow."

Brenda surprised me with an envelope containing money for a new coat, but she needed to return the burned jacket along with the receipts. After Henry popped into Crowsville and had a word with him, Sonny agreed to pay for a new hacking jacket, even though mine was a well-used year old. The dry cleaner did not want his new location to lose the trade of the riding community. If I had packed the jacket, it would have been at the bottom of my trunk. I gladly gave the singed coat to Brenda.

We exchanged addresses and promised to write.

After lunch I pushed my final essential items into the crevices of my overstuffed trunk, but there was one small problem: now the lid would not close.

"Gillian, please give me a hand."

"There's something sticking out between the top lid and the bottom of the trunk." I opened the lid and stuffed the offender into the trunk, and *oops*, now the lid would shut but the latches would not close.

Gillian sat on the top. "Good, now the latches will snap shut, but don't get up, Gillian, or the hinges will break."

Fiona saw us struggling and started to laugh; her sense of humor had at last returned. "Don't move," she said, and she zipped off. She was back in a few moments with two luggage straps. Gillian and Fiona sat on the trunk, and I tightened the straps. Mrs. Highstaff reassured me the shipping company would put steel bands around the trunk once they checked the paperwork.

I had the rest of the afternoon off. I put my rubber and leather Wellies in the hallway for the last time. Jeremy could figure out what he wanted to do with them later. I changed from the work clothes I was leaving behind into street clothes.

Mrs. Highstaff gave me a stack of forms to fill out. I neatly printed, in triplicate, the contents of the trunk and my contact information. We left the space for the weight blank. The company would have to weigh the bulging trunk when they picked it up from the Hall; it was quite a bit heavier than when it arrived last June.

I wandered around the stable yard, and I pet the horses and said my goodbyes. I hugged Wizard and whispered to him, "You are a true champion." I kissed Rob Roy on the nose. "Be a good boy." I wouldn't be riding again until some unknown time in the future. Even Sword of Justice seemed kind; he may have been happy I was leaving.

It was hard to describe my emotions. I felt elated to pass, drained from stress, happy to be traveling with Mom, and sad to be leaving Heels Down Hall. I loved all these horses and ponies; this had been my whole world for the past year.

Mr. Benson could take us away after the tack cleaning was finished. He arrived earlier than planned, so he and I had a cup of tea with April in the kitchen while Gillian gathered her things. I found out Cricket's real name was Christine. April helped me a lot while I was here; she was kind to everyone. I told her I thought Cricket would make a great Pony Clubber.

Apollo and Artemis were sitting on the steps hoping to get into our room. I petted them goodbye.

Mr. Benson and Gillian put our luggage in the boot of his car. Then he drove around to the front door of the Hall. Gillian was sitting in the back seat.

Today I was to leave Heels Down Hall through the front door, instead of the usual route around the tack room and out to the car park.

A student leaving the school for their last time was a formal occasion.

Mrs. Highstaff with her dogs, Lord Daffy and Sir Dawdle, were waiting by the door of the study. I gave each of the dogs a pat on the head. Dawdle shook hands with me.

Tearfully, I said, "Goodbye, Mrs. Highstaff."

She gave me a kiss on the forehead. "Have a safe journey home."

I took her hand and thanked her for everything. "I promise to stay in touch."

I walked down the steps and got into the car.

Mrs. Highstaff and the dogs walked out onto the porch.

As Mr. Benson drove us down the driveway, I waved goodbye. Mrs. Highstaff waved and went back inside followed by her faithful dogs. Soon she would be doing the evening stable check.

Acknowledgements

This book is dedicated to my parents, Jack and Zelda Kear, who reluctantly allowed me to pursue a career with horses, and to my horses of memory.

I thank my many instructors, many of whom were Olympic competitors and coaches, and those in the British Horse Society for giving me a sound education.

Special thanks to my brother and sister-in-law, Robert and Sheree Kear, for their support and encouragement.

The illustrator of this book, J. Johnson, and I have shared many adventures over the years. Writing this book is certainly one of them. I thank her for listening, page by page, to the first draft, which was vastly different from this story, and then listening to the entire rewrite, and, of course, for imagining and creating the wonderful illustrations.

Thank you to Robert E. Cacchione, founder of the Intercollegiate Horse Shows Association, and Debra D. McCarthy, a former Pace University student, for writing the foreword for this book. Debra is a talented horsewoman trained in the USA and GB. She is a horse show and racing official, an equine educator, and riding coach. Debra listened to the saga, story by story, and helped with the references to horse racing.

Many thanks to my neighbor Mark P. Young, a beta reader, who also patiently helped me with many technical issues.

In the read-to-dog school of thought, my faithful friend Molly Moodle patiently lay by my chair and listened to me read the story over and over for the past two years. She never criticized, but then again, she was paid in biscuits. My literary cat, Dusty Hemingway, could have cared less about the whole thing, except for occasionally shredding paper and jumping on the desk.

Special Thanks to the Launch Team

A special shout out to all those on the *Heels Down Hall: Adventures of a Working Pupil* Launch Team. There is no way I could place one of these people above another, so I have listed them in alphabetical order by last name.

Carey Beam

Margaret Bignell, Dip. Cot., musician and folk singer, published poet

Debra Grasley, lifelong hippophile

Linda Kerstetter

Aly Lock, BA (Honors.), purveyor of all things fine!

Cathy Lycholaj

Arno Mares

Arlene A. McHale

Julia Peterson, independent film producer and retired college professor

Jane Richardson, fifteen years stud hand, six years hunt groom, twenty-one years racing secretary

Sharon Right

Mikki Schattilly

Terry Wentworth, president, Empire Saddlery, Inc.

Linda Wolfe

About the Illustrator

J. Johnson

J. Johnson was born and raised in the Midlands. She attended the School of Arts, St. Georges Avenue, Northamptonshire, before spending a year as a working pupil at a British Horse Society Riding School.

After working with Thoroughbred mares and foals for several years, she married a farmer. She enjoys gardening and walking in the English countryside with her dog.

Throughout her life, she continues to draw and paint as a hobby. She likes to amuse her friends with her cards and drawings.

About the Author

Regina Kear Reid

Since the age of seventeen, Regina Kear Reid has traveled the world, pursuing a career as a professional equestrian, freelance journalist, published poet, and artist.

Her formal training includes a BA and MA from East Carolina University and years of intensive training at British Horse Society riding schools in various locations in the UK.

Her love of horses has taken her across the United States and around the world. She lived in Ethiopia and England and has visited over forty countries.

Regina's travels have influenced her teaching, writing, and artwork. Her articles and poems have been published in anthologies, and regional and national magazines. Her artwork has appeared in juried shows, galleries, and Art in Public Places.

During her equestrian career, Regina directed the Pace University (New York) Equine Studies programs for fifteen years. She competed in major horse shows in hunters, jumpers, and ladies' hunters side-saddle. She coached regional and national champions in the Intercollegiate Horse Shows Association in hunt seat and stock seat equitation. Trained by Olympic coaches and riders, Regina successfully competed in One-day Events, trained young horses, played and coached arena polo, hunted, and worked with Pony Clubs in the US and UK.

After fifteen years at Pace, Regina married and co-owned a working farm where they boarded horses, raised ponies, and owned a tack shop.

Heels Down Hall: Adventures of a Working Pupil, Regina's first novel, is based on a true story and is a tribute to her early training.

A Note to Readers

Thank you for reading *Heels Down Hall: Adventures of a Working Pupil.* If you enjoyed this book, I would be grateful if you would post a short review on Amazon. Your support makes a difference.

To leave a review or purchase copies of *Heels Down Hall*
in ebook or in print, please visit Amazon:
https://www.amazon.com/dp/B09VWRZ5P9

Please visit our website:
www.hoofbeatsandhorsetales.com

Sign up for a monthly newsletter of fun facts about 1967,
horsemanship, upcoming events, new releases, and more.

Find us on Facebook:
facebook.com/hoofbeatsandhorsetales

Do you enjoy poetry? Check out *Reflections*:
amazon.com/Reflections-Space-Writers-Poetry-Anthology-ebook.
Two of Regina's poems appear in this anthology,
along with those of other Guild members.

For more information about the Space Coast Writers' Guild:
scwg.org

Discover how to be involved with horses
while pursuing your college education by visiting
the Intercollegiate Horse Shows Association:
ihsainc.com

Made in the USA
Las Vegas, NV
09 April 2022

47136267R00238